To Virginia:
I really enjoyed
all the best

"The Gun Hunter"

MW00440067

The Gem Hunter

True Adventures of an American in Afghanistan

Gary W. Bowersox

Editing By:
Jonathan Ross, T. M. Jordan, March Davenport

GeoVision, Inc.
www.gems-afghan.com

The Gem Hunter – True Adventures
of an American in Afghanistan

Gary W. Bowersox

www.gems-afghan.com

First published by GeoVision, Inc. 2004.

Published by
GeoVision, Inc.
P.O. Box 89646
Honolulu, HI 96830 U.S.A.
Cover design by Josh Visser
Book design by Shirley Lund

No part of this book may be reproduced by any mechanical, photographic, or electronic process, or in the form of a phonographic recording, nor may it be stored in a retrieval system, transmitted, or otherwise copied for public or private use, without written permission from the publisher.

Copyright First Edition 2004 by Gary W. Bowersox
Reprinted 2006
Printed in China by Twin Age Limited, Hong Kong

Library of Congress-in-Publication Data

Bowersox, Gary W.
    The Gem Hunter - True Adventures of an American in Afghanistan /
    Gary W. Bowersox
    p. cm.
    Includes bibliographical references and index
    ISBN 0-9747323-1-1 The Gem Hunter (hardcover)

1. Afghanistan 2. Gems 3. Geography 4. Travel 5. Military 6. Politics
7. Gary W. Bowersox 8. Pakistan 9. Central Asia

Many of the Gem Hunter's tales take place within the rectangular area shown on this topographical map

Forward

During my more than 25 years with the Afghan resistance movement, I have heard a lot about the Gem Hunter, Gary Bowersox. Gary's friendship with my people has benefited Afghanistan in crucial ways. He has volunteered himself as goodwill ambassador by introducing intriguing aspects of our national character to the outside world, and he has single-handedly instituted training programs to improve mining and marketing precious stones, one of our most valuable natural resources. Especially profitable have been his introduction of new mining techniques and his advice on the requirements of the international gem trade. By improving business strategies, Gary has aided the economy of Afghanistan's mining areas and has also helped lay the groundwork for making our gem industry an important contribution to reconstruction.

Before coming to the United States, I owned and edited the Payame Mujahid, (Mujahid Message) newspaper in Afghanistan. Now my government has sent me to Washington, DC, to explain what is happening in Afghanistan in terms of international terrorism, war, narcotics, women's rights, human rights, and foreign influences.

After attending one of Gary's *Afghan Events*, I recognize how greatly Gary is helping Americans gain a balanced understanding of the often distorted media images of my country. Through talking about his own experiences, Gary portrays things that give our society its own character: food, customs, and friendships. I greatly appreciate that Gary is a true lover of Afghanistan and its people.

Engineer Mohammad Es'Haq
Director of the Afghanistan Mission to Washington, DC

Introduction

I have written the true tales and facts in this book from my personal research and adventures in Central Asia, primarily Afghanistan. For 30 years, I have had the privilege of walking in the footsteps of Alexander the Great, Ollie Olufsen, Marco Polo, Jean Baptiste Tavernier, and Captain John Woods. In the crags of the Hindu Kush and the bazaars of ancient cities, I have discovered spectacular gems and formed fascinating relationships with gem miners, tribal peoples, government officials, scientists, and intelligence operatives in this war-torn area.

As a restless young man I set out for excitement and precious gems. I found both – but not without risking life and limb, enduring close calls with rockets, bullets, bombs, and land mines; rebounding from deceits and robberies; contracting sheepherder's disease, poison ivy, hepatitis, and food poisoning; enduring vicious assaults of poison flies and fleas; and suffering from blisters, bruises, and missing toenails.

In sharing my experiences of discovery and ancient mines, be ready to encounter danger, intrigue, and people, good and bad. Through my personal involvement with the leaders and politics of the region, I provide you with firsthand insights into the complexities of what is known to historians as *The Great Game*.

I have a deep respect and love for the Central Asian people. Politically and historically, Central Asia, particularly Afghanistan, continues to grow in importance. So I write this book wishing to widen ancient trails and to leave behind paths of knowledge of personal contacts and understanding for merchants, scientists, politicians, and other adventurers to follow.

Happy trails…..**GWB**

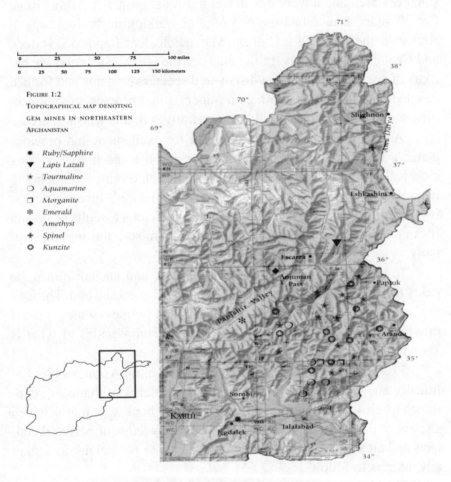

FIGURE 1:2
TOPOGRAPHICAL MAP DENOTING
GEM MINES IN NORTHEASTERN
AFGHANISTAN

● Ruby/Sapphire
▼ Lapis Lazuli
★ Tourmaline
○ Aquamarine
▢ Morganite
✳ Emerald
◆ Amethyst
✛ Spinel
✪ Kunzite

Topographical Map of North Eastern Afghanistan

Much of this story takes place amid the high mountains and deep valleys of Afghanistan, where man has existed for over 100,000 years. A country of incredible beauty and ancient mysteries, Afghanistan has some 270,000 square miles of land – roughly the size of Texas or France. It is completely landlocked by its neighbors: Iran, Turkmenistan, Uzbekistan, Tajikistan, China and Pakistan. Difficult terrain has always hindered transportation and communication among the various tribal groups. Historically, the Afghans have been as hard to conquer as their mountains are to climb. Through the years, Afghans have learned to rely only on strong family ties and loyalty to their tribe or ethnic group. Basic survival demands self-sufficiency – growing the necessary food and raising the necessary animals. Shopping in the bazaars has little to offer. No foreigner stays for long, as life there soon becomes threatening to one's health.

On the other hand, Afghanistan is rich in gems and minerals. It is one of the few third world countries with real potential for providing its population with a good standard of living. The introduction of technology and equipment to extract the country's wealth could provide employment, wages and foreign currency to Afghanistan. Today, however, most Afghans remain desperately poor, suffering from the devastating effects of more than 25 years of conflict in their country. At present, day-to-day survival is their primary concern.

Dedication

This book is dedicated to those who have walked through these pages and physically departed this world or are missing from my life. Each one has in some way – and often in many ways on many occasions – contributed to my knowledge and understanding of Afghanistan.

DECEASED:

Sayed Roohullah Bacha, Afghan/Soviet code breaker and good friend, for being my traveling companion.

Adolph Dubs, U.S. Ambassador to Afghanistan, for encouragement, advice, security briefings and access to Embassy staff and contacts.

Louis Dupree, anthropologist, author, consultant and friend, for his savvy political advice and for the many hours of laughter we shared.

Zia ul-Haq, President of Pakistan, for arranging a tour of Pakistan and for words of encouragement.

Eugene Foord, geologist, U.S. Geological Survey Team, for his instruction at GeoVision, Inc. Symposiums, for co-authoring articles, and for years of friendship and advice.

Dr. Mohammad Yaqob Lali, Afghanistan Minister of Mines and Industry, for his advice and counsel on Afghan gems and mineralogical data.

Akbar Khan, owner of Crystal Gem, Peshawar, Pakistan, for his friendship and companionship, and for sharing his business acumen.

Ahmed Shah Massoud, Commander-Northern Alliance, for his friendship, project support, and unwavering devotion to the cause of freedom for his countrymen.

Sparky M. Matsunaga, U.S. Senator, decorated veteran and peacemaker, for our time in Washington, DC and Honolulu discussing the Afghan situation and his U.S. Institute of Peace.

Dr. Nassaeri, Professor of Geology, University of Kabul, for his wisdom, friendship and knowledge of the Afghan gem and mineral industry.

MISSING:

Assadullah Amin, Afghan Ministry of Commerce, Kabul, Afghanistan. He attended the Symposium in Hawaii. I think he may be living in the U.S.

S. Hashim Dehzad, Director of Lapis, Afghanistan Ministry of Mines. He attended the Symposium in Hawaii. Later imprisoned in Afghanistan after the Soviets invaded. Disappeared sometime after his release.

V. Prokofiev, United Nations Project Manager, Afghanistan. My main lapis contact in Kabul and good friend. He returned to Russia after the Soviets invaded Afghanistan.

Kim Tae-Ik, Korean Army Provost Marshals Office, Pusan, Korea, and the Chosan Beach Hotel. A good friend and hunting companion who taught me much about Korea and Korean life among the mountain people.

Dr. Ahmed Q. Zia-Zadah, President, Mineral Exploitation Department Ministry of Mines, Kabul, Afghanistan. He ably assisted me in buying and exporting Afghan lapis and other gems.

If you have any knowledge of or know the whereabouts of any of the above persons listed as *Missing*, please, contact me via E-mail at: MrGary77@aol.com

Prologue

Washington, DC
In the aftermath of 9-11-2001

They called me into the room. There were four of them. They did not smile. They introduced themselves, but I'm not sure the names they used were real. They did not want to talk. They wanted me to talk. And talk I did, for three consecutive days.

Sometimes there were other faces – never women, only men. They came in, listened for a while, asked a question or two, listened intently to my answers, and then left. There were no social niceties; there was

Gary W. Bowersox in Badakhshan, Afghanistan

no chit-chat. Their faces were grim. Nobody took notes. I assumed that the session was recorded.

I told them what I knew, in response to their questions. I tried not to sound aggressive or critical. I spoke from memory, occasionally consulting my journal to refresh my recollection.

We met in a hotel room. Occasionally I would ask for a break or for water to soothe my drying throat. This seemed to discomfit them; they were not set up to welcome guests. One of them would go off in search of a glass or a coffee cup and bring it back filled with tap water. As time went on, they would order sandwiches or ask the hotel to supply us with pitchers of water and glasses. That's okay. I wasn't there for the hospitality. I was there to offer what I knew – all of it – to men desperate to make sense of something senseless; in fact, of numerous senseless things.

Toward the end of the third day they reminded me – more than once – that our discussions were confidential. They had me sign forms. Then they thanked me. They were finished. I was not destined to know what they had concluded, how they evaluated my comments, whether they disagreed. That was unfortunate; a Socratic discussion could have refined a number of issues. But that was not their way. I was merely a source, an expert. I was not one of them, and they barely trusted their own. I only hoped I had helped, but I'll never know if I did.

In the aftermath of 9-11, I was one of the few Americans who knew about the geology, terrain and politics of Afghanistan. That's why they wanted to talk to me. I was happy to comply. It wasn't just the Department of Defense who wanted my views. So did Diane Sawyer on *Good Morning America.* I was glad to talk to anyone who would listen. But my message was always the same. Our government had been supporting the wrong guys. In some cases, we still are. The reasons, while complex, have as much to do with oil and drugs and money and foreign intervention as they do with the Taliban and al-Qaeda and Osama bin Laden. And the sooner we, the people, understand the issues, the sooner we will be able to apply our energies where they will do the most good.

Table of Contents

Elma & Millard Bowersox
(parents)

Kalamazoo, MI   Gary, age 7

Family 1962   Family Home   Captain Gary 1965

Chapter One
Young Man Seeking

2001, August 10

The wind rushed through the small, round window; feelings of excitement and anticipation stirred within me as I peered into the after-noon light. Over the throbbing clatter of the rotor blades, I could hear the droning of the engine. It was a wheezy hum, oscillating up and down. Hardly robust enough to lift us off the earth. And yet we were lifted skyward. The wobbly g-force of our ascent pushed me back into my canvas seat. No need for a seatbelt yet; good thing, since there wasn't one. The helicopter veered left, and I caught a glimpse of our shadow against the peaks jutting straight up, treeless, from the valley floor.

Two hours before, I had been sitting in the Embassy of Afghanistan in Dushanbe, Tajikistan talking with Saleh Registani, the Defense Attaché of Ahmed Shah Massoud, Commander of Afghanistan's Northern Alliance.

Saleh Registani

"What's the situation in the Panjsher Valley? Have the Taliban advanced?" I asked Saleh.

"Do not worry," he replied. "Your helicopter is probably more dangerous than the war!"

After our meeting ended, Saleh's driver drove me to the airfield in a black Soviet-made sedan. We entered the field through the back gate, were waved past by the military guards who recognized the car, and drove down the runway to a bullet-riddled helicopter. This worn and weary magic carpet would carry me across the Amu Darya River, which was the border between Tajikistan and Afghanistan, and over valleys flanked by snow-capped peaks.

I was bound for the Panjsher Valley, a beautiful, fertile 93-mile long valley in northeastern Afghanistan, filled with corn and wheat fields, apple and apricot trees and more than a few emerald mines. The valley with its steep, high, mountainous walls was militarily defensible. For this reason it served as a permanent base for Commander

Panjsher Valley

Massoud's Northern Alliance.

I am not always the reflective type. I sometimes act before I analyze. Ready. Fire. Aim. But I found myself thinking how far I had come
from Kalamazoo, Michigan in my thirty-some years as a *gem hunter.*
Wondering if I had changed much. And wondering what pushed me
forward into dodgy situations, time after time. But I knew why I was
flying into a war zone of my own volition. I wanted to help my friends
there create a viable economy to support their way of life and a *Free
Afghanistan.* The personal relationships and the excitement of the hunt
meant more to me than the riches coming from the magnificent gem
discoveries we had made together.

In my early years, living a comfortable and conventional life, had
I known that something else existed? As I remember it, I was often
surrounded by the laughter of a close-knit family and friendly neighbors, the smell of Mom's fresh-baked cookies, and the click of the Ping-
Pong ball in our nightly after-dinner games. Dad's accounting job at a
nearby paper company afforded us a life centered around lunches eaten
together at home, summer vacations at a cabin in the woods, and ice
fishing and skating at the lake during winters. The dimensions of my
world did not yet extend to Viet Nam or Afghanistan or any of the

dozens of countries I would later visit, except as images flitting across a TV screen. Cub Scouts. Boy Scouts. Fishing. Hunting. Hiking trips. Bike trips. Always doing, always moving. My life was full. Wasn't that enough?

Later on came trips by car. I'd like to think I went further afield, always hungry to explore what lay beyond. That would explain these thirty years. But in fact, I never really ventured that far. My perimeter expanded when I went off to Western Michigan University – all of ten miles away! I started out as an engineering student but finally majored in accounting and business. Some adventure! I had a job, an active social life, ROTC and Alpha Kappa Psi fraternity. I was happy. I was not restless. That's the truth of it.

My brother still lives in Michigan, happily dealing real estate while his wife and three daughters pursue careers in teaching and engineering. Mom and Dad, at 85 and 91, still live independently in their large ranch-style home at the end of a cul-de-sac. My semi-annual visits home are redolent with crumb pies, punctuated by good-natured, after-dinner games of euchre. All-American. I think Ozzie and Harriet lived down the street…

But were there hints that I was different? I took flying lessons and was soon flying solo at the controls of a Piper Cub. Freedom to go wherever I wanted. Life had so much to offer … but so much what? I still remember the scene in my living room when I told my parents that I wanted to travel around the world – alone – before attending graduate school. These were both family firsts; no one else had considered either. I had saved $3,000 for my dream trip. A round-the-world air ticket only cost $1,200! I figured I could make it on about $2,000 if I stayed in private homes, YMCA's, and youth hostels. Well, maybe not quite enough to make it but "Hey, why not go for it. It'll work out."

The Soviet-made helicopter dropped into an air-pocket, bringing my stomach to the back of my throat, a startling reminder of where I was. I looked out the window and saw that we were flying over the Amu Darya River. We had just crossed into Afghanistan and were now flying in a war zone. For a while, I watched the changing scenery unfold, but soon my thoughts drifted back to earlier times in my life.

In high school, life had been football, basketball and baseball.

And, of course Ping-Pong. School. Dating. So many games, so many sports. I was raised on them, and I was good at them. Maybe all this adventuring was just an extension of that: a love of the game. Well, if so, I had sure picked a good one – the one historians have called *The Great Game* – the complex geo-political scramble among the powerful and the developing countries to win the prize: Afghan land, gems, minerals, oil right-of-ways, and natural gas. Money. Land. Drugs.

Was all this adventuring stuff just a ruse? Myth-spinning? Was I just another misguided adventurer on a fool's errand? A pawn in some ill-defined geo-political game? Maybe. Maybe not. My stream-of-consciousness was cresting over the bank…

The engine stalled, just long enough to drop us a few meters, then roared back to life. Water in the gas line or something worse? We were descending into the Panjsher Valley. I was back from my reverie, my idle speculations on my motivations. Below, green hillocks and golden wheat fields striped the narrow side valleys of the Panjsher. I saw more and more mud houses as we proceeded south and downward.

The helicopter slowly settled on a field the color of em-

Soviet Hind Helicopter

eralds near the rush of the Panjsher River. A red Toyota four-by-four approached as the engine and blades whirred to a stop. The only other people nearby were two soldiers armed with AK-47s, guarding the dirt track entrance to the helipad. A few curious locals gathered along the riverbank near a large metallic hulk, the remnants of a Soviet tank long abandoned to the roaring water.

My driver smiled at me and reached for my bags. I was expected. We headed south on the dirt road to Bazarak. Saleh had warned me that serious fighting was in progress on the other side of the mountain to the west of us. As we approached the small village, the dirt road gradually filled with locals going about their everyday business among gun-

Panjsher Bazaar

bearing soldiers.

This ancient place abounded with striking contrasts – a farmer in the golden field with oxen walking in a circle to thresh the wheat next to abandoned rusting Soviet tanks; men on horseback riding beneath the contrails of jets breaking the sound barrier; homes with no running water and sparse furniture equipped with satellite telephones.

We entered the bazaar, a series of one-room wooden shops built on long rock platforms. The locals gathered in small groups, sitting on rock walls, conversing about the day and as they saw my face, this new foreign visitor. Most of the strangers they encountered were French medical teams here to treat war-related injuries. I don't know what I looked like to them, other than foreign. The mixture of ripe fruits, live humans, and dead animals emitted exotic earthy scents, which both lured me in and turned me away. As always, the merchants stood around or sat cross-legged on blankets outside their shops, waiting for buyers – much like village merchants the world over. Some negotiated a purchase with two or three customers; most just sat and talked to pass the time. Many customers drank tea supplied by the shop owners. A few of the shopkeepers had moved into metal shipping containers left over from the war and now put to better use than when they first arrived loaded with arms. They sold fruit, clothing, and pots. I searched for the meat man's shop with its carcasses of goats hanging on hooks.

From previous trips, I knew that directly across from the meat man's shop I would find Tajuddin's home. Until a few years ago, Tajuddin had been one of Commander Massoud's top lieutenants. He still worked for Massoud, but more importantly for me, he operated a guesthouse for visitors. To my pleasant surprise, Tajuddin, my longtime friend Jon Mohammad, and Dr. Abdullah stood in the road watching our approach. As I jumped out of the Toyota, a big smile lit up Jon Mohammad's face.

"Mr. Gary, Mr. Gary!" That's how I am known in Central Asia.

Jon Mohammad, my cherished friend, approached me rapidly with open arms. As we exchanged hugs, tears welled up in our eyes. I recalled the countless times Jon Mohammad had smuggled me across the Pakistan-Af-

L-R: Jon Mohammad, Dr. Abdullah, and Tajuddin

ghanistan border during violent years. Close to my own age and now with graying hair, his intelligence and wit still showed in his dark eyes. He is alert but always calm. And his gait is nimble as a mountain goat.

Next to Jon Mohammad stood Dr. Abdullah, Afghan Foreign Minister. I had accompanied him by car from Tashkent, Uzbekistan to Dushanbe, Tajikistan the week before. We shook hands, then the three of us huddled in the road as Dr. Abdullah spoke.

"Mr. Gary, I have talked with Commander Massoud. He has approved your plans for further emerald exploration and mapping. And he has approved your request to make a documentary film of the emerald and lapis mines. He also approved your offer to create a website for him on the Internet."

"Excellent," I thought. I welcomed the news delivered by Dr. Abdullah. My trip was off to very a good start!

Dr. Abdullah continued, "Engineer Es'Haq is expecting you. Get some rest tonight, and Jon Mohammad will come tomorrow morning with transportation to take you to Rokha, close to the front lines. Es'Haq has set up an office there. I am going north to Takhar to be with Commander Massoud. When you finish your work here in Panjsher, we will send a helicopter to bring you to Takhar. From there you can return to Dushanbe."

"Give Commander Massoud my greetings," I responded, after thanking Dr. Abdullah.

Dr. Abdullah and Jon Mohammad quickly shook my hand, one after the other. They were in a hurry to go. They climbed into an idling jeep and were gone.

Tajuddin, waiting nearby, motioned for me to follow him into his home. Tajuddin's home, with its five guest-rooms, was built in a modern Western-style and contained a library built especially for Commander Massoud, his son-in-law. Tajuddin does not speak English, and my Dari is practically nonexistent. Using hand motions, I learned

Commander Massoud

I was to stay in the same room I had occupied the year before, comfortably furnished with two chairs, a coffee table, a dresser, and a bed – rarities in this part of Afghanistan. It was now late afternoon. Tajuddin left me alone, and I lay down on the bed in a familiar state of tired-but-alert relaxation. The whirring of the helicopter still rang in my ears.

I felt at home here with these people. They were among the most important representatives of the Northern Alliance. But to me, they were friends, whom I had known for years, even decades.

* * * * *

How did I get to Panjsher? I immediately began graduate studies in accounting and finance at Western Michigan University after returning from my solo trip around the world. That trip had been an adventure with a capital *A*. It was a life-changing experience in ways I would not recognize for years.

Following the trip, I held an entirely new perspective on life's possibilities. I was convinced that much of life is chance. One bus arrives on time; another ten minutes late; another goes over a cliff, never to arrive at all. As a wanderer, with no set agenda, I could equally well have been on any of them. Something about this *randomness* excited me. It was so different from the planned, structured life I had known. I resolved to bring more chance into my life or at least recognize it when it occurred. Foreshadowing of this mindset had appeared years earlier during my first year of college.

At the start of my freshman semester, I had to choose whether to sign up for ROTC – the Reserve Officers Training Corps. I flipped a coin and signed the papers! Joining ROTC set in motion a series of later events that shaped much of my adult life. My military deferment ended after a year of graduate school. I entered the U.S. Army as a Second Lieutenant in January 1963.

I learned military accounting at the Army Finance School at Fort Benjamin Harrison in Indianapolis. I was then assigned to a Finance Office in Pusan, Korea. I supervised payrolls and accounting plus served as Company Commander for the enlisted men. Ensuring that our U.S. troops and native employees were paid on time, without incident or theft, proved to be a challenge. It went like this: fly to Seoul, pick up $500,000 in payroll, fly back to the base in Pusan escorted by armed guards, exchange $100,000 in U.S. cash for Korean won to pay native employees. I had Military Police, Korean police, sedans, and aircraft at my disposal. Once we secured the money in the vehicles under armed military and civilian police guards, we transferred it between the vaults in the Finance Office and the Pusan Bank by racing through the streets of Pusan with sirens blaring, laughing aloud at the noise we made!

On most weekends, I hunted pheasant in the mountains with a Korean friend, Kim Tae-Ik. We slept with the mountain people in small village huts.

My Korean tour only lasted one year. From it, I learned that I enjoyed living in and adapting to a foreign land and working with people whose culture and background were different from mine.

My next assignment took me back to the U.S. Army Finance Cen-

ter at Fort Ben in Indianapolis. I
learned data processing and com-
puters there, years before the ad-
vent of PCs and the Internet. Such
things were rarities, complex and
miraculous. I seemed to rise to
their challenge. In December
1966, after another promotion
and almost three years at Fort
Ben, I received a call from Washington, DC.

L-R: Col. Yoon, Mrs Tae-Ik w/daughter,
Gary, Kim's brother, Kim, and daughter

"Captain Bowersox," the voice on the other end of the phone
asked, "Would you consider an assignment in Honolulu, Hawaii with
the U.S. Army Audit Agency?"

The sun had not shone in Indianapolis for over a week. Ah, that
randomness thing again!

"Let me think about it – but don't hang up. My answer is yes!"

The Hawaiian office serviced Japan, Korea, Okinawa, Taiwan,
and Viet Nam. I spent almost all of my time traveling around the Western Pacific as an Administration and Security Officer along with commanding 30 enlisted men. I thrived in these exotic locales. In 1969 the
US Army promoted me to the rank of Major. By then, even though the
Vietnam War would not officially end until 1973, the Army was scal-
ing back in size. This meant fewer long-term career opportunities and
chances for further rapid promotions. I decided to resign my commission.

What did I have in mind? I had seen quite a bit of how the world
works. The Army is good for that. It taught me about the dynamics of
power and money. And I knew I wanted some of each. I wanted to go
into business – whatever that meant.

While taking graduate school courses at the University of Hawaii, a Marine F-14 pilot Captain John Dohrman and I began studying
together. Soon after, we were making plans to open a business in Honolulu. We purchased a jewelry store at the front of the International
Marketplace in Waikiki and renamed it The Gem Tree. We had run
numbers on jewelry store profit margins, done a competitive market

The Gem Tree, International Market Place, Honolulu, Hawaii

analysis, and concluded that the jewelry business was a winner. At the time, I had no particular knowledge of or passion for gems and neither did John. But it looked like an excellent business opportunity.

Within two years we owned controlling interest in 12 companies, which employed over eight hundred people. But rapid growth and a couple of bad acquisitions developed into management and financial burdens we had not anticipated. I guess our eyes were bigger than our stomachs. Sadly for our friendship, with financial problems came partnership problems. We decided to sell the businesses and dissolve the partnership. Our parting was strained, but each of us left with $100,000 in cash. And now I knew the gem business.

With investors and profits from the sale, I opened a wholesale gem operation. My market was going to be Hawaii and the U.S. mainland, Japan and Hong Kong.

Starting in 1972, I began traveling to acquire cut gems: to New York City for diamonds; to Brazil for amethyst and citrine; to India, Burma and Thailand for sapphires and zircons; to Madagascar for gemological specimens; to Kenya for garnets; and to South Africa for tiger eye. My goal was to bypass the middlemen by going directly to the source and buying rough material or cut gems from the miners or their agents. In this way, I could pass along the savings to my buyers, have a competitive advantage over other dealers, and still earn a handsome profit for my company.

I soon learned that, in some cases, I could increase my profit margins by buying rough material in one country and taking it to another country which specialized in gem cutting. Brazil, Hong Kong and Thailand were noted for their gem cutting industries. I used all three. I loved the adventure, the travel, the cultural diversity and the bargaining. And I loved rubbing shoulders with the fascinating figures of the international gem trade.

Soon my business began to grow. I worked very hard buying here and selling there. I was happy, and in that frame of mind something opened up in me. I fell in love with a woman from Honolulu.

Wilma was both beautiful and exotic: half-Italian and half-Japanese. She was similar to me in many ways: we both liked nice things,

and we both felt that we were somehow different from other people. I proposed; she accepted, and we married. Later I would discover how different we really were – sadly, from each other.

I loved the travel and adventure of my work more than Wilma did, but she was a good sport about coming along. In 1975, we welcomed the birth of our beautiful

L-R: Prokofiev, Wilma, Brandi, Gary, and Prokofiev's son

daughter Brandi. Her arrival added a new and joyful dimension to my life.

Brandi turned out to be a good traveler; at the age of two months she began accompanying Wilma and me in globetrotting. In 1977, the three of us visited Afghanistan. Making our way through Kabul's Chicken Street Bazaar, piled high with richly colored Afghan carpets and surrounded by old guns and artifacts, we watched some workers washing and grading lapis at the government store. They let Brandi try rinsing the stones in water, making their brilliant deep blues and sparkling golds leap out! This was play to her! She didn't want to stop! And neither did I.

I was totally engaged: my family, my work, my love of travel, my thirst for adventure, all seamlessly blended together. It seemed too good to be true. And it was. Near ruin lay just around the corner.

* * * * *

Now, resting on a small bed in a small village in a remote area of northeastern Afghanistan, I waited for Tajuddin to call me to dinner. In the warmth of that August evening, I idled away the minutes, reflecting over the past thirty years. I never imagined the catastrophic events which would occur in both the United States and Afghanistan a few weeks later.

Brother Dennis, wife Laura and children,
Bree, Corry, and Blair with Brandi

*L-R: Brandi, Sen. Sparky
Matsunaga, and Gary*

*US Capitol, Washington, DC,
Brandi and Gary*

Central Asia

Chapter Two
Man of Action: Diamond and Lapis

The Decade of 1970s

When I get the urge to go, I think and act quickly. Only after I return from some faraway place do I completely reflect on what drove me there. And when I think about my underlying penchant for exotic travel, I see doors.

It seems to me that the universe, in all its randomness, continually places us next to *doors*. And I like to jiggle doorknobs. Some might continue straight down the corridor of life, whereas, I slow my pace and jiggle the doorknob of whichever door draws me to it. It just happens – I don't plan it. If the door opens, I go in. And I react instinctually to whatever I find. Only later do I take the time to look back at events and analyze them. There's my cycle: think; act; react; reflect, distill. I seem to repeat it in almost everything I do. When I find myself by chance next to a particular door, without a thought, I act. I jiggle the knob. No planning, no forethought. Just me and a door. And things go well when I operate like that.

Take this business of gems. I got into it for *rational* motives. John Dohrman and I had run some numbers of different retail businesses and the numbers looked better for the retail jewelry business than any of the others. If the numbers had been different, John and I could just as easily have ended up in the *widget* business. Who knows, maybe I would have discovered a passion for widgets. Just like good MBAs, we based our decision on the numbers – rationally and unemotionally. I wasn't attuned then to my intuition – the inner voice that is often a truer guide.

Later, when we were dissolving our company and selling off the assets, I discovered how much I loved the gem business. I realized my passion. Perhaps even at the time, what seemed to me to be rational and fact-based decision making was just my intuitive jiggling of a door that chance put next to me.

But why Afghanistan? I'd like to think that even before my first visit there in 1972, Afghanistan stirred something in me. The land itself is steeped in history evoking Kipling's tales, Alexander the Great, Genghis Khan, Timur, Babur, Marco Polo and a host of others. Except, I had not read Kipling since childhood, didn't remember much about Alexander or Marco Polo, and had never heard of Timur and Babur. I did find the country and the people intriguing, and Afghanistan promised a door to adventure. But so did Burma and Thailand and Madagascar. Business and adventure were my driving forces, but why in this place?

Afghanistan had one thing going for it. Just by chance, I had an *in* there. In 1972 my friend in the U.S. Department of Commerce (USDOC), familiar with my gem experience, asked if I could be of assistance in moving Afghanistan's rich blue lapis lazuli into the marketplace. The Afghans had a large amount to sell, and the country was something of a new frontier.

The United Nations, Russia, and the U.S. were well into the latter half of the Twentieth Century's version of *The Great Game* there. Each of the players had a different idea about how to generate exports and earn the hard currency that would help jump-start the Afghan economy. Geo-political stakes were on the table, and the players were serious. Afghanistan was heating up. Both Russia and the U.S. were providing foreign aid to Afghanistan. The U.S. was trying to match the Soviets by improving business and infrastructure development and funding construction projects.

On paper, Afghanistan had the potential to develop into a profitable exporter of gems and minerals. But in reality, the country was rural, agrarian, and mostly backward; it had transportation difficulties and erratic communications, and no organized mining was taking place, other than lapis. Moreover, differing tribal and ethnic factions, presided over by their own elected or self-appointed leaders, controlled different regions of the country. Poppies for opium and marijuana were openly grown, and Kabul, the capital, had rightly earned its reputation as a haven for hippies seeking easy access to illicit drugs.

On the other hand, Afghanistan held the most beautiful lapis lazuli the world over, and export quantities were now available! If sufficient international demand could be developed, Afghanistan stood to gain desperately-needed foreign currency. From my perspective as an international gem dealer, it looked as though I had a ground floor opportunity to help create and supply the U.S. market with lapis. I was intrigued!

At about the same time, again by chance, I met Omar Nassaeri, a student attending the University of Hawaii in Honolulu. It just so happened that Omar's father, Dr. Nassaeri, had recently retired as a geology professor at the University of Kabul. He was still living there and agreed to meet with me should I decide to go. Not long thereafter, I was on a plane bound for Kabul.

My introduction to Omar's father proved fortuitous. Dr. Nassaeri was a fountain of information. He offered a crash course in Afghan gems and minerals, along with expertise on geological research and exploration in Afghanistan. He taught me about the country, the people and the customs. We became fast friends. Looking back on those early years in Afghanistan, I warm to the memories of the many evenings I spent with Dr. Nassaeri and his family, sitting around a fire pit in the middle of their Kabul home, toasting our feet over the hot coals while the snow fell outside.

In addition to my meetings with Dr. Nassaeri, I drew heavily on the knowledge and contacts of the Commercial Attaché at the U.S. Embassy in Kabul. Through the Embassy, I was introduced to M. Faird Rafiq, President, Export Promotion Department. Rafiq had attended Harvard, spoke excellent English, and was committed to increasing Afghanistan's exports. His help and advice proved invaluable. As time went by, we both worked hard to develop programs to promote the sale and export of Afghan lapis. It was good for them, good for me, and good for Afghanistan. In fact, *life* was good!

I made many useful contacts in Kabul, but two in particular stood out. In 1974, I became acquainted with Dehzad, and Prokofiev. Dehzad, or more formerly, Engineer S. Hashem Dehzad, was the Director of Lapis Lazuli and Gemstone Sorting within the Afghan Ministry of Mines. We soon became good friends and remained so for many years, until I lost track of him during the turmoil in the mid-1980s.

V. Prokofiev was a Soviet advisor working for the United Nations. Officially, Prokofiev served as an economic development advisor to the Afghan Export Ministry in his capacity as a Project Manager for the United Nations Conference for Trade and Development (UNCTAD).

Unofficially, this generic job description meant that besides whatever he was doing for the U.N., he was probably also either working for or reporting to the Soviet Committee for State Security – the notorious KGB. M. Farid Rafiq appointed Prokofiev to be my direct contact.

Prokofiev was like-able and well-connected at many levels within the Afghan government. I respected his abilities to survive and to get things done under difficult and sometimes turbulent working conditions. And on some visceral level, I sensed that he was not just out for himself; he felt that his U.N. work in helping to develop Afghanistan's

L-R: Prokofiev, Ministry of Mines Staff, surrounding Gary

exports was important and could make a difference to this impoverished country.

In 1974, I founded United Gem Merchants. I initially occupied a small office in the Bank of Hawaii building in Waikiki. The company prospered, and by 1976, I had a staff of five employees. That year, we moved into larger quarters in the Pioneer Plaza building in downtown Honolulu. I soon increased the staff to ten, including two gem cutters, an appraiser, and a three-man sales team. Meanwhile my friends Tom Sullivan and Ralph Valentine started marketing my gems in Ohio and Michigan, respectively.

You might wonder what my early motivation was. Was it just about money? Yes, in the beginning, it was – but that was back then. I had yet to learn that there were much larger stakes involved. For some of us, we have to learn a lesson more than once to fully grasp it.

By 1975, after nearly fours years of buying lapis directly from the Afghan government – and being the only American who legally could – I asked Rafiq to formally appoint me as the exclusive importer of Afghan lapis into the United States. Rafiq and Prokofiev both supported the idea. Rafiq gave me a verbal approval but reminded me that official government approval might take some time. The following year, the official approval came through. In October 1976, four years after that chance phone call about Afghan lapis from my friend at the U.S. Commerce Department, the Government of Afghanistan formally appointed me the exclusive importer and distributor of Afghan lapis in the United States.

During the years from 1973 through 1979, I made three or four buying trips a year to Afghanistan. Getting there was never easy. The difficulties of arranging a trip to Kabul usually required a week to ten days just to plan my itinerary and set up appointments. Even making a phone call there was difficult as calls had to be booked in advance with an operator in Paris, France. If the call to Kabul was not answered I had to rebook the call for another time. Once in Kabul, I would spend another two or three weeks inspecting, grading and selecting the lapis I wanted to buy. Then I would prepare my offer and eventually negotiate an acceptable price. Finally, I would arrange for shipment of my purchased goods, except the best quality lapis. I would usually hand-carry these gems with me back to Hawaii. I would often take the medium-to-high quality pieces to Hong Kong, to have them cut into statues or figurines or made into beads.

I soon learned my way around the Afghan bureaucracy. Fortunately, the officers and staff of the various Afghan Ministries I dealt with were diligent, friendly, and willing to provide assistance. As in many developing countries, ministerial staffs were small, with very few assistants. Secretaries and clerical help did not exist. Under such conditions, the pace of business and negotiations moved slowly.

During these same years, I expanded my travels to other countries to buy other colored gems and crystals. I mainly went to Brazil, Hong Kong and Thailand, sometimes buying cut gems; at other times buying *rough* in one country and taking it to another to be cut into beads, cabochons or a variety of faceted shapes. Several trips to Burma, Kenya, Madagascar and Sri Lanka did not hold much promise for good business for a variety of reasons.

When I accumulated enough inventory, I distributed some to my two sales offices on the U.S. mainland and parceled out some to my

Corporate Meeting on the beach at Makaha, Hawaii.
L-R: Front row: Brandi
2nd row: Jean and Bill Yellin
3rd row: Carol Sullivan, Betty and Jack Reigot
Back row: Sonia, Konno, Gary, Sue Valentine, Ellie Maddox,
Ralph Valentine, Larry Maddox

Directors Meeting
L to R: Bill Yellin, Tom Sullivan, Sue and Ralph Valentine, Gary and Brandi,
Ellie and Larry Maddox, Ed and Jean Rossi

Hawaii office to service our existing accounts. My Honolulu sales staff called on jewelers throughout Hawaii; my Detroit staff serviced the Midwest, and my Los Angeles office worked Southern California. I called on my Japanese and Hong Kong dealers personally.

My colored stones business was prospering; the lapis business from Afghanistan had proved to be such a bonus that I was now looking at other newly-discovered Afghan gems as well; and my wholesale diamond business had become profitable. Unfortunately, as I mentioned earlier, near ruin lay just around the corner. Diamonds proved to be the catalyst. Here is the story of what happened and the devastating effect it had on my life.

* * * * *

In 1974 as I was setting up United Gem Industries, I learned about a growing consumer demand for high quality diamonds among Japan's younger professional class. My experiences with Gem Tree in Honolulu had given me a jeweler's understanding of the diamond trade, and buying gems in the international market had exposed me to the periphery of the international diamond market on the wholesale side. To be successful in wholesaling diamonds to Japanese dealers, I would have to learn the ins and outs of the small Japanese diamond guild. I didn't think that would be a major obstacle.

Entering the Japanese market looked like an excellent opportunity, but would it be worth the risk? During my Army career I had been to Japan many times and knew my way around Tokyo. I liked Japan. I liked the Japanese. I admired their culture and was somewhat familiar with their business customs. These factors might give me a competitive advantage over any other American diamond merchants with similar ideas.

Decision time. Pursuing this endeavor would mean committing a substantial amount of my start-up capital to a diamond inventory. That was risky business, but I jiggled the doorknob and stepped inside.

First, I had to acquire an inventory of diamonds. Relying on contacts and introductions set up by colleagues in the gem industry, I flew to New York City and headed for the city's famous *Diamond District*. Within a few days, I had concluded meetings with several dealers. I settled on the firm of Landau & Co., in Rockefeller Center.

*L -R: Jack Reigot of Landau,
Jean and Bill Yellin,
Corporate Attorney*

Landau was a well-established and reputable diamond cutter and dealer with direct access to DeBeers. Moreover, two members of that firm, Jack Reigot and Bert Reinhold, were both enthusiastic and confident about my business prospects in Japan. By the time I left New York, I had bought tens of thousands of dollars worth of high-quality diamonds from Jack and Bert. I returned to Hawaii and began planning my trip to Japan.

By the clock, a flight from Honolulu to Tokyo took almost nine hours. In entertainment terms, it was a two-movie flight. Metered in food intake, it was two meals and a snack. When I finally landed in Tokyo, I was tired but alert. I hoped that my first experience as an international diamond dealer would go smoothly.

As I entered the scramble of Japanese Customs, a Japanese Customs officer asked me if I had anything to declare. I said yes – I had a commercial shipment of diamonds that I personally owned in my briefcase. He then advised me that due to the high value of the diamonds, I would have to make a formal customs entry using a customs broker. Until then, Customs would take my diamonds into custody and hold them until I either left Japan or arranged for a formal clearance! He then locked my briefcase, wrapped it in a brown paper bag, and had me write my signature across the bag. He then sealed it with wax and moved it to a secure holding area. When he returned, he simply waved me on and moved to the next traveler. Tired and confused, I hailed a taxi and

Max Miles

checked into the Imperial Hotel in downtown Tokyo. Sleep eluded me that night!

Early the next morning, I marched directly to the U.S. Department of Commerce's (USDOC) Tokyo Trade Center to see if they could help. I was directed to Mr. Max Miles, the Deputy Director, a professional and friendly man. After I explained what happened, he arranged for a series of phone calls to be made on my behalf.

"Don't worry, everything will work out," he said.

It wasn't that simple. But after more phone calls, the intervention of his Japanese assistant, and finally Max talking directly to a Japanese Customs supervisor, my diamonds were released to the U.S. Trade Center. A Customs officer would deliver the sealed package with my diamonds inside. I was to cut the wax seal in his presence, inspect my diamonds, and sign a release form.

Hanging up the phone, Max suggested that I hire one of the Trade Center's part-time interpreters to help me search for potential customers. I agreed. Hiring an interpreter solved the language problem, and I would soon have my diamonds back. Had my inventory been stolen or confiscated, my diamond career would have ended before it began.

During the next week I sold enough inventory to pay my travel and hotel expenses. More importantly, I learned about Tokyo's Jewelry Trade Center at Hamamatsu-Cho, where gems and jewelry were sold to Japanese diamond wholesalers. To my surprise, many of the Japanese wholesalers there did not have a ready or reliable source of diamonds. I resolved to remedy that problem!

My entry into the Japanese wholesale diamond business had been a *learn-as-you-go* experience. By the end of four weeks, I had acquired a good working knowledge of the market. My most valuable resource was Mr. Tetsuo Akiyama, president of a wholesale gem importing firm called Manston Trading

Tetsuo Akiyama and Gary after fishing for tuna on Konno Coast, Hawaii

Company. Manston's bookkeeper, Mr. Tadokuro, joined us at our dinner meetings and acted as interpreter since he spoke excellent English, and Mr. Akiyama didn't speak it at all.

When I returned to Hawaii, I studied the USDOC's *World Trade Data Reports* to research the Japanese companies with whom I had met. But out of all the Japanese companies I had visited, only three were large enough to merit an USDOC report. All three reports were favorable, including one on Manston Trading Company. The Economic Officer officially signed each at the U.S. Embassy in Tokyo.

Within a month, using the *Trade Data* reports, I was back in Tokyo selecting reliable business associates. Relying on the *Trade Data* report for Manston Trading and the personal rapport I had established with Akiyama on my first trip, I entered into a business relationship with Akiyama in which I sold him diamonds on credit.

As my Japanese diamond business started to grow, I began to make cold calls on diamond wholesalers in Hong Kong as well. During one trip I met Warren and Casey Leong, third generation jewelers and diamond wholesalers. Their company, B. Green Ltd., was located in a high-rise building on Hong Kong Island only a few blocks from the Star Ferry. We struck up a fine friendship, and they began purchasing small quantities of diamonds from me.

Before long, I was making bi-monthly trips to Japan and Hong Kong with my briefcase full of diamonds. What could be better than that? Fair dealing at fair prices with friends; traveling to exotic destinations and warm welcomes upon arrival. A *win-win* combination in the game of life, with jackpots for all!

I dealt only in extremely high-quality diamonds with carat weights just below the standard one carat, one-half carat, one-third carat, and one-quarter carat sizes preferred in the American market. The slightly smaller diamonds I sold, in carat weights that were hard to move in the U.S. market, were most welcome in Japan and Hong Kong. My profit margins were slim, but I managed to cover my expenses and still have a little spare change.

As the months went by and our diamond sales increased, Akiyama attempted to learn English. Our business relationship grew and so did our friendship. Akiyama made several visits to Hawaii. Joe Phillips, one of my corporate directors, had a sailboat he kept at the Waikiki Yacht Club, and the three of us spent many enjoyable days sailing. On other occasions I took Akiyama deep-sea fishing off Hawaii's Kona Coast.

A year or so passed by. Although I felt confident about my business with Akiyama and Manston, with so much money and inventory at risk I continued to order updated credit reports on Manston. And then, in 1976 just three weeks after receiving an updated USDOC report which recommended Manston as a reliable trading partner, disaster struck. I received the proverbial phone call in the middle of the night! It was Mr. Tadokuro, Akiyama's bookkeeper.

"Mr. Bowersox, you should come to Tokyo immediately," he said with an odd strain in his voice. Over the miles of underwater cable, he sounded *very* concerned, his voice full of alarm. Before I could reply, he rushed on.

"There is a problem with your diamond account. I am a Christian and I need to tell you something about Mr. Akiyama that may cause you to lose your money."

Tadokuro now had my undivided attention. I had trusted my judgment of others. I was in my mid-thirties. I had crisscrossed the world buying and selling gems. I had commanded troops. I had been a Major in the United States Army for God's sake! What was happening?

Hours later I was on a Pan Am flight to Tokyo. While I was checking into the Imperial Hotel, I spotted Tadokuro waiting for me. He informed me that he feared Akiyama might possibly leave Japan and go into hiding. Two large diamond dealers with debts totaling over ten million dollars had just filed for bankruptcy and one of them owed a considerable amount to Manston Trading.

Mr. Tadokuro and I grabbed a taxi and were soon in the Manston office. As we walked in, Akiyama saw me. The look on his face was one of stunned disbelief. I confronted him and told him I was there to review my account. Akiyama confirmed Tadokuro's story that two of his customers had filed bankruptcy and would not be able to pay him, and he would, therefore, not be able to pay me. I asked if he thought he could work himself out of this crisis if I continued selling to him on an extended credit basis – *if* I could get Landau & Co., my New York diamond supplier, to agree.

I had already alerted Landau and explained the situation to them. They had agreed to extend some forbearance on Akiyama's behalf – really though, on my behalf – if I thought I could work things out with Akiyama. Akiyama and I managed to reach a preliminary agreement of sorting out the shortfall in his account. With the basics of a workout plan in place, I privately thanked Tadokuro. I returned to Honolulu, worried but hopeful.

Back in my office in Honolulu, I kept thinking how risky and difficult this was going to be. Akiyama had assured me he would keep his commitments, but why had Tadokuro called me, not Akiyama. I felt, though, that if Tadokuro witnessed anything amiss, he would call me again. I was right about Tadokuro but wrong about Akiyama. The following Saturday morning, I was awakened by a telephone call. I heard Tadokuro's voice.

"Mr. Bowersox, this is Mr. Tadokuro. Mr. Akiyama has left Japan and all the diamonds are gone!" The panic in his voice was genuine.

That very night, I was back on a flight to Tokyo, trying not to panic before hearing all the details. There had to be a solution.

On arriving at the Imperial Hotel, I met Mr. Tadokuro and a Manston colleague. I learned that Akiyama had disappeared after taking virtually all the diamonds and cash still at Manston. No one had any indication of where he was hiding, and he evidently did not plan on returning since along with the diamonds and cash, he had also taken his prized sword collection, which he kept in his office.

At the Manston office the next morning, Tadokuro and I went over the records. I came face-to-face with the dire straits I was now in. Besides absconding with $150,000 of my diamonds, another $30,000 in cash owed to me from previous sales was also missing. It was no consolation that three other dealers' gems and money were also missing. Akiyama gouged one diamond merchant from India for over a million dollars!

Over the next few days, I made numerous trips to the U.S Trade Center, the U.S. Embassy, the Japanese Police and a Japanese attorney I retained. Max Miles from the Trade Center and his wife Trish graciously extended the hospitality of their home to me so that I might keep my expenses to a minimum. Unfortunately, the rest of my efforts to recover either money or diamonds were for naught.

Over the next six or eight months, I returned to Japan once to attend the court hearing of my civil suit against Akiyama and Manston. At the hearing, the court awarded me a judgment for $180,000, the entire amount of my loss. With that judgment in hand and knowing that Akiyama was now living in South Africa, we tried to get the Japanese authorities to have Akiyama apprehended. No luck. While they did consider it to be a criminal matter, my civil suit judgment against Akiyama barred them from proceeding with criminal charges. In short, the Japanese authorities would do nothing. Akiyama would go unpunished.

With the loss of so much of my diamond inventory and working capital, I slowly spiraled into debt. With the overhead of a large new office, additional staff, and the beginning of a downturn in the U.S. economy, my expenses remained high and jewelry sales declined.

Through the end of the 1970s and into the early 1980s, I struggled to recover financially. I continued my overseas trips to Afghanistan, Japan, Hong Kong and elsewhere. I managed a respectable level of sales, but Akiyama's theft had dealt my company a mortal wound. And we were slowly bleeding to death.

The burden of this debt also weighed heavily on my personal life. The strain took its toll on my marriage. I was forced to take my company into Chapter 11 bankruptcy. I hoped that with court protection from my creditors I would be able to reorganize the business, regain solid footing, and pay off my company's debt. But all this disarray proved too great for my wife, and we decided that it was best to separate. In the first half of the 1980s, we divorced, and my Chapter 11 reorganization became a Chapter 7 complete liquidation of my company.

I was living a nightmare. I was over forty, nearly broke, had no place to live and couldn't even draw unemployment, as I had refused to draw a salary from my company for two years while I tried to save the business. I had lost my company and the monies friends had invested in it, caused the loss of jobs of people I cared about, and the monies from suppliers who had relied on me, and on a personal level, lost my wife and a small fortune in personal assets. I was shattered.

Fortunately for me, friends and former gem suppliers, to whom I shall always be grateful, came to my rescue. Without them, I am unsure what would have become of me. On several occasions, I camped out at friends' houses or apartments for weeks at a time, with no place to go and nothing to do but take long walks on the beach.

Several former gem suppliers offered to provide me with inventory and generous repayment terms if I decided that I wanted to start over again. This was just the break I needed – a means to get back into the gem business. Life is interesting – as some doors close, others swing open.

However, before United Gem Merchants faded into oblivion, other forces and events had come into play in the intervening years. Those forces and events would tie my future and my eventual recovery much more closely to Afghanistan than I could ever have imagined.

MINISTRY OF COMMERCE

Dept. (Export Promotion

No. ....

Date .October..30.,..1976

تجارت وزارت

)   (ریاست

) . (مدیریت

)   (خانگه

مبر ع.........

نیته و د ۱۳۰

REPUBLIC OF AFGHANISTAN

United Gem Merchants
2222 Kalakaua Avenue
Suite 1305/Honolulu
Hawaii 96815
U.S.A.

Dear Mr. G. Bowersox,

    This letter is to inform anyone interested that United Gem

Merchants is the Ministry of Commerce of Afghanistan exclusive

U.S. Importer and Distributor of Lapis-Lazuli.

Faird Rafiq, President
Export Promotion Department

US Exclusive Agreement for the sale of lapis

Kabul (Caboul) Area Map – Late 1600s

Chapter Three
Danger in Kabul

September – October 1979

A phone call from my Soviet friend Prokofiev in Kabul alerted me that something out of the ordinary – even by Afghan standards – was in the works. As always, Prokofiev phoned me at a pre-agreed time and a particular public pay phone in Honolulu. (*Specialists* had warned me that it might be unwise to receive calls from Afghanistan on my home phone.) Prokofiev's news was not altogether startling but it was certainly interesting.

"The Afghan government is anxious to sell their current supply of lapis, tourmaline, kunzite – and maybe some emeralds before everything falls apart." As if to emphasize the message, his voice began to break up because of the poor connection from Kabul through Paris. His reference to "before everything falls apart" was prescient. The Soviets were definitely preparing to do something – and something big – but nobody was sure what.

At the time of Prokofiev's call in late September 1979, a good friend and business associate was visiting me in Honolulu. Joao Bosco Monteiro, an attorney educated in Brazil and now an international gem wholesaler, had arrived a day or so earlier, bringing a variety of colored gems from Brazil: aquamarines, amethysts, citrines and topazes.

The morning after Prokofiev's call, I went to my office with Joao and worked until noon grading stones and selecting the ones I wanted. I ended up purchasing several thousand dollars of Joao's merchandise, but three hours of peering at stones through a 10-power jewelers loupe under bright lights had worn me out. I was ready for a nap on the beach. I needed to rest my strained eyes, and I wanted some quiet time to mull over Prokofiev's intriguing news.

The beach winds were kind, and the palms swayed gently against the blue of the Hawaiian sky. Joao and I placed our grass mats on the sand not far from the shoreline near Waikiki's famous *Pink Palace,* the pink-hued Royal Hawaiian Hotel. The summer tourist season was nearly over, and the beach was quiet except for two young boys playing in the surf. I lay down to take a nap, but Joao remained vigilant, on the lookout for any bikini-clad girls who might wander by.

I was dozing off when I heard Joao exclaim, "Wow! Take a look at her!"

I slit my eyes open just long enough to appreciate what had caught Joao's full attention – an unusually pretty girl in a very small bikini walking seductively down the beach. Ipanema in Honolulu! Joao, being young, single, and Latin, was fantasizing out loud.

Gary and Joao inspecting matched pair of triangle-shaped kunzites weighing a total of 405 carats

Closing my eyes again, I said, "You want some *real* excitement? Why not come with me to Afghanistan!"

"Afghanistan? Isn't that dangerous?"

Leaving his question unanswered, I asked, "Well, do you want to go along? My contacts there want to keep our gem business alive."

"Can I buy rough?"

"Sure. They have more than I can afford to purchase."

"I'll call Brazil tomorrow to make sure the money is available."

"You have enough time," I assured him. "It will take me about ten days to set up the trip."

I did not tell Joao that I would be calling my Honolulu contact with the Central Intelligence Agency the next morning. In the midst of the Cold War, meeting with the CIA, or the KGB for that matter, would have labeled me a *spook* – a spy – and made me a walking target in Central Asia. For security reasons, I didn't tell anyone – not even my family and associates – about my frequent visits to the CIA in Honolulu.

Initially, I had been contacted by a CIA officer working out of their downtown Honolulu office. Apparently, my regular travels to so many third world countries had come to their attention. They thought I might be able to provide a different point of view from that of their

Waikiki Beach, Oahu, Hawaii

own resources. I agreed to be *debriefed* from time to time, but in exchange I asked for permission to query them on political and safety issues for the countries I was visiting. Money was never an issue. It was never offered, and if it had been, I would have refused.

Usually, we met to exchange information. I told them what I had seen on the ground during my visits. Sometimes we expanded our discussion to include Middle Eastern and Central Asian politics. At times my information was more current than theirs. But on this occasion, *I* wanted an up-to-date assessment of the unfolding Afghan situation.

About eighteen months earlier (in April 1978), a coup d'etat in Kabul had brought the Communist Peoples Democratic Party (PDPA) into power. Then, in February 1979, Adolph Dubs, the U.S. Ambassador to Afghanistan, had been kidnapped and then killed during a rescue operation. And just one week prior to my meeting with the CIA, the President of Afghanistan, Nur Mohammad Taraki, had been assassinated. Clearly, Kabul was unstable. After a thirty-minute conversation with my CIA contact, I felt reasonably confident that my trip to Kabul would be relatively safe. Hopefully, it would also prove to be successful.

At eleven that evening in Honolulu, it was two-thirty the next afternoon in Kabul – half a world away. The rain was falling and the trade winds had picked up. The wind and the dampness made it seem uncomfortably cool. I was at the appointed place at the appointed time – the neighborhood pay phone in Honolulu. I dialed the Paris operator to check on my reserved call time for my phone call to Afghanistan. The Paris operator replied she was having difficulty getting through to Kabul. She tried again and continued every few minutes until the wee hours, but to no avail. There was nothing for me to do but wait impatiently outside the phone booth for the callback. I finally gave up and returned to my apartment; tired, frustrated, and thoroughly chilled. The second night wasn't any better. Finally, on the third night at one in the morning, the call went through and Prokofiev answered. The poor connection crackled like bacon frying in a pan.

"Hello, hello," speaking slowly and loudly, I repeated over and over.

Finally I heard Prokofiev's familiar voice. "I am so happy to hear from you!"

Sparing no time for niceties, I jumped into the business at hand.

"I'm planning to come to Kabul as soon as possible, and I'm bringing my friend. He's an international gem dealer; his name is Joao."

"It is safe for you. You and your friend are welcome anytime. I will inform your friend Dehzad, and we will prepare the gems for your inspection."

With my call to Prokofiev completed, I set about choosing the best route to Kabul. Deciding on which airlines to use always involved a combination of educated guesswork and a fair amount of luck. This time, based on my assessment of the best connecting times to make the fastest trip (and weighing the reliability of the airlines involved and the cost), I chose a route that would take us to Kabul via Seoul, Bangkok, and New Delhi. I always hoped for the best, but I knew from experience that chance was apt to intervene. We would probably be slowed down, if not waylaid. It happened in New Delhi; we were stopped in our tracks after thirty hours of mind-numbing travel.

At the New Delhi airport, the Indian officials led Joao, our planeload of motley passengers, and me into a dirty, airless, crowded

40-foot by 40-foot marble-floored room completely devoid of furniture. This was the *lounge* for transiting passengers, and it was already packed with about one hundred people. There were two lavatories. One was out of order; the other was filthy. We were told that our connecting flight to Kabul on Ariana Afghan Airways was delayed for 12 hours. Unaccustomed to this type of travel, Joao asked in a dismayed tone what we were going to do for the next 12 hours.

"Joao," I told him, "In this part of the world, I've never taken a plane that left on schedule. What do we do? *Carpe diem!* We sleep."

The Transit Lounge reeked of unwashed bodies. I was glad I had trained myself, years ago, to sleep nearly anywhere. Glancing around to assess our situation, I pointed to a spot ten feet away.

"There's room for you between those two fellows over there. Be sure to use your bag as a pillow. That way, if somebody grabs it, you'll wake up when your head hits the marble floor!"

Leaving my friend and stepping over a number of sleeping men, I bedded down between two malodorous turbaned characters. Just before dozing off, I glanced over at Joao and saw him sitting forlornly atop his carry-on. He resembled a silhouette of Rio de Janeiro's Corcovado, hulking over his own little sea of reeking humanity. He had lit a cigarette, but then realized that the only ashtray available was the square yard of real estate where he would soon lay his head. He cupped the ashes in his hand, gave up, and finally rubbed them into his trousers. Amused by his performance but wanting to rest, I closed my eyes and drifted off to sleep.

Time seems irrelevant to most people in this part of the world. I tried to adopt their approach – a resigned stoicism. I slept fitfully, turning frequently until I was equally bruised on all sides, trying to save up energy for whatever might lie ahead. The hours passed slowly and uncomfortably, marked only by my changes of position.

I awoke to the sound of voices in strange tongues. Our flight had arrived and was ready to board. We were elated to leave that lounge after the 15 miserable hours we had spent there. The date was October 14, 1979. We were hungry and jet-lagged. As we waited in line to board our flight to Kabul, I calculated that we had already been enroute more than 45 hours.

On the flight, we eagerly ate whatever was offered. To this day I have no memory of the food, only of the sweet tea, which, cup by cup, gradually revived me. Our *horizontal visit* to New Delhi faded from memory.

The final leg of our flight proved uneventful. As we exited the plane in Kabul, a polished-looking young man with an olive complexion and straight black hair approached the ramp. From the top of the ramp, he appeared shorter than his 5'6" frame. Introducing himself and shaking my hand, he told me in accented English that he had been sent by his boss, Mr. Prokofiev, to escort us to the UN compound. His name was Meghdessian, and he was from Lebanon.

During the 1970s, English was the *lingua franca* among Afghanistan's eight major languages and 20-odd dialects. English was taught locally beginning in grade schools and continuing through university level at Kabul University. I had mastered a few Arabic words and phrases from lessons I had taken in Hawaii, plus I had picked up bits and pieces of other languages, but I was really like the punch line of the old joke: "What word describes someone who speaks only one language? ... American!"

Still, it was strange to see a banner in English, which spanned the entire roof of the airport terminal building, proclaiming "WELCOME TO THE LAND OF THE NEW MODERN REVOLUTION." I don't know if Joao read anything into the sign, but to me it rang of socialist cant. I confess to a deep-seated and perhaps irrational suspicion of that sort of rhetoric. Hailing from the land where advertising has been lifted to an art form, I expect a higher caliber of propaganda. To be fair, perhaps the words were wishful. Or perhaps being saturated on Western-style rhetoric, I was being too cynical. But the Kabul I witnessed through the window of Prokofiev's UN vehicle put the lie to the banner's words.

Kabul, in late 1979, had very little new or modern about it. The city's once historic grace, chronicled by the travel writer Nancy Dupree in her guidebooks, was nowhere to be seen in any part of Kabul. Only a few sidewalk tables and brightly-colored umbrellas beckoned weary sightseers. The streets were crowded with people – Afghans, Soviets, Pakistanis, Pashtuns, and assorted others – brushing by each other as they nervously hurried along. Horses with turbaned riders galloped down narrow alleyways. Taxi horns blared. The last vestiges of the hippie culture that had made Kabul a mandatory stop on their hedonistic trail were seen here and there, standing in small groups looking uneasy or bewildered as if they had lost their tribe. More to the point, the place seemed to have an air of worried expectancy and an almost palpable sense of danger.

Geography and destiny are intertwined. This ancient capital had been a center of trade and conflict for more than a thousand years. Through the ages, Afghanistan's mountain passes provided passageways to Iran, Central Asia, India, Pakistan, and the Arabian Sea. Afghanistan often served as a buffer among competing empires and political ideologies, in an area where many foreign armies have marched. And Kabul, seldom able to resist, has more or less accepted them all: diplomats, businessmen, displaced tribal farmers, hippies, drifters, and the occasional archeologist and gem dealer.

Our trip from Hawaii had taken nearly 50 hours. Meghdessian checked us into the United Nations Guest House and told us lunch would be served in the dining room in 20 minutes. I went to my room just long enough to rinse a layer of road dirt off of my hands and face.

The United Nations Guest House was by no means posh, but it was decent. It housed various

L-R: Joao, Gary, and Meghdessian at United Nations Guest House, Kabul

dignitaries and officials when they came to visit. There were some military uniforms about, representing some degree of safety. After a lunch of roasted chicken, fresh tomatoes, cucumbers, and green tea, we returned to our shared room primed for sleep. Before I settled down for a nap, Prokofiev phoned, welcomed us to Kabul and advised that he would be sending a car and driver for us the following morning. I then phoned Mr. Freres, the U.S. Embassy's Commercial Officer, to report our presence in Afghanistan and to receive a quick briefing on the current situation in Kabul. Then I slept.

I awakened to the ringing phone. It was seven p.m. Through the fog of exhaustion, I heard Prokofiev's concerned voice.

"There have been some security problems on the southern road out of Kabul," he warned me, "…and in Rishkur just a few miles south of Kabul. I will have to stay in the Soviet Compound until the danger has passed and the problems are resolved. I will call you again tomorrow morning at eight."

I immediately thought back to our conversation when I was in Hawaii. Prokofiev had told me "It is safe for you." Had things really changed so quickly?

Fifteen minutes later, Freres called:

"A division of Afghan Army soldiers has attempted a *coup d'etat* in Kabul. The city is teetering on the edge of violence. We've been receiving *Alert* status reports more often than weather reports."

I tried to assimilate the information. I knew that the alert status levels ranged from *Routine* to *Travel only as necessary within Kabul* to *Stay inside* to *Take cover in your building* to *Proceed to evacuation point.* We were at Phase Two: Stay inside. What might the status level mean for me and for the safety of Joao, who had put himself into my keeping? Not realizing the seriousness of my conversation, Joao had fallen back into a deep sleep.

 **via** **Graphnet**

3E D102 1-1 P908 25 10/01/79 09:37 00000 0049L JTZ

GARY W BOWERSOX PRESIDENT
UNITED GEM MERCHANTS
HONOLULU HI
TEL (808) 923-1288 OR 923-1911

HAVE RECEIVED YOUR CABLE INFORMING US OF YOUR PROPOSED
OCTOBER 14 ARRIVAL AT KABUL. PLEASE CONTACT EMBASSY UPON
ARRIVAL FOR LATEST READING OF SECURITY SITUATION.
REGARDS, FRERES, CHIEF, ECON-COMMERCIAL SECTION
AMERICAN EMBASSY KABUL AFGHANISTAN 7233

FAXGram received in Hawaiian office on 10/18 after
Joao and Gary had departed

"The curfew in Kabul is 2300 hours each night," continued the diplomat, "…with a large number of searchlights being turned on the terrain around Kabul, as well as several blockades set up. Hafizullah Amin has appointed himself Chairman of the Revolutionary Council, Prime Minister, and Secretary General of the Peoples' Democratic Party. The announcement came after he had smothered Taraki, the last President, with his own pillow. He is definitely a hard-line revolutionary."

"I've received several anonymous reports of Soviet advisors being killed," he added, "One of those happened a week ago. Two Soviets, walking through a bazaar, had been stabbed in the back by Afghans. The identities of their assailants are still not known. In addition, fighting broke out near the Peoples House and in a park area in the Shahrenaw district."

"OK, I understand. I'll see you around noon tomorrow," I said, replacing the phone. I walked to the bed and fell hard asleep. Some information is best processed that way.

Half an hour later, we were awakened by the "rat-tat-tat-tat-tat" of automatic weapons, followed by a loud KABOOM. Joao's feet hit the floor; the walls moved in and out, and furniture bounced in place as the building shuddered from the impact.

"What was that?" Joao cried out, terrified.

"In Vietnam we called that a rocket," I told him with a little grin. Perhaps it was because of my combat experience, perhaps I was slow to wake, but I remained calm, even bemused by Joao's response.

"Rat-tat-tat-tat." More gunfire. And now the phone was ringing. I answered. Silence. I hung up. It rang again.

I could hear a faint voice, "Hello, hello, hello." Then dead silence again. The phone rang again. It was Prokofiev.

"We have a situation!"

Yes, we do, I thought.

"Stay where you are and I will call back in 30 minutes."

"Yes, yes, I understand," I said, hanging up. Joao, wide-eyed, was peeking out the window, barely moving the curtain so he wouldn't attract attention. He wanted to know what was going on outside but was afraid to look lest he find out. No way we were leaving our room.

The phone rang again. The connection still wasn't good, but I recognized it was Freres again. "There are attacks in the streets."

"Yes, we know. Prokofiev just called to tell us that some Afghans called *Freedom Fighters* are in the city with guns. He told us not to worry, as the government forces have been sent to arrest them," I said matter-of-factly, thinking that this was all there was to the situation.

Sounding alarmed at my relaxed attitude, Ferres insisted, "Information has it that some of the Afghan government forces have joined the Freedom Fighters. Now the Soviet security forces are battling both units."

The gravity of our situation now struck me. I compensated for my growing concern by joking, "Thanks for the good news."

Only hearing my half of the conversation, Joao nervously asked, "What was that about?"

"The Soviets are now fighting the Afghans."

Rat-a-tat-a-tat-tat ! More gunfire! Automatic weapons – closer this time – no more than a block from our building. Another loud KABOOM resonated through the dark night, followed by a red glow that lit up the streets of the city. In a near panic, Joao shouted, "I didn't come here to fight a war!"

I was still trying to make light of the situation, in order not to alarm Joao. I joked, "Don't worry, I'll ship your body back in the most beautiful lapis box that Brazil has ever seen. You'll be famous."

"Thanks, Major," a name with which he had tagged me because of my former rank in the U.S. Army.

An hour later, the gunfire and bombing were letting up. Prokofiev called again, "All is safe inside the city."

"Thanks for taking care of the problem," I said, jokingly. "We will see you in the morning."

I turned to Joao and repeated Prokofiev's message. We were still exhausted from our trip. "Tomorrow's going to be a busy day. We have business to do. Let's try to get some sleep," I suggested, as I crawled back into my single bed, pulling its worn-but-crisp cotton sheets over my shoulder, far too tired to process the intermittent warfare going on around us.

Dawn brought with it the distant sounds of continued fighting.

The city was awakening; we watched through the window of the Guest House. People cautiously began to move through the eerie quiet of the streets. At around 8 a.m., Prokofiev arrived, dressed in a coat and tie. His driver was wearing a shalwar kamese, the long knee-length shirt worn over balloon pants by most Afghans. Joao and I had just finished a hearty breakfast of fried eggs, toast, and coffee, which we enjoyed as if it might be our last.

As the driver opened the old black sedan door for us, Prokofiev greeted us. I introduced Joao and then he informed us, "The attempted coup was effectively crushed, but there are still some pockets of resistance." The sound of gunfire echoed only two or three miles away. Joao looked scared. I was concerned as well, although my bearded, stoic, Germanic face didn't show it

Engineer S. Hashem Dehzad

Safely arriving at the Ministry of Mines office, Dehzad was at the door waiting for us. He smiled and wrapped his arms around me, "Mr. Gary, it is good to see you," he said.

After apologizing for the political situation, he turned into a large office and introduced us to Dr. Zia-Zadah, the new Minister of Mines. The pandemonium that was occurring in Kabul had not outwardly touched the Minister or his office quarters. Professional in manner and dressed in a Western suit and tie, he invited us to join him for tea. He was clearly a power player in the game of Afghan politics, yet gracious, with a touch of formality.

The Minister explained how the gem purchase would proceed, "Gentlemen, you must understand that all purchases must be approved by the Afghan Government Cabinet before the gems can be exported."

Whispering to Joao, I joked, "This will pose a great problem. Trying to get a group of Afghans to agree on anything is like trying to get a horse to drink whiskey!"

Indicating that the formality of the social tea had concluded, our host arose.

"We have arranged for you to inspect our inventory."

He led us across the narrow street from the President's office to an unadorned Soviet-built cement building. I had no doubt that the

L-R: Unknown, Eng. Dehzad, Unknown, Unknown, Finance
Minister, Gary, Dr. Zia-Zadah, and Assadullah Amin

guards – who were everywhere and all armed with AK-47s – were at full alert and instantly ready to fire.

An escort waited to lead us down into a long, narrow, whitewashed but dimly lit hallway in the basement. All of the doors along the hallway were padlocked. Just before the end of the passage we approached a door guarded by two soldiers with old British Enfield rifles. I could feel the anticipation running up my spine. In the faint light we could see the door was sealed with a four-inch padlock securely wrapped with a roll of white adhesive tape. The tape was covered with graffiti-like signatures in blue and black ink.

Joao, looking puzzled, asked me softly, "What is this about?"

"It is the communist system of distrust," I responded. "The owners of these signatures must be present to open and close the door." And indeed, by now the Ministers of Mines, Finance, Lapis, and Security were all present.

Without a word, Dr. Zia-Zadah handed one of the guards his Swiss Army knife to cut the tape, while the Minister of Finance handed the other guard a three-inch-long key. Turning the key in the padlock, the guard opened the lock, removed it and pressed the heavy metal door open. Joao and I stepped into the edge of a small windowless room, under the watchful eyes of all present. Wow! The room was filled with an enormous pile of royal blue rock rising to the top of the eight-foot ceiling. I had never dreamed of such a large hoard of lapis.

Dr. Zia-Zadah said, "Please step back outside."

Two guards arrived with buckets of water. Joao and I stepped outside to give them room and to watch through the doorway as they splashed water on the pile of lapis. The royal blue color jumped.

Joao and I stood mesmerized at the sight. Dr. Zia-Zadah explained, "This lapis has been collected over the past hundred years. This is some of the finest lapis our country has produced. There are more than 50 tons here. It comes from mines that date back before 4000 B.C. My doctoral dissertation was completed on lapis at the Soviet University." I struggled to keep my eyes from popping out of their sockets!

From behind us Dehzad announced, "We would like to sell this lapis to you, Mr. Gary."

Joao glanced at me. We both restrained our excitement, as we spent the next 20 minutes washing individual pieces in water to get an idea of the color, quality and corresponding worth of the lapis. It soon became apparent that the appraisal would take several days and that the assessed value would be vastly more than we could finance on this trip. But I played it cool, as if I were unimpressed or accustomed to seeing such riches. Rising and turning to leave the overcrowded room, I asked Dr. Zia-Zadah, "What else do you have to show us?"

"After lunch tomorrow we will schedule another appointment to view emerald, tourmaline, and kunzite. It is not available today." A guard blew out the lantern, locked the door, taped the lock, and held it steady for our hosts to write their names. Leaving two guards behind, we silently followed the other guards back the way we had entered the building through the lengthy basement hallway.

On the drive back to the UN compound after lunch, Prokofiev warned us, "It would best be for you if I stay out of the negotiations. There are people who want to take the lapis to Russia without payment." Out of concern for our safety, he warned us, "Soviets are beginning to get a bad name here. When you meet new Afghan people, immediately tell them you are Americans."

That afternoon Mr. Meghdessian, Prokofiev's Lebanese assistant, came to visit Joao and me at the compound. More than curious, I asked the assistant very purposeful questions, which he answered surprisingly freely. What I learned put the current disorder into perspective.

The Soviets were violently disliked by many Afghans both for and against the current administration, led by Hafizullah Amin, a hard-line Stalinist revolutionary and Soviet puppet. The Soviets had supplied the Afghan Government with a large number of the latest tanks including T-60s and T-55s, as well as helicopter gun-ships, which apparently were doing great damage, both psychologically and physically, to the citizens of Afghanistan. The Soviets had built a *security installation*, or military base, approximately 60 kilometers from Kabul. The Soviets and/or the Afghan leaders had also constructed ground-to-ground missile sites within the Kabul area for future use.

Meghdessian went on to say that unknown numbers of Soviets were being killed throughout Afghanistan on a regular basis and that it was his belief that Amin's government would be short-lived because Amin did not have the full backing of his Soviet handlers in Kabul. Apparently, the Soviet leadership wasn't satisfied with his responsiveness to their demands!

The next morning when Dehzad arrived, I invited him to have tea with us. Dehzad and I were certainly friends, but even so, given the dangerous political climate, I found his absolute candor surprising.

"Among the Afghan people," Dehzad told us, "Prime Minister Amin was referred to sarcastically as the Governor of Kabul. He has no control over the country outside of the capitol, and only holds power within Kabul thanks to his tanks, guns, and Soviet supporters. The USSR supplies him with vast amounts of ammunition. They have built three bridges at Termez, Uzbekistan, on the northern Afghanistan border, just to bring down armaments. Mr. Amin is extremely Stalinist. He is strong-headed, with extremely hard-line policies aimed at self-preservation rather than the good of the people. The vast majority of the Afghan people would like to be rid of both the Soviets and the current government, their lackeys. So they defy Amin's policies. There is much desertion amongst the military ranks and resistance among the civilian population. Just when you were arriving, more than two thousand Afghan military deserters attempted a military coup. They were all killed. There are pockets of conflict around the country, and the Soviets have responded by dropping bombs on the Afghan people in their own homeland. The situation in Kabul is very tense."

Dehzad stopped and sighed.

I wondered why Dehzad was being so forthcoming. I didn't have to wait long for an answer.

"Mr. Gary, the economy in Afghanistan is in a deplorable state. But we need arms and ammunition to fight the Soviets. So we need to get as much money into our country as possible. We need hard currency – foreign money."

Now I understood why they were so eager to sell the lapis before the Soviets spirited it away. But who could be trusted? Which ministers where on which side of this? What was I getting myself into? I tossed and turned through the night, while distant explosions interrupted my thoughts.

The next day, we entered the room next to the Ministry of Mines' central office. On the table lay tourmaline and kunzite for our appraisal. "What about Panjsher emerald?" I asked Dehzad, while examining the heap of crystals. Handing me a six-inch test tube of emeralds sealed at the top with tape, he informed me that they were only samples and not for sale. Holding the vial up to the light in the window, I saw that they were of very low quality, with little value.

We turned our attention to the tourmaline and kunzite. We fell into examining and grading the gems, and the hours flew by. Finally, in keeping with the long-standing local custom, I asked the Minister to keep the gems sealed until we completed our negotiations. Such requests have been honored since the times of Marco Polo, when the parcels were sealed in wax. The Minister wrapped the gems in white paper and taped them; I signed the packages. He then wrapped them with clear tape. They would not be reopened without my presence. There would be no breach. Even in this time of turmoil, I trusted that promise.

Joao and I spent the rest of the afternoon at the UN Compound discussing our approach to the negotiations with the Cabinet. We realized that they would probably reject our first and second offers as is the normal practice here in Afghanistan. A knowledgeable buyer would never start with his bottom price. Yet, our first offer had to be an adequate amount to demonstrate our genuineness. We decided to bid one-third

Lapis Lazuli

The world of gems considers lapis lazuli and Afghanistan synonymous. In the Upper Valley of the Kokcha River, *blue river* in Turkish, lay the mines of Lajwurd, which men have worked for over seven thousand years. By 4000 B.C. Afghanistan exported lapis to Egypt to produce scarabs, personal seals, and pharaoh masks. Transport took as long as three years. Later, Cleopatra, queen of Egypt from 69 to 30 B.C., exaggerated her exotic features with powdered lapis eye shadow. The painters of Europe ground lapis for royal blue paint pigment, which they called *ultra-marine*.

Darius the Great of Persia, 521-485 B.C., proudly adorned his palace in Susa with lapis. Following preset traditions of Aryan artistic excellence, Alexander the Great, 356-323 B.C., returned to Greece with lapis from Afghanistan after he had conquered the region near the mines. The Greeks shared knowledge of lapis with their subsequent conquerors, the Romans.

Legionnaires of Augustus Caesar of Rome, 63 B.C. to A.D. 14, wore seal rings of lapis. In his book *Natural History*, Pliny, A.D. 23-79, referred to the blue stone with gold flecks as *sapphirus*.

In about 1500 B.C. Moses assigned his elder brother Aaron to act as the high priest of the Twelve Tribes of Israel. Then Moses commanded Aaron to fashion a jeweled breastplate with 12 stones to represent the different tribes. Each gem measured about two-inches square. The gems were set in four rows of three stones across. Lapis lazuli, the fifth stone, symbolized the tribe of Issachar. In the mid-1200s during a visit to Badakhshan, Marco Polo noted, "In these mountains lies the most beautiful azure in the world." Much of the lapis trade in Europe was in the hands of monks in monasteries, who painted their parchment illuminations in medieval ecclesiastic manuscripts with lapis pigment. Also alchemists and theologians used lapis as eyewash. Years later, Michelangelo, 1474-1564, employed powdered lapis lazuli to paint the miraculous blues in the Sistine chapel. Peter Carl Fabergé, 1846-1920, selected lapis lazuli as part of his legacy— the jewelry for three Czars of Imperial Russia, Alexander II, Alexander III, and Nicholas II, whose cumulative reigns spanned 1855-1917.

of the highest price we were willing to pay. Together we organized the written weights and the number of pieces in each lot. I wanted to purchase some of the top quality lapis and tourmaline, and Joao wanted the better quality kunzite. We were willing to take large amounts – but not fifty tons of lapis!

When we approached Dr. Zia-Zadah the next morning with our written offer, he seemed annoyed and immediately rejected it and asked us to reconsider. The next morning we raised our bid to one-half of our final target price. The awkwardness of that moment was unforgettable.

"I am embarrassed," he responded as he reviewed our written proposal again, "but I will present your offer to the Cabinet this afternoon." He got back to us the next day. Nothing less than three times our highest offer. The deal was off!

Dehzad rode with us to Prokofiev's office to tell him the results of three days of meetings. The streets in this area of town were unusually quiet. We saw only a few people with carts of melons and cloth. As we entered Prokofiev's small office with one desk and two chairs for guests, he got to his feet and stretched out his hand to greet us. The walls were lined with shelves of books. Such a library was unusual for Afghanistan. Then I spotted a 2-½ foot long rocket lying on his desk.

"Are you in the arms business now?" I inquired.

"No, this landed on the steps of my house last night. If it had exploded as it was designed to, I would not be here talking to you."

Turning the rocket over, I saw there was an imprint on it –*USSR*.

Prokofiev responded to my unasked question. "If it had gone off, it wouldn't matter which country's name was on it." Solemnly he positioned the rocket on a nearby shelf and continued the conversation, "I am happy that my wife and son returned to Moscow the first week in October. If I get the chance, I will probably leave myself soon."

Changing the subject as he returned to his desk, "Tell me about your meeting this morning." He followed the back-and-forth of our story intently. "They are being unreasonable! I will attempt to negotiate further after your departure."

"Thank you, Prokofiev. If anyone can convince them, you can. It's getting dangerous around here – for all of us."

After Dezhad's disclosures, I had begun to wonder which side Prokofiev was on; he had invited us here to buy gems, and he was Soviet. But Dezhad said they were selling the gems to get money to fight the Soviets. Were these two in cahoots? Or was something else going on? And why would an USSR rocket be aimed at Prokofiev's house? Instinctively, I trusted Prokofiev. But I had trusted before – in Japan and elsewhere – and been left nearly destitute by that error in judgment. It was becoming increasingly difficult to tell who was *in* and who was *out* and even more difficult to predict what was going to happen next.

Dezhad told us that President Amin had a new nickname. He was now called *The Butcher* because he had ordered the execution of twelve thousand prisoners in the Pul-e-Charky Prison, officially announced on October 25, 1979. And it was rumored that this figure was low. The government was beginning a purge, arresting and killing anyone suspected of resisting. They were murdering well-esteemed prominent religious and tribal leaders. They were kidnapping children off the streets – deporting them to *schools* in Russia – for indoctrination. Students, teachers, lecturers, and intellectuals protested fervently against the current horrific events. Throughout the city Afghans were holding illegal underground meetings. It was time for Joao and me to go home.

As we continued our conversation, I asked Prokofiev what he foresaw for the future of a project we had discussed for sometime. We both felt that the general knowledge of gem mining in Afghanistan was almost non-existent and that a training program would greatly benefit the country by increasing the output and value of the gem mines.

Prokofiev replied as he offhandedly pointed to a second rocket on his desk, "I have been giving it some thought. Would you consider providing training at your company headquarters for some representatives of the Afghan gem business?"

"Sure, why not? If the political situation here continues, it will be the only way to safely continue our work. It would allow us to build a sound collaboration while building our distribution system."

"Then please think about it, and send me some estimated expenses along with thoughts on how to proceed with the training," Prokofiev urged. "I will work with the UNDP to get the project approved." Dehzad interjected, "I would like to be the first to go to America." Prokofiev stood up and said, "Let's see what we can do about that."

As we prepared to leave, Prokofiev urged Joao and me to present Dr. Zia-Zadah with one more offer. We decided we had nothing to lose, so we decided that we would again submit an offer for the same amount that we originally decided was our best price. If the Cabinet would change their decision, our offer was still good.

Indicating that our meeting was over, we all shook hands and agreed to keep in touch. Turning to leave, Dehzad lightened the conversation by suggesting that we find a carpet in the bazaar for Joao to take home. We left Prokofiev to his papers; he left us to our thoughts.

It's odd how differently we react to fear. Joao was Latin, and you could read him like a book. Even if he tried to bluster his way through, his emotions were there for all to see, written on his face and in his gestures. Prokofiev, Slavic, was cerebral and cool, even in the face of the threat of death. His manner garnered respect from the Afghans, who were loath to be seen as weak, afraid, or feminine. Prokofiev was one cool customer.

Pandemonium reigned in the streets. Shops were closing early. Our car, clearly marked as a UN vehicle, moved slowly through the crowd. We had no idea if the UN designation offered us protection or made us a target. Over a hundred demonstrators were yelling and waving red flags. Dehzad pointed to them saying, "Government employees are being forced to demonstrate on the behalf of the new government."

"As a government employee, will you have to demonstrate?"

Demonstrators marching down the street towards our vehicle

"Not if I can help it. I'm attempting to stay out of politics. At this time it is very dangerous to be in politics in Afghanistan."

Dehzad escorted us to the bazaar where Joao hurriedly purchased a carpet before returning us to our hotel where we bade him farewell and quickly packed for the 11,000-mile 32-hour trip back to Hawaii.

Early the next morning Joao and I checked out of the Guest House and rode to the airport in the car which Prokofiev had arranged for us. Much to our relief we left Kabul without further incident. It might take weeks or even months before we would hear whether our final offer to Dr. Zia-Zadah had been accepted or rejected, but I was already planning the mechanics and the curriculum of the Afghan gem symposium Prokofiev and I had so often discussed.

Old Kabul Fort

INTERNATIONAL TRADE CENTRE

UNITED NATIONS CONFERENCE
ON TRADE AND DEVELOPMENT

GENERAL AGREEMENT
ON TARIFFS AND TRADE

Cooperation with the Government
of the Democratic Republic of Afghanistan
in Export Promotion

Mail address:

U.N.D.P. Office
P.O. Box 5
Kabul, Afghanistan
Cables: UNDEVPRO, KABUL

Ref.: ITC/1145/R/79

Ministry of Commerce,
Darulaman Road
Kabul, Afghanistan.
Phone: 41041 Ext. 5
40511

November 6, 1979

Dear Mr. Bowersox,

I refer to your visit here and the purchase of tourmalines and
kunzite. Approval of the prices is expected in a few days and then
(if approved) a proforma-invoice will be forwarded to you immediately.

To have your Afghan partners better qualified in your future
negotiations we seem to have agreed here that two officers, one from
the Mining Department and one from the Export Promotion Department of
the Ministry of Commerce, be sent for training in Gem business with
strong orientation to the stones Afghanistan has in commercial quantities.
We thought a professional Gem dealer can provide can secure adequate
training and we wish to request your company to extend this kind of
cooperation.

All normal expenses will be paid by us (air tickets, per diems
including hotel) and we are prepared to pay a fee to whoever will be in
charge of the above training. We assume that 45 days will be a sufficient period for the training and the two men can come to your place
second half February - March.

As we see today the basic directions in training should include
the following:

- Identification of Gems in general.

- Sorting and grading (internationally accepted) of Lapis-Lazuli,
  Kunzite, tourmalines.

- Pricing of the above stones.

- Familiarizing with emeralds, rubies and garnets. These Gems
  might be available here in future.

- Marketing methods.

- Basics in business correspondence and proper preparation of
  commercial documents (contracts, proforma-invoice, shipping
  documents as required by a L/C provisions, etc.)

We would also welcome your ideas to extend the training programme.

Looking forward to your early comments,

Yours sincerely,

Mr. G. W. Bowersox
President, United Gem Merchants

V. Prokofiev
ITC Project Manager a.i.

MR BOWERSOX UNITED GEM MERCHANTS 900 FORT STREET MALL SUITE
900 FORT STREET MALL
1605 HONOLULU HAWAII 96813

USA

EIGHT ITEMS PRECIOUS STONES IN SIX CASES PACKED AND SEALED IN
THE PRESENCE OF AUTHORISED OFFICIAL OF THIS DEPARTMENT THE ABOVE
GOODS DESPATCHED BY AIR ON 5 APRIL TO YOU PLEASE TRANSFERRUSDOLLAR.
160469/85 TO DA AFGHANISTAN BANK KABUL IN OUR FAVOUR IMMEDIATELY
     KABUL MINES

COLN 900 1605   160469/ 85

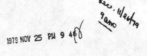

HNNN RW
ZCZC WHH809   DP4131TG003 KAG053 0325   1979 NOV 25 PM 9 40
HWHU CO AFKL 024
KABOUL 24/23 26 1100

GARY BOWERSOX
UNITED GEM MERCHANTS
HONOLULU HAWAI

WE HAVE RECEIVED OFFER FROM USSR PLEASE SEND (YOUR OFFER
FOR 50685.100 LAPIS SOON)
     KABUL MINES

COL 50685.109

L-R: Assadullah Amin, Katarina Thome, Hashem Dezhad, Joao Monteiro, Gary Bowersox, Tookie Evans, Sandi Morin, and Sky Petersen at Symposium in headquarters office, 1980

Chapter Four
The First Gem Symposium – The Great Game

1980 – 1982

Time is relative. Sometimes it seems to fly; sometimes it drags interminably, each second an exercise in suffering. As we flew home, I felt sadness for the suffering I knew was happening all over Afghanistan. Things were going to get worse.

The value of money is relative as well. Not enough money on one day is just enough on another. Two weeks after our return to Hawaii, Prokofiev cabled me that the Ministry of Mines and Industry had agreed to accept our offer to purchase the gem materials. I guess they figured that something was better than nothing.

Evidently the political situation in Kabul had deteriorated since our departure. I was eager to buy the lapis, but communication with any of my contacts there had become completely impossible. After four months of trying, I finally reached Prokofiev. Speaking only in general terms, in case anyone was listening, we decided to go ahead with our plans to run a symposium on gem mining techniques, to be held in Hawaii and co-sponsored by the UNCTAD (United Nations Conference on Trade and Development).

I asked Prokofiev whether he had been able to obtain a copy of Dr. Zia-Zadah's doctoral paper on lapis lazuli, which he had promised to send me. Zia-Zadah, Prokofiev informed me, had been removed from his position as Minister of Mines because of inefficiency. I could read between the lines and realized that the doctor, a decent and well-educated guy (like so many others who were caught up in the political purges), had been thrown out of his job. I found myself hoping that he was not in prison – or worse. I never learned what became of him.

Joao and I had left Kabul in late October. On December 27, 1979, the USSR officially invaded Afghanistan. Troops had begun streaming into Northern Afghanistan on December 24, on the pretext of stopping internal disturbances from spreading into Soviet territory – the vodka version of the Monroe Doctrine, I suppose. They placed Babrak Karmal in power in the same forceful way they had commandeered the governments in Mongolia, Hungary, and Czechoslovakia. Once under the control of the Soviet Union, leaders tended to hold onto the power. Their methods were well-known formulas of concoction, coercion, and forced conversion. It is easy to demonize them. The US has supported horrible regimes in Guatemala, Nicaragua, and Chile. Our Monroe Doctrine in action.

I hoped that this political change would not sidetrack the plan Prokofiev and I had worked up to train Afghans in the gem business. I was a businessman, intent upon developing a network for finding, mining, and distributing some of Afghanistan's riches. I certainly didn't like the Soviet style of governing, but whatever our reasons might be, we both wanted to hold this *Gem Symposium* in Hawaii the following March. We were committed to doing it. Prokofiev arranged for the UNCTAD approval to co-sponsor the Symposium along with my company, United Gem Merchants (UGM). We proceeded apace, exchanging telexes with program suggestions, lecture outlines, budget

00904

RW

ZCZC WHH693   DP4131TG005 KAG100 604

HWHU CO AFKL 026

KABUL 29 2 1510

: :"R 2 /U I 47

UNITED GEM MERCHANTS
900 FORT ST. SUIT 1195
IONOLULU HI 96813

UGMBXXXXX UGMHI

HONOLULU(USA)

I-S M-F 531-6811
I/H GARY BOWERSOX 3613920

GARY. BOWERSOX TRAINEES ASSAD AND DEHZAD ARRIVING HONOLULU MARCH 5 FLIGHT WA 102 STOP PLEASE FORWARD HERE BILL TUITION FEES ALSO CLASS MATERIALS WISHING SUCCESSFUL TRAINING PROKOFIEV

COL 5 102

Notice of Dehzad and Amin's arrival in Honolulu, Hawaii

data, and itineraries. Politics to
be ignored!

I half-expected that the
U.S. government would show
disapproval of the Soviet
occupation by refusing to allow
representatives of its puppet
government to visit the United
States. And yet, they issued U.S.
visas to my friend Dehzad, (now
titled General Director of Lapis
Lazuli Mineral Exploitation),
and Assadullah Amin, from the

Sorting and grading lapis
L-R: Tookie, Sky, Gary, Amin,
and Dezhad

Afghan Ministry of Commerce office in Kabul. Perhaps they thought,
as I was beginning to, that any contact between Afghans and the outside
world would be a blow against the hegemony of the tyrants in power.
Still, I was amazed that no one objected when, in March 1980, Dehzad
and Amin boarded a plane for Hawaii.

They shared a bedroom in my two-bedroom two-level apartment
near Waikiki Beach. An adjoining bathroom allowed them privacy for
washing and preparation for their prayers. Like faithful Moslems
everywhere, they would wash their faces, hands and feet five times a
day before they prayed. I had stocked the shelves with simple foods I
hoped they would enjoy.

I had also invited Joao Monteiro to fly up from Brazil and Katarina
Thome from Singapore to join with our Hawaii staff members Sandi
Morin, Tookie Evans and Sky Petersen. They were asked to lecture on
their area of expertise.

We filled the next 30 days with intense, thorough discussions,
demonstrations, field trips and classes. The curriculum was rigorous:
history of gems and minerals; gem and mineral identification, sorting
and grading; faceting and cabbing rough; appraising and pricing
methods; locations of the world's supply of gems; and gem markets
and trade routes. We also covered exploration and extraction; marketing
and sales; banking procedures, including accounts, letters-of-credit,
loans, money transfers, and foreign exchange; packaging and shipping

gems and minerals; customs procedures on export and import; and lastly, business correspondence, negotiations and contracts. I had learned all of these things through experience and hard knocks. The symposium provided a virtual Ph.D. in the gem trade.

Interestingly, the subject of invoicing, billing, and record keeping proved strange to them. In Afghanistan businessmen only had to remember who owed them and whom they owed, so keeping books was simple. With taxes and audits in other parts of the world, Afghan dealers would be required by international law to keep full accounts and business records.

We ended our sessions at three o'clock each day. Then Amin and Dehzad would go on an excursion around the island or they would have free time to walk back to my apartment. I would usually return home at seven after staff meetings, phone calls, and clearing my desk of paperwork. Joao had taken over the downstairs couch, and Brandi, having given up her bedroom to the Afghans, moved to a Japanese bed in my room.

We now had a full household. By the time I arrived home, everyone else had convened for drinks and conversation. Dehzad and Amin had green tea, Brandi soda, and Joao and I cocktails. While talking about the day and world affairs, we munched on Afghan raisins and nuts and

American snacks. Then we either ate dinner at a restaurant or had food delivered. On a few occasions Dehzad and Amin cooked for other dinner guests and us. Their exotic cuisine made for popular evenings. A few times we left the office early to sail along the

L-R: Amin, Gregg Arth, Dehzad,Katarina,
Sonia, Mitsi, Sandi, Sky, Omar Nassaeri,
and two Afghans

Honolulu coast with Joe Phillips, a Director of UGM. Sometimes we attended luaus or other local events and parades.

To end the Symposium, we had a staff party. We awarded

certificates of attendance, and as a parting gift I accompanied Dehzad and Amin to Los Angeles, where I introduced them to the staff of the Gemological Institute of America and its research laboratory. After touring the facilities we drove to Anaheim, California, where we spent the night at a motel. We got up early the next day to tour Disneyland. Like kids in fantasyland, we rushed from exhibit to rides to exhibit to rides for 14 hours before returning to the motel sated with sights and fun.

The next morning I drove them to Amin's cousin's home in Los Angeles. They were both bright-eyed with memories of Hawaii and Disneyland yet sad over our parting company. When I checked in on Amin and Dehzad three days later, after completing my business in Los Angeles, I met two long faces. Amin's relatives had heard that fighting in Kabul and other parts of Afghanistan had escalated. Amin had decided to stay with his relatives in America, but Dehzad was determined to return home.

Dehzad and I took a long walk to discuss his situation. Given his American connections, I was very concerned for his safety. He had been taught engineering by an American professor at the University of Kabul and was now in America with many friends. I feared that he would either be shot or imprisoned if he returned to Kabul. This was happening to most of his associates even as we discussed the situation at home. I offered to help him stay in the US, but he was concerned about his family, particularly his son. He feared that if he did not return, the government would punish them, so I respected his decision. I realized how desperate and determined I would feel if Brandi's life were threatened. Dehzad and I said goodbye to each other with full hearts. Months later, my feelings were partially and temporarily relieved when I received a letter from him.

Throughout 1982 as the situation became graver in Afghanistan, Prokofiev and I continued to correspond periodically. We kept our letters brief, pertaining only to our future gem project. Our aim was just to keep in touch because I was sure someone else was reading our letters and telexes. Any correspondence between a Soviet and an American would have been considered suspect. The authorities would have dismissed the truth – that we were writing as friends.

Dehzad Letter

Dear Sirs:

I feel very sorry for not being able to correspond with your good self and hope you may consider it as an excuse. I always remember your nice treatment of hospitality which you rendered to me during my mission in the U.S.A.

We are feeling well and everything is going well and life is normal, hoping this letter will find you well and prosperous.

I hope you may convey my sincere respect to your family and your office staff, especially Mr. Tokey, Mrs. Sandy, Mr. Sky and your daughter Miss Brandi.

Mr. Gary, from all gemstones only we have the stock of 50 tons of Lapis Lazuli that you have observed during your last trip in our country. For further information and details please do not hesitate and write directly to our department.

Dear Mr. Gary, during my stay in your country I had seen a book under the title of A Field Guide in Colour of Minerals, Rocks and Precious Stones in your office but I could not get it from GIA bookstore. If this would not cause you inconvenience, please do send the above book to me, which will be very much helpful to my fieldwork.

Dear Gary, if you want to come in Afghanistan, please inform me before your coming in our country.

Yours faithfully,
 (Signed)

S. H. Dehzad,
General Director of Lapis Lazuli
Mineral Exploitation, Ministry of Mines and Industry

Neither Prokofiev nor I mentioned Amin's remaining in the US or the fact that the United Nations had never reimbursed my company for their share of the Symposium expenses. Nor did we refer to the meals we had together or our families' meeting. Brandi still played with the black plastic poodle Prokofiev's son had given her when they first met at the Intercontinental Hotel.

One day I heard via some Afghan friends that there were plans to attack Kabul. I telexed Prokofiev the following message: "Dear V. Prokofiev: I've heard news of plans to attack Kabul and highly suggest you leave immediately. We are concerned about your welfare. Gary."

Prokofiev immediately telexed me back with appreciation for my concern. He stated that he had plans to return to Russia. That telex was the last time I heard from my Soviet friend. I still wonder if he made it home safely? Was he KGB? Was V. Prokofiev his real name?

Desiring to stay on the Afghan scene and develop business, I decided to visit Washington, DC to discuss the situation with the Desk Officer for Afghanistan at the State Department and Amin, who was now driving a taxi in DC. Through these two meetings and my file search for the latest Afghan news at the Library of Congress, I learned that Kabul had spun out of control. It had become a very dangerous place to live or even to visit.

The Soviet puppet government was throwing people into prison and having them shot. The Mujahideen were passing out pamphlets to the non-Soviet ethnic groups. One such pamphlet read:

> You are in Afghanistan as soldiers of an imperialist occupation army. You are fighting against peaceful people who have never done you any harm. With your hands you are serving the political system in the USSR that has deprived men of their basic democratic freedoms and created a new ruling class of oppressors. You are shedding your blood and the blood of innocent Afghans in order to colonize a foreign country. Your dead friends are sent home in sealed coffins and their families are told that they have been killed during maneuvers.

As I flew back to Hawaii I analyzed all I had learned in

Washington. Amin had not heard from either Dehzad or Prokofiev. Neither had I, and they were my only hope for keeping this affair going. Relations between the US and Russia were tense over Russia's occupation and aggression. The winds were changing, and I would have to change my strategy if I wanted to stay my course and continue my Afghan gem project. At the same time, I felt allegiance to Dehzad, Amin, and the U.S. anti-Soviet policy, and disgust with the Soviets.

It was up to me to act – I would find a way to work through the Mujahideen in and out of Pakistan. Before landing in Honolulu, I had decided to visit Peshawar, Pakistan and the border areas of Afghanistan to searh for partners in keeping this project alive. I had researched The Great Game and the major players in the area, and I was most impressed by the scuttlebutt about a guy named Massoud. I didn't know how I would find him, but I was coming to trust my instincts and chance to lead me to where I should be.

"The Great Game"

(World's oldest established imperial rivalry)

During the 1800s Peshawar storytellers told about The Great Game played by the British, the Indians, and the Soviets for the control and domination of Central Asia and Afghanistan. They told stories about the two British wars with the Afghans, the siege of Chitral in the 1890s, the Pashtun and Chitral revolt against British claims to their territory; and the spying intrigue between the British and the Soviets. The Great Game has now broadened to a world power struggle for vast oil and gas rights of this region – the last untapped reserves of energy in the world today.

By the 1930s, the Soviets had joined with the British and Americans against the Germans. With obvious pressure from the US and Britain, in a letter dated December 5, 1938, Attiq Rafiq, a high Afghan official, stated that an expulsion order was in effect against all Germans. Afghanistan was to ignore the German offer of assistance in reclaiming the historical lands in the NWFP, which had been occupied by the British for the last century. The port city of Karachi, located on Pakistan's southern shore, was included in this offer. On August 17, 1940, Zahir Shah proclaimed Afghan neutrality.

The next year Afghanistan found itself surrounded on three sides by allied co-belligerents-China, the USSR, and British India. Allied-dominated Iran formed the fourth side. During August 1941, the USSR and British joined forces to conquer Iran. By October, diplomatic pressure from the two world powers were pressuring Kabul to remove all non-diplomatic Axis personnel.

After the end of hostilities in 1946, the Morrisson-Knudsen Company of Boise, Idaho, established itself in

Afghanistan with the mission to repair and construct irrigation channels, dams, and highways. Their employees were the US Government's eyes and ears inside and outside of Kabul. That project lasted 32 years until 1978, when insurgency against the newly installed regime put the lives of the American staff in jeopardy.

By 1950 the Soviets began stating that Afghanistan was once again a target of US aggression and conspiracy. They believed that the USA had concentrated all its imperialistic efforts on diverting Afghanistan from its policy of non-alignment and had drawn it into joining an aggressive military bloc. On the other hand, it was obvious to the United States that Russia was continuing its policy of encroachment toward Afghanistan that it had begun in the 19th century. The true Afghans concurred with the words of Abdur Rahman Khan, the Iron Amir who ruled from 1880 to 1901, when he described his country's vulnerable position:

How can a small power like Afghanistan, which is like a goat between two lions or a grain of wheat between two strong millstones of the grinding mill, stand in the way of the two stones without being ground to dust?

Afghanistan found itself in this position again as The Great Game continued.

After 1950, Russia and the US struggled covertly. In 1960 the Soviets shot down Gary Powers, pilot of the American U-2 spy-plane who had taken off from Badaber, near Peshawar. Badaber served as an American radar communications center from 1954 until it was closed in 1969.

Then, in February 1979, the American Ambassador Adolph Dubs was abducted and murdered in downtown Kabul. The US accused Soviet agents of the heinous act. Shortly thereafter, the Americans pulled back from Kabul to Peshawar, and the CIA took over covert operations with a budget of hundreds of millions of dollars.

When Zbigniew Brzezinski, President Carter's National Security Advisor, visited Peshawar, he posed before cameras on the Khyber Pass with a Chinese submachine gun in his hands aimed toward Afghanistan. A sea and air bridge was established between Pakistan and Egypt to supply Soviet weapons to support the counterrevolutionary forces fighting against the Kabul government. They used Soviet weapons instead of American arms in an attempt to avoid news of direct American involvement.

The ISI (Inter Service Intelligence), Pakistan's secret police, and the CIA assisted with setting up an Afghanistan Government in Exile, which met in Peshawar and Islamabad, Pakistan. One of the key figures was Gulbuddin Hekmatyar, a Pashtun leader of Hesb-i-Islami. It was rumored in Kabul that Hafizullah Amin, the new leader of Afghanistan, sent people to Peshawar for secret meetings to support his position with Hekmatyar and others. The Soviets accused Amin of liquidating hundreds of upright Afghans when he killed the legitimate head of state, Nur Mohammed Taraki, and jailed Taraki's family.

The Afghan counterrevolutionaries, aided and abetted by the USA, turned Pakistan into their logistical support base to launch operations aimed at destabilizing the situation in Afghanistan. An open war was developing between the US and the Soviet Union. With the aid of his Special Forces, General Zia ul-Haq, President of Pakistan, knowing that Pakistan was deeply in debt, readily supported shipments of American arms. In 1979 he appointed General Akhtar as Director-General of ISI. Son of a physician in Peshawar, Akhtar had obtained a Masters Degree in Economics in 1945 from the Government College in Lahore, India. In addition, reports cited him as a champion boxer, wrestler, and cyclist. General Zia ul-Haq is said to have directed General Akhtar in 1984 to establish a *Seven-Party Alliance in Pakistan*, with representation from the seven major Afghan parties. Pakistan sought a way to exert influence on all the commanders.

To obtain weapons from Pakistan, the field commanders in the Alliance had to prove they could deliver operational efficiency, a distribution system, and successful strikes against critical strategic targets. The favored commanders willingly followed Pakistan's instructions in exchange for arms and money:

Abdul Rasul Sayyaf, an Afghan long settled in Saudi Arabia and supported by the Wahabbis;

Maulvi Younis Khalis, a mullah and Hesb-i-Islami leader;

Gulbuddin Hekmatyar, an engineering student from Kabul University, leader of Hesb-i-Islami, and well-connected to the Pakistan ISI;

Ahmed Shah Massoud, from Kabul's French Lycee and connected with Afghaninistan's Jamiat-i-Islami party;

Pir Sayed Gailani, head of the Qaderiyah order and related to ex-King Zahir Shah.

Ahmed Shah Massoud's connection to this group was through Burhanuddin Rabani. Massoud himself, however, remained in Afghanistan, not caring to take directions from Pakistani military or political officials. Later he assumed national importance in the northern region.

Hekmatyar was blamed for a 1983 attempt on the life of Burhanuddin Rabani, the leader of the Jamiat-i-Islami, who supported Ahmed Shah Massoud. An intruder had entered Rabani's home in Peshawar and opened fire with a submachine gun, killing two people and wounding 12. Later in the year Sebqatullah Mujaddedi, leader of another political group,

Nejate-Melli, escaped death by sheer luck. Once again, Hekmatyar was blamed. The Mujaddedi family had been kingmakers in Afghanistan for centuries. They had started an anti-government campaign against the Afghanistan government in Jalalabad, protesting land reform that had been supported by Zahir Shah, the king at that time. Mujaddedi had formed the National Liberation Front with headquarters in Peshawar. Despite the charges against him in connection with the Mujaddedi attack, Hekmatyar continued to be Pakistan's favorite son, a position he had enjoyed and profited from since 1973.

In 1984, President Reagan declared US support for the Afghan counterrevolutionaries backed by Pakistan in their fight against the Soviets and their minions, the puppet government installed in Kabul. ISI moved tens of thousands of tons of arms and ammunition to the Mujahideen, with Hekmatyar receiving the lion's share. These arms gave him and his Pashtun tribal followers an edge over the other field commanders.

The Soviets in MIG fighter planes answered with direct strikes against Afghan encampments and convoys. In addition, Soviet Hind-24 helicopter gun-ships, the ultimate terror of Afghanistan skies, leveled villages in less than 15 seconds. MI-8 choppers, gutted for troop transport, then followed with hardened troops to destroy remaining villages and buildings and to set up an outpost.

*Historical map showing that Afghanistan once encompassed
the major cities within current Pakistan*

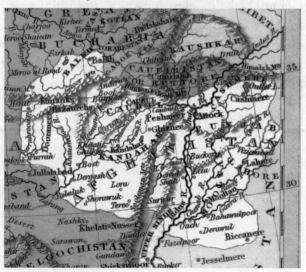

Chapter Five
Peshawar, The Spy Capital

1983 – 1988

Peshawar goes by many names. To some, it is *The City of Storytellers.* To others, it is *Smuggler's City*, a busy marketplace for black money, arms, heroin, and jewels. Rudyard Kipling described Peshawar as *a city of evil countenances.* Of course, this frontier town is best known as the capital of the Northwest Frontier Province (NWFP) of Pakistan. But to me it will always remain the *Spy Capital*, for good reason. Peshawar's origin is lost in history, but it dates back to at least the sixth century B.C. Some historians write that the Kashan Kings of Gandhara founded it over two thousand years ago. Wars over the centuries have often shifted borders in this contentious area, and Peshawar has, at different times, flown the flags of Afghanistan, India and Pakistan. In an 1893 agreement among Afghanistan, Russia, and India, the British overlords redrew the borders to place Peshawar in the NWFP of Pakistan. It rests there on the map, but its residents bear allegiance to a host of interests, most of all their own. On any given

1699 Map

Gary in turban purchasing kunzite

day, it is a hotbed of plots and conspiracies, of curious deaths and strange bedfellows.

Until the mid-1950s Peshawar existed within a city wall with 16 gates. Ringed by tall, narrow buildings bearing intricately carved wooden shutters and balconies, the old bazaar, the place of storytellers, lies within the old city. As Peshawar grew from its original fort, it naturally divided into districts. A short distance away from the inner city, the Andarshahr Jewelry Bazaar became known for gold, silver, and antique jewelry. The Khyber Bazaar, near the old fort, is for selling carpets and storytelling; Saddar Bazaar features clothing and books; Qissa Khawani and Shinwari Bazaar offers jewelry, antiques, and money changing; and at Namak Mandi, it is salt, rubber, and gems.

Five Star Hotel

My first visit to Peshawar, city of mystery, intrigue, and bad hotels, was in 1983. I came to trade in gemstones, to

seek news of my missing friends and
colleagues, and perhaps to cross
paths with the Mujahideen. I needed
to convince them to trade with me,
for my benefit and theirs. I could
help supply them with foreign
currency, which they would use to
resist the Soviets.

De-Cent Restaurant

In a rickety taxi, I headed for
the north side of the city where most
of the gem dealers locate their small
offices. Namak Mandi, the salt
market in the olden days, was comprised mostly of two-story wooden
structures, in which few repairs have ever been made. My business
was in a similar state of repair, my ambitions thwarted by the Soviet
presence and civil unrest.

Peshawar awakens early with merchants preparing to do business
and men cooking corn, shish kebab, and nuts on open grills. A few

Namak Mandi Restaurant, Peshawar, Pakistan

beggars work the street, and children display trays of stacked washcloths, shoestrings, and pocketknives or sell candy and gum from black leather straps hung around their necks. Shopkeepers get quite personal in their sales approach, venturing onto the sidewalk to coax and cajole potential customers into their shops with guarantees of better goods and prices than their adjacent competition. The whole world, it seems, is in the streets, swallowing the diesel particulate that darkens the sky by early afternoon. On Fridays, the religious holiday, Peshawar feels like a ghost town in the Old West with a relentless wind blowing dust and stealing unsecured wares from careless merchants.

By day, the city displays a particular rhythm and hum: the rumble-roll of horse-pulled carts loaded high with goods bulging inside muslin sacks, the rude honking of car horns, the quiet buzz of a bicycle rickshaw speeding by, the sharp clanging of bells on teeming buses, the clack-clack of the horse hooves, and the early morning calls to prayer fill the dusty air over the streaming people and animals. This is the commerce of a population of 750,000, plus an indeterminable number of Afghan refugees

Foreign women visitors have to be especially wary in the crowded

Street scene Namak Mandi

Gary and Mohebullah negotiating the purchase of lapis

bazaar alleys. Local men, using sleight of hand, are out to touch female tourists anywhere they can. Such an act is forbidden with their own women, who show contemporary-looking faces but cover their heads with traditional chadors. Arrayed in their 22-karat thin-hammered handcrafted jewelry, they overlay mysteriously sensuous soft-fabric trousers with ankle-length dresses, ornately embroidered and trimmed. Usually though, the Peshawar women take exception to conservatism in footwear, preferring wedge-heeled pumps called *mules* in the Western world.

But at nightfall, Peshawar lurks. In the dark, even the shadows have shadows. After sunset, the unlit streets can be spookily deserted, except for the occasional furtive stranger and the ubiquitous poor sleeping in alleys. It is a gateway to Afghanistan, some two hundred kilometers away. Through that gate pass arms, drugs, gems and secrets untold. Not a good place to overnight.

Nor, as it turned out, was Dean's Hotel. The rooms opened on to deceptively beautiful grounds filled with green lawns and flower gardens. However, I was keenly aware that anyone entering the complex had direct access to my door. On several occasions, strangers came knocking, which disturbed me. I would answer to find a questionable-looking stranger who was clearly expecting to find someone else. They made little eye contact and quickly scuttled away like insects.

Sometime during the first week, a dead man and a live cobra were discovered in a bathroom two doors away from my room. The man had died from snakebite. The snake showed no human tooth marks and was apparently fine. A cobra is a rarity in Peshawar. A murder is not. I decided that Dean's Hotel was too unsafe for me.

Instead, I took a room at the upscale Pearl Continental – no relation to the famous hotel chain. The grounds were landscaped and groomed. Marble faced the floor and walls of the lobby, and the rooms were clean. But the food was often bad, and the posh atmosphere of the hotel intimidated my Afghan miner friends. Preferring international guests of nobility, the hotel staff glared at my rough-and-ready guests, still clad in dirty clothes from the long, demanding journey to Peshawar from the gem mines in Afghanistan. But my choices were few.

In 1984, I met Akbar Khan, a thin man who stands about five-foot-six with pitch-black hair. We became friends. Soon afterwards, we began to find ways to work together. At 14, he had started collecting gems and selling them in his village just outside Peshawar. When I met him, he already had 19-years' experience in brokering and shipping gems from Pakistan. He was assisting the Afghans in selling their rough gems to foreigners. Prospering in business, he had a nice office in Namak Mandi.

*Akbar Khan holding
188 carat rough emerald*

I told him about the gem market in the US, about which he knew nothing. He was a savvy merchant and saw its potential instantly. A few years later, Akbar Khan started coming to the US to share space with me at the International Gem and Mineral Show in Tucson, Arizona. And when I was in Peshawar between field trips, I stayed in his office and stored my field and gem equipment there. This proved to be a solid, three-star alternative to my other hotel

Arif Chaudhary, manager, Green's Hotel

opportunities. But that was before I discovered Green's Hotel.

The first time I stood outside Green's Hotel uniformed military and civilian policemen, armed with AK-47s, were everywhere. When I entered Green's, the uniformed armed guard, his green beret aslant over his dark hair, exhibited a large toothy grin from under his black mustache. He had posted himself strategically where he could catch the dusty downdraft from a ceiling fan just inside the entrance.

I walked directly into the lobby, a meeting place for men with questionable agendas. I waved hello to Arif Chaudhary, the Hotel Manager and Shuja Uddin the desk manager, who were standing in the lobby. They waved back as I made my way up the steps to the left of the lobby. I entered Lala's restaurant, established in 1984, shortly later USSR invaded Afghanistan. The table covers were oil cloth topped with small bouquets of plastic flowers. As I waited and

waited some more, I realized that Lala's evidently subscribed to the tenets of the *Slow Food* movement which was emerging in Italy at that very same moment. Slow was good. No hurry. The food was the best I had tasted in Peshawar, and the prices were fair.

During the Soviet invasion of Afghanistan, newcomers to Peshawar unwittingly identified themselves by their delight in grabbing the often-vacant table next to the front windows.

Shuja Uddin, desk manager, Green's Hotel

Their rush to get a street view brought smirks to the faces of old-timers, who, ever watchful, were busy spinning their wildly exaggerated stories at the back tables. These innocent first-timers did not know about the frequent drive-by shootings or the time the visage of the hotel had been *exfoliated* by a facial of *plastique*.

The scene inside promised even more fascination than the street view. Undercover Soviet KGB, American CIA, British MI-6, Pakistani ISI, Afghanistan KHAD, and Iranian SAVAK agents, as well as foreign journalists, frequented this retreat and mingled on a regular basis. Battle tactics were tested with forks and saltshakers. Spy cells and shell corporations were forged and merged, formed and disbanded. They combed their environments like hungry paramecia, seeking materiel to support various wars, crusades, and jihads. Hushed whispers were the rule, and information was the currency. Money, which speaks every dialect known to man, served as the *lingua franca.* Speculation was a local sport. Old-timers wagered about the missions of the soldiers-of-fortune seated hither and yon with drinks for the winner. Reporters sat culling through the rumors for hours they crafted their stories from the latest word from the front before heading to the telex office a mile away on Fort Road to relay their stories to the folks back home.

In 1986, the Lala's clientele were turning their gossip to Libya's Mu'ammar Gadhafi. Lunch and dinner at Lala's, home of the fattest grapevine in town, were pro forma for most foreign organizations. But the Americans chose another course. They forbade personnel from American Government-funded organizations from visiting Lala's. They also banned riding in rickshaws, the three-wheeled covered scooters with a double seat built on the back.

I had thought that a foolish restriction until April 17, when the Americans bombed Libya's Gadhafi. The next morning a bomb destroyed the British Airways office in the hotel lobby next door to Lala's. The blast rocked me out of my bed. I was in Room 101, the best room in the hotel, but on that day, the one closest to the explosion *du jour.* But that has been my room in Green's, my home in Peshawar, ever since my early visits.

Later that day, Mr. Gadhafi commanded his people over the radio to *kill all Americans.* Crowds gathered in different market areas to discuss the anti-American developments. Rickshaw drivers would not pick up an American or white European unless he waved, high in the air, twice the normal fare in cash. Akbar Khan and I rapidly concluded our purchases of new gems for my inventory.

Two days later I was on a plane to Karachi, Pakistan and then to the USA. In Karachi there was a 15-hour layover. I decided to go directly to the Midway Hotel next to the airport to rest and avoid any possible encounters with Libyans. Poor choice.

Zahid, the hotel manager, was a friend of mine from many previous stopovers. He happened to be in the lobby as I walked in. " *Salaam Alaikum* (Welcome)!" he said with a big friendly smile.

"*Alaikum Salaam* (Peace be upon you)," I replied, as we shook hands. Glancing at my dirty clothes and exhausted appearance, Zahid handed me a room key and said, "Go take a shower, relax, and come down later to sign for the room."

An hour later I walked out of the elevator on the first floor, clean and refreshed, ready to register. But as I approached the front desk, I noticed a prominently placed four-by-six-foot blackboard, which I had not noticed before. Staring at it, I could hardly believe the message; written in large, white chalk letters were the words ALL LIBYAN FLIGHTS ARE CANCELLED INDEFINITELY!

I hurried into Zahid's office, down the hall and around the corner from the front desk. Zahid was sipping tea at his desk. "Mr. Gary, come join me," he invited in a relaxed voice.

"First, Zahid, tell me how many Libyans are staying in this hotel!"

"About 50."

So here I was in a hotel full of Libyans after their exalted leader had exhorted them to *kill all Americans.* Even though I accepted Zahid's courtesies, I said, "I plan to depart ASAP. Do you know anything about flights to the US or Japan?" When he said he didn't, I told him, "Then after this tea I'm going upstairs to get back into my dirty shalwar kamese so I look like a Pakistani. Then I'm going straight to the airport. I'll come back for my bags when I find a flight. By the way, do you expect more Libyans tonight?"

"Yes, we expect at least another hundred. Because of the bombing, all their flights have been cancelled."

"It's past time for me to leave Karachi." I put down my cup and headed out the door.

Local men usually wore colorful turbans, so with appropriate headgear and my beard, I could change my appearance instantly. Looking like a Pakistani, I hurried to the airport and obtained a ticket on Japan

Airlines departing at two o'clock in the morning. Then I returned directly to the Midway Hotel. Detecting no Libyans in the restaurant, I purchased food and proceeded to my room, firmly locking the door. I stayed there until I left for the airport at eleven-thirty.

The plane finally lifted off the runway two hours late due to security checks. I heaved an involuntary sigh and sank back into my seat. "My God, when just being an American is enough to get you hated, even killed! I'm no spy, I'm no cold warrior…" I shook my head in disbelief and dozed off.

My plan had been to make connections to keep my gem trade with Afghanistan going. But I had been chased away from Peshawar by Libyans before I could connect with any Mujahideen. I had the sense that Afghanistan lay at the heart of my business strategy. I was still a business guy, thinking in dollars and cents. I had not yet learned – or I had learned and forgotten – the importance of hearing my inner voice. I had one or two things to learn.

And learn them I did, thanks to the rough tutelage of the School of Hard Knocks.

Because I had connections for gems at good prices, I came up with a new marketing concept for my retail gem business. I promoted *Afghan Connection* gem events in large third- and fourth-generation retail jewelry stores. The jeweler would provide eight to ten cases to

Gary riding camel to promote gem event

display my gems and mineral specimens and widely advertise the events. Besides selling, I held live TV and radio interviews, did slide show lectures in the stores, and spoke to groups – Rotarians and students. I billed myself as *The American Gem Hunter*. Some might find this positioning hokey, but it felt natural to me. Life on the road was not so easy, but somehow it beat staying home. I liked showing up in a *shalwar kamese and turban*, exotic and mysterious. Good theatre. Good business. It took some ego strength to appear in public in turbans and such, but my efforts were rewarded.

I got to Hawaii with a new supply of gems from Afghanistan in January 1988. I gathered my show supplies for an event in Detroit and ticketed a TWA flight via New York. Just before boarding in Hawaii, an attendant complained about my four carry-ons. He demanded that I check at least one more bag. I selected the one with the least inventory and received a receipt. I thought nothing of it.

You can guess what happened. When I got to New York, my checked bag was missing. My search of the miles of Samsonite at the lost luggage warehouse produced nothing. After making a report to TWA, I called my attorney and friend, Steve Hastings, whose law firm represented TWA in the Los Angeles courts. He gave me the bad news regarding TWA's liability in my case. He said the most he could do was arrange for me to visit TWA's lost baggage warehouse, where at least I could search for my bag.

The next morning a TWA employee and I walked up and down the warehouse aisles searching for my bag – to no avail. Then I called the FBI to report that $80,000 worth of gems had disappeared with my bag. The agent on the line started a report and told me to call back. The following week the airline had completed its search. Even though I made many calls to both the FBI and the airline during the next two months, I had nothing to show for my worry. This loss devastated me!

Six months later, on July 7, 1988, upon returning to Hawaii after a series of gem events, I called my friend Dan LaLonde, a gemologist and gem wholesaler. He said, "Gary, I've been trying to contact you. A young man tried to sell me some of your inventory."

"How did you know it was mine?" I asked.   *Dan LaLonde*

"I recognized your handwriting on one of the packages."

"Did you get his name and number?"

"Yes, it was Danny," and LaLonde read me his number.

Immediately I called the FBI. The local agent said he would review my five-month old case.

An hour later another agent called, "We have the case, but the number you gave us isn't good," he said, "Do you have a description of the man?"

"No," I replied, "but my friend Dan LaLonde can describe him. He's expecting your call."

An hour later he rang again. "Some good news," he said. "LaLonde provided a description of the man and the name of another jeweler who had recommended him to LaLonde. He's in Kaimuki. When I phoned him, he gave me the same description but a different number. I checked out this new number, and guess what?"

"No idea," I said, frustrated but willing to play the game.

"It's the baggage area at Hawaiian Airlines! The last name the jeweler gave us checks out with one of the handlers on duty the night your bag disappeared. We have these names in our file from your original inquiry. We'd like to meet with you as soon as possible."

An hour later a broad-shouldered man in his early '40s standing slightly over my height of six feet, knocked at my door. He introduced me to his partner, a thinner, shorter, brown-haired man in his late '30s. Over coffee they outlined their plan. I enjoyed a new feeling of hope.

"We want the Kaimuki jeweler to ask the suspect to return with some more gems to sell. The jeweler will tell the suspect that he has found someone to buy them for a ten percent commission. If the suspect agrees, he'll set a time and date, and you'll pose as the buyer. I'll pose as a bench worker, and we'll have three other agents in the area to arrest the man if he shows you any of your stolen gems. You just have to nod your head and we will be on him." He hesitated. "Before agreeing to this plan, you must consider that the man may be armed."

"Let's do it!" I said.

Four days later the agents called to say that the suspect had agreed to meet the jeweler the next day at noon. "We'll pick you up at ten-thirty and drive to the store."

By ten-fifty the next morning I had met the Kaimuki jeweler, and the second agent had put on one of the jeweler's bibs at the workbench. Another agent was stationed at a bus stop about 40 yards away, while two others hid in the store. The agents told me to go out and walk around until eleven forty-five.

At two minutes after twelve the suspect entered the store. The jeweler said, "Hello, Dan," and went around the counter, motioning for me to meet him, a clean-cut sandy-haired young man in his early '20s. Given his slight build – all of 140 pounds – he certainly didn't look dangerous.

"I hear you have some gems to sell," I said, as calmly as I could manage.

"Yes." He looked at me confidently. The *snake*! I thought.

Slowly he reached into his pocket and pulled out some plain paper all twisted up. I played it cool as he took his time unwrapping the goods. When he placed four blue topazes in front of me on the counter, I must have given him a look of great disappointment. "Is that all you have?"

"What are you looking for?" he asked.

"I collect more expensive gems like emeralds and tourmaline," I said. "Do you have anything else?"

He didn't reply, so I continued, "If you have more expensive gems, I'm interested, but I'm not interested in blue topaz."

"That's all I have now," he said.

I shrugged and said, "Well, call the jeweler if you locate some more."

He walked out of the store a free man.

The agent came off his bench, cell phone in hand.

"You didn't recognize them as yours?" he asked heavily.

"No, they were just regular Brazilian cut. They could have come from any wholesaler." I answered with only a shade of the disappointment I felt. I hoped to have seen some of my special gems or some that I had personally cut.

"We appreciate your not having him arrested for gems you couldn't identify to the court under oath," the dark-haired agent stated.

Over lunch they informed me that because of the small dollar amount, they would have to drop my case shortly. I didn't answer, but $80,000 seemed like a lot of money to me. I was wondering if the FBI is only mandated to serve the very rich.

The late Eli Livian holding 8.79 carat
Panjsher emerald cut from nodule. He
sold this gem in 1987 for $165,000
($18,771/carat).

Hanoh Stark faceting 36 carat
rough into 8.79 carat cut emerald

36 carat emerald crystal with nodule
to be cut by Hanoh Stark

The tall dark-haired agent told me, "I'm sure we have the right man. Maybe we can get a judge to allow us to search his apartment." Then he added, "It's a tough call, but the fact that he was working for the airline the night of your loss and then showed Dan LaLonde a folded gem paper with your writing on it is pretty convincing."

"I don't think we'll hear from him again through the jeweler," I said. "He seemed too nervous. He suspected something." I had dealt with enough other gem dealers to read his body language. We tried to enjoy a fine Island lunch of mahimahi with happy talk of how the two mainland agents were adapting to Island life.

The next morning around eleven they called to say that they had gotten permission to search Danny's apartment. They wanted to conduct the search after they had placed another agent at the airport to assure the suspect was at work. I was to go along to identify my goods. The next day the landlord let the agents into the apartment while I waited in the lobby. They searched for over an hour without locating a single gem.

Looking very disappointed, they added more bad news. "Our superiors will only allow us another 48 hours to crack the case before transferring us to another assignment." Because of all the evidence, the agents recommended that I consider a civil suit against Danny. They said that I could have copies of their report tying the suspect to the airport and the handling of my baggage. They thought that information coupled with Dan LaLonde as a witness would provide a successful case.

After a long walk on the beach, I decided not to prosecute. It seemed too risky to go further in debt by paying attorney's fees for litigation. Anyway, I felt sure that the young man would shortly disappear.

Exactly three months later I was hit again, this time in Tel Aviv while I was having a beer in a hotel restaurant with Richard Homer, who was accompanying me on the trip. He had been my instructor in a course on faceting gemstones at the Gemological Institute of America. Our plane had been late landing after a 20-hour flight from the US, and our contact at Hargem, Hanoh Stark, had gone home for the night.

Hanoh is a gem cutter I have known for many years. He had been purchasing Afghan emerald rough from me and allowing me to cut my tourmaline rough in his factory. I would pre-form, or shape, the crystals, and Hanoh's people would facet and polish them into gemstones.

Next to my chair I set my briefcase filled with Hanoh's aquamarines and my own rough tourmaline and rubies. When I bent to pick it up, it was gone, along with my passport and other important papers. Although the city police informed me they were too busy with all the Israeli-Arab problems to investigate such cases as mine, they agreed to take a report the next morning. There it was in writing, the initial $70,000 (which after inventory had been taken later turned out to be a $120,000) recorded with an official stamp, but my previous experiences with robberies gave me no real hope.

Later Richard and I entered the towering sky-rise where Hanoh's offices were located, a highly secured building in Ramat-Gan. Ramat-Gan is the gem center of Tel Aviv with numerous high-rise offices containing multi-million-dollar gem cutting operations. After greeting Hanoh, I complained to him about the lassitude of the police. He was so upset that he phoned a police relative in another city. Concerned calls from Hanoh and from his relative finally persuaded the Tel Aviv police to look into my case. It took only a few interviews at the restaurant for the police detective to establish that the waitress had seen the cook in the kitchen opening a briefcase like mine. The police started a search for the Arab cook and three days later found that he was already in jail – for another theft.

When I heard that news, I knew I would never find my stolen goods. What's more, I knew I would never survive in this business.

Disheartened, I arranged for a new passport to replace the stolen one and flew back to the US. A letter from Guy Clutterbuck, a British gem merchant, was waiting in Hawaii. It said, "Commander Ahmed Shah Massoud has sent a message through his brother Wali in London. Massoud is interested in our gem program for Afghanistan!"

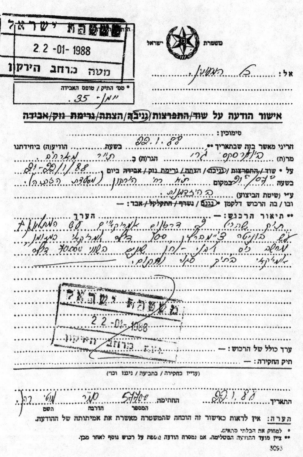

Police report of Tel Aviv theft claiming loss of briefcase containing passports, workpapers, airline tickets, small computer, gem materials, and cash for a total value of $70,000.

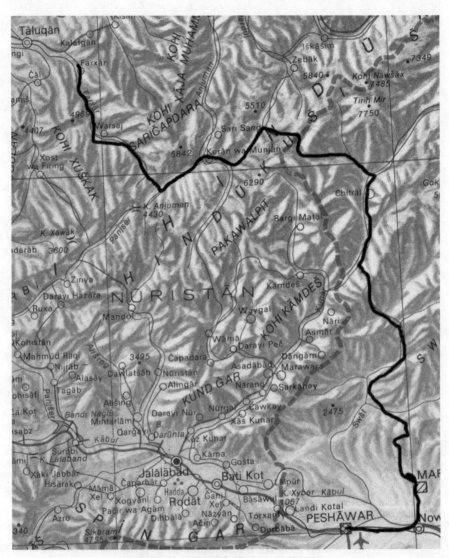

Route taken from Peshawar to Farkhar

Chapter Six
Into the Lion's Den

1989

Chitral nestles high in the Hindu Kush in Northern Pakistan on the border with Nuristan and Badakhshan, two provinces of Afghanistan. North of Chitral the old road bends before K2's 26,500 feet and continues to Mastuj and to Gilget beyond. Luxuriant rice fields green the Chitral valley between rugged mountains. "Hindu Kush" means Hindu Killer because its passes, over millennia, have killed thousands who tried to cross it in one direction or the other.

Disguised as an Afghan in my shalwar kamese, I sat in the crammed public minibus during the dusty 13-hour trip from Peshawar. Near Swat, the bus rolled to a slow stop. A guard slinging a Kalashnikov swaggered over from the check post. With another guard, he mounted the bus and started his search for guns, non-citizens, or whatever else he might find. No Westerner came here to pick daisies. If you were here, you were up to no good, and the guard's superiors wanted to know which no good you were up to and for whom. I lowered my head out of instinct and habit, turning my face away from his eager eyes. He did not spot me, and he finally stepped off, waving the minibus on its way with the muzzle of his weapon. I straightened with relief. I had passed undetected.

Mount Tirich Mir (26,000 ft), north of Chitral Pakistan

Chitral Fort famed by 1895 Seige of Chitral

We rumbled down the hole-spotted road. The road got narrower and turned from macadam to packed earth to dusty ridges baked into the once-muddy trail. After another two hours, we reached a dirt lot, euphemistically called the Timargarha Village Transportation Center. It was filled with other minibuses and trucks parked at every possible angle to one another. Within minutes, I had honed in on a driver yelling "Chitral, Chitral, Chitral" into the throng. Ten others had heeded the same call, so pressed shoulder to shoulder, 11 of us stepped into the back of a Toyota pickup. With his full load, the driver could stop hawking his wares. We rolled and swayed our way though Dir and on to Chitral over the 10,400-foot Lawari Pass with its 42 sharp switchbacks, each and every one of which I had already traveled too many times. The excitement of meeting Commander Massoud somehow vanquished my weariness.

In the summer of 1989, the political situation in Afghanistan was unstable. Before coming to Chitral, I had stopped in Peshawar to meet with Yahya and Ahmed Zia, Commander Massoud's brothers, who had been notified of my reason for coming to Afghanistan. They had been frank: getting to Massoud would not be a cakewalk. To reach Massoud I would be passing through territory held, barely, by Soviet troops. The roads – and often even the adjacent fields and hills – would often be

The Chitral Mosque

mined, since Afghanistan is the most heavily land mined country in the world. Estimates of the number of mines range from six to eight million. Land mines are very egalitarian. They don't care who you are. As a precaution, Massoud's brothers had recommended that I hire a trusted guide who had made many trips from Chitral to Massoud's camps.

At last, the truck stopped in the middle of Chitral Village. I had just enough energy left to claim my bags and carry them uphill through the small bazaar to the Mountain Inn. Fortunately, the evening was

comfortably warm. My fatigue was forgotten when I saw the smiling face of my good friend Haider Ali Shah, the innkeeper, and his aging father Ataliq Jafar Ali Shah, who had once been an advisor to the king of Chitral, when Chitral had a king. Of medium height and build, his salt-and-pepper hair was just now beginning to show his 50 years. Haider greeted me with a handshake and gestured me into his hotel lobby. I had missed this quiet man. Behind his polite shyness lay genuine caring. Although I had been fooled before, I still trusted my instincts about people.

Haider Ali Shah, owner,
Chitral Mountain Inn

Jon Mohammad at Garam Chasma

I was glad enough to surrender my heavy cases to his houseboy. "Jon Mohammad was here earlier today looking for you. He will be here after dark, around eight-thirty, so I will have your dinner sent to your room."

Jon Mohammad, the six-foot, well-built Supply Officer for Massoud, made sure that war and food supplies from the Pakistani border in Chitral reached Commander Massoud in the Panjsher Valley. His supply route into the valley included passes at 14,000 feet and higher. A son of the valley, he knew it as if genetically. Jon Mohammad and I had liked each other since our first meeting in Garam Chasma two years before. Later, it was he who responded to my letter to Commander Massoud about my gem research and desire to explore the Panjsher region. His answer was polite but noncommittal. The next summer I sent a second letter in which I proposed surveying the emerald-producing areas and presenting formal training in modern mining techniques to the Afghans. That seemed to produce more interest on their part. Since emeralds were only discovered there in the early 1970's, according to local lore, there was no long-standing tradition of mining nor knowledge of proper procedures.

Refreshed by the meal and a shower, I sat on the edge of my bed, imagining what lay ahead. But eight-thirty came and went, with no news from Jon Mohammad. The moon shone through the open shutters of my room window, a beacon in a cloudless sky. I checked my gear and busied myself checking it again. Finally, there was a faint tap on the door. It was Jon Mohammad. He glanced over his shoulder and entered quietly, saying nothing until he and his slim, tanned, young Afghan companion were both inside. With a big hug Jon Mohammad lifted me to my toes and greeted me with not much more than a whisper. "This is Mohammad. He will come to get you tonight." Then turning to leave, he instructed me, "Be ready anytime after midnight. Must go."

Cautiously he opened the door and peered into the darkness before leaving. The two men slipped back into the night as stealthily as they had come seconds before.

I slept fully clothed on my bed in the dark room. I was awakened by another gentle knock. Grabbing my pack, I opened the door. The young Afghan was back. My watch glowed in the dark room, nearly as bright as the moon, which was now gone from the window – one o'clock. Looking around the shadows, the Afghan said only, "*Azoo* (Let's go)." He shouldered one of my bags and motioned me out.

We skirted the lobby and the night guard. Mohammad led me around the back of the hotel and over a low stone wall. We hurried down the empty dirt road to a jeep with engine running and driver waiting. I threw my full duffel into the back of the jeep and sat down next to Guy Clutterbuck, through whom the message had come that Commander Massoud wanted to see us. Each of my visits to Central Asia had brought me new associates. Last summer Guy and I had met at the Mountain Inn while he was buying lapis for the British market. We had both expressed our desire to visit with Commander Massoud and had agreed to request the trip together. "Glad you made it. Did you have any problems?" I asked.

Guy shook his head no as we sped through the empty bazaar. We saw the metal sliding doors secured with chains and large keyed padlocks that girded each shop against the night. Splashing through one irrigation channel and stream after another, we followed the dirt path as it tracked a river north into the inky quiet of the moonlit night. We were on our way to Garam Chasma, north of Chitral, high in the Hindu Kush at the Afghan border. The only sound was our engine thrumming and revving in sine waves. We did not converse but stayed each with his thoughts. Roads in these mountains require concentration from passengers as well as drivers. It was all we could do to cling to the side bar of the open jeep through every steep, sharp curve and the driver's double-clutching on the treacherous turns.

Suddenly we jarred to an abrupt stop. We were not yet in Garam Chasma. Mohammad jumped out and motioned emphatically to Guy and me to follow. Now! On the roadside 50 yards ahead we could just make out the silhouette of an armed guard at his post. Our young Afghan escort seemed to become one with the mountain, and Guy and I knew we had to follow. Not doing so could cost us our lives. This is a lawless place. I felt adrenaline surge to meet the challenge of fear and exertion. It wasn't a long trek. We trailed Mohammad through the fields along water channels to the back of Prince Shuja's single-story, whitewashed-cement hotel with its 15 to 20 rooms and sulfurous thermal pool.

Garam Chasma is a settlement with a bazaar extending two hundred yards along the river. The war had transformed it into a boom village. Supplies spilled from the six-by-six foot shops, cobbled together out of scrap wood. During the day hundreds of travelers traded supplies

Garam Chasma bazaar

for trips into Afghanistan.

Swiftly we moved through the darkened, deserted lobby. The young Afghan opened a door into a small, musty, windowless room with two army cots and one old torn padded chair. Mohammad instructed us to stay in hiding for the rest of the night and the following day. Food would be delivered to us. He would come late the next night to take us across the border. Guy and I knew that if the Chitrali Scouts, the police of this region, found out we were here, we would be returned under guard to Chitral and barred from crossing the border, perhaps forever. The Scouts are what passes for legal authority – the Pakistan Army and police stay out under an agreement with the government of this autonomous region. We had heard that some Scouts would take *baksheesh*, whereas others, who did not want to see anyone assist the Afghans, would thwart us, at best. At worst, we could be disposed of, our trail covered with some trumped-up nonsense. Who would take the word of two sneaky Westerners against that of a Chitrali Scout?

Two hours later, our silent vigil was broken by loud footsteps in the hall and a familiar voice thundering our names, "Gary, Guy, I know you're here. Where are you?" John Gunston, I thought angrily. We ignored his call. The British journalist was not supposed to have been part of our journey or even to have known our plans. Didn't he realize that he was risking our mission? Fortunately, his little game of *Marco Polo* went nowhere, and he went away. We hoped no one had heard him calling our names. How could he know that we were here? Probably from someone at Lala's, home of the Peshawar rumor mill.

Somehow I was sure we would be safe. This meeting with Massoud had been a long time coming. I had made proposals, as had Guy and others, to do business with commanders in the North. It wasn't until Guy and I pitched together and made the proposal about economic development, not just short-term profits, that Massoud, the most powerful among them, wanted to hear our plans for gem exploration and training programs for the miners. Now we had his attention and as long as he knew our motives were good, somehow this would happen. In those hours of waiting and not knowing, I wondered how we would look to someone like Massoud. Would he wonder what brought me here? Surely there are easier ways to make a living than running guard posts and sneaking across borders. What were my motives? Yes, some of it was my quest for adventure and my childlike fascination for the new, the different and whatever lies behind the closed door. Massoud might find that charming for a few minutes, but he lives in the realm of adult men, of leaders making important decisions that affect the lives of many others. Boyish charm was not going to impress him.

What did I really know about Massoud? I had compiled a dossier on him and kept clippings for years.

Massoud was the most powerful leader in the north. From what I had heard, he was charismatic and willing to shoulder the burden of leadership. Even his detractors said he acted to benefit his people, and they saw his altruism and followed. He sought what was good for them, not for himself, unlike the legions of corrupt officials in Pakistan and Afghanistan. He was an idealist but also pragmatic. After all, he wanted to talk about doing bsiness with us. I found myself wondering whether money was an end for him or a means and whether he would actually live up to his star billing.

I noticed there was no forward movement when our proposal was just about mines and money. When we illustrated benefits like educating miners and technical support, however, things moved. I question whether I would have made that observation prior to the TWA fiasco and the Tel Aviv debacle. I doubt it. It wouldn't have fit my paradigm, my frame of reference as a businessman. But these last two misadventures had left me empty both financially and somehow – oddly for me – spiritually. Running around the world, going for weeks without bathing, and getting shot at by dangerous people propelled by profit motive alone seemed somehow idle, pointless, and incongruous. The risk-return curve was flat – more risk than being an accountant, gem store owner or schoolteacher and equal *financial* payback, perhaps even less, at the rate I was losing gems to thieves. So, what was I here for? Was it money? No. I didn't care about big houses, bank accounts, and social status. Was it adventure? Well, I liked being a nomad, with no fixed abode, but there was still more. An idea kept recurring to me: it wasn't about winning and losing. It was about how – and why we played the game, this Great Game of Life. I was realizing that I was different, and it was okay with me because there was some larger code of honor, or set of rules, by which I played. I was changing.

Guy and I, still in the small, dank, dark room, studied my maps and waited tensely for signs that our journey was to continue. The Dorah Pass stands at 14,250 feet above sea level on some maps and at 14,800 feet on others. The border to Afghanistan is just before the pass. At either altitude I could see we were in for a long arduous climb. In Peshawar, Massoud's brothers, Ahmed Zia and Yahya, had been explicit about the problems we would face at the border from Pakistan into Afghanistan, even though we had legal visas for both countries. Those visas meant little in the treacherous mountain areas. More than 15 guard stations prevent all foreigners from crossing the narrow valley from Garam Chasma to the Dorah Pass. Having foreigners around would only create problems. Besides blundering into the middle of a battle zone, *tourists* might present complications by drawing attention to the area. We might meet people who didn't want us helping the Afghans. If caught, we could easily be forced back to Peshawar empty-handed and under armed guard. Or worse.

Maybe Gunston had opened his mouth, annoyed that he couldn't find us. Maybe the Chitrali Scouts would swoop down any minute and bundle us off to some fetid cell for a few rounds of unpleasant interrogation. The hours dragged on. We took turns trying to stretch and exercise in the cramped space. Even while dozing, I wondered why I was there and how we would look to Massoud. And I kept concluding, like Massoud (or at least the Massoud of legend), I was not in it for the money.

Finally, the quiet knock signaling our departure came late the next evening. We opened to find a tall, distinguished-looking blond, Paul Costello, a Swiss journalist whom Guy had worked with on previous assignments. He said in a hushed voice, "Four Mujahideen are outside in a four-by-four ready to take us to meet Massoud in Farkhar." "Four, four-by-four…" I thought silently. We gathered our packs quietly as he explained the plan. Two of the Mujahideen would escort us on foot around the uncooperative border guards while the other two crossed through the checkpoints in the jeep. Our guides would carry the packs filled with our heavy equipment, leaving us with only our lighter packs. The rationale was that the border guards would recognize American,

L-R: Guy and Gary preparing to ride on

Swiss, or English goods, cameras, and camping equipment. They were less likely to search and confiscate our items if the guides were carrying the bags. The guards might even smile, I thought, seeing that someone had bamboozled some Westerners out of some attractive goods. Without saying another word, the three of us slipped down the darkened hallway to join the waiting Mujahideen.

The first guard post posed no impediment. Our escorts knew the guard on duty that night, and, as prearranged, handed over a bundle of Pakistani *rupees* in exchange for his lifting the wooden gate for our vehicle to pass.

Fifteen minutes later, the guard at the second post demanded US$150 each from both Guy and me. We argued for 15 minutes before settling on US$20 each. Our escorts encouraged us to pay more, which raised our suspicion that they might be sharing in the toll. Bribery makes doors open in many parts of the world. It's just part of the way of life. But why would Massoud send slippery types to escort us? Maybe his legendary moral rectitude was just a crock or good PR. My anger served no purpose but burned on anyway.

Mohammad warned us that the next posts would be more difficult.

We would have to evade the guards entirely. We had a plan. Our driver was to stop a quarter of a mile before each post to let Guy, Paul, and me jump out and follow our guides to the far side. A quarter moon would help hide us but light our way, dimly, through the fields to a rendezvous with our jeep a half-mile past the danger. Once we crawled and walked more than a mile with our gear because there was no other way to stay hidden. Twice we missed our connection because the driver and our guides had not accurately defined our meeting place. Searching up and down the road for the truck cost us precious time. Sometimes it's hard to know who your friends are, but you have to play the hand you are dealt. There was no folding in this game.

Dawn broke before we cleared the last guard post; we had to hide until the cover of dark the following night. One of our guides walked ahead to arrange for us to spend the day in the tent of an Afghan engineer who was working on the road with a mixed crew of Pakistani and Afghan laborers and guards. We slept until mid-afternoon but were awakened by voices outside our tent. They were speaking Urdu, not a good sign. Afraid of discovery, we hardly breathed during their conversation, which seemed to drag on for hours. There we lay silently staring at the roof of the tent. The voices finally wandered off, but our guard was up. When our blue-eyed engineer-benefactor, Moinuddin, came in with food, we were plenty edgy. We almost jumped him!

"How much do we owe you for the food and assistance?" I asked.

"Nothing," he said, then placed his finger across his lips. He stayed with us for 20 minutes, without any conversation, watching us eat, before he returned to his work. The tension had not dulled our appetites, and we ate like silent, focused, feral beasts, storing up energy for a hard road ahead.

Guy whispered that he had to relieve himself. I motioned back that he couldn't leave the tent. Soon I heard the sound of water pouring on metal and turned to see which vessel Guy had found. After that, as thirsty as I got, I could never bring myself to drink from his canteen.

Lying there in silence, night seemed long in coming. So much waiting, so many hours for speculation to spin about in my head. About an hour after dark, our guide reappeared, silently motioning us to follow. We wanted to talk, to ask what was going on, but his fierce look kept us quiet. Outside the tent about 25 yards away, several men stood talking around a campfire. Three of them wore Pakistani military uniforms and guns. We knew if they spotted us, we would have trouble. We were forbidden to be in this area without written permission, or perhaps even with it, depending on who did the writing and reading. We stood frozen, not knowing whether to run, hide, or go back in the tent. Suddenly out of nowhere, a new Afghan face materialized. Quickly and silently he started away. We set out after the man, managing to creep unnoticed around the road, camp and on up the mountain. From there, we went, half-

Guy Clutterbuck, British gem dealer

crawling, half-walking, the next two hundred yards. Our new guide stood up suddenly and turned to face us. We did not know what to expect, and I stood ready to drop my bags and run – but where? Then he announced, with a hint of pride in his voice, "Welcome to Afghanistan."

After hours of internment, we were ready to move. Now we could move upright on the path, as long as we had the narrow light of the moon. But when she slipped behind the clouds, we had to press on in almost total darkness. In the extraordinary expanse of sky and mountains, every view extended to infinity. The Hindu Kush night absorbed all light, like black velvet, yet it enhanced star shine and moon glow. It muffled all sound yet telegraphed the faintest crackle or whisper across the vast expanse. The darkness separated us into a piercing solitude yet bound us together out of a need to survive. The climb induced an extraordinary, dream-like experience. We heard the murmur of voices and clip-clop of horses to our left. We headed toward the sounds into an open valley, where five horsemen awaited us in the blackness. With them was the guide and interpreter Guy and I had hired on the recommendation of Massoud's brother.

"Move quickly," he said in English. "We fear the Pakistani soldiers might have followed you."

After we had tied our loaded bags onto the horses, we climbed large rocks in order to mount. Instead of saddles, we had to straddle our bags. Riding astride our bulky equipment was new to me, and my pack didn't feel secure. I was forced to sit too high in the makeshift saddle. From the horse's first steps, I struggled to keep my balance. No time to stop for adjustments. We headed up the mountain toward Dorah Pass.

The mountains cast an ominous shadow over the trail, and the night was still except for the scuff of our horses atop the rocks. In the world of cities, it is hard to imagine how black and silent the Afghan mountains can be. We kept the tight silence of men careful to hide their whereabouts from the prospect of unseen enemies. Occasionally, the horses stumbled while they negotiated the mountain trail, which quickly narrowed to 15 inches. To my left the treeless mountain merged with the sky, somewhere beyond my vision. To my right the scree, stirred by our progress, slid some yards then hurtled into the void. The drop-off seemed bottomless.

Suddenly my horse faltered. His right hind leg gave way – and my balance with it. I grappled for the rope that held the bags. Straining to regain his footing, again the horse slipped. The bags began to slide from beneath me off to the right. Oh, no! The horse lunged forward to avoid falling while I desperately grasped his neck, but my bags slid from beneath me. All I could do was hold on as the stallion whinnied and shook. He swayed, pulled in the direction of the bags, leaned the other way to compensate, lost his footing, and fell down the slope, heaving and careening sideways down the mountain. Too late to dismount, I fell with the horse. Several feet before hitting the ground, my right leg clung to his side as if pressed by g-forces. Then my hip crashed onto a boulder. I saw a bright flash; then pain radiated sharply up my side. I could feel the warm ooze of blood running down my leg. In those seconds of terror, I was certain the horse would die, and with a crushed leg, I would never walk again. And then I blacked out.

Ahmed Shah Massoud

1953-2001

Ahmed Shah Massoud was born in 1953 in the village of Jangalak in the Bazarak district of Panjsher Valley. The name of his family was "Nawroozkhel." Dost Mohammad, Massoud's father, was an army officer who spent most of his life in Kabul. Massoud received his primary and secondary education in Lycee Isteqlal. Later he joined Pole-e-Technic University of Kabul to study engineering and architecture. He was a passionate reader of prose and poetry.

King Mohammad Zahir Shah was overthrown in 1973 by his cousin and the former Prime Minister, Sardar Daoud Khan, who declared a republic. Daoud Khan abolished the monarchy and declared himself President until he was assassinated in 1978. It is said that he worked for modernization and reform within the government, including the unveiling and educating of women. He passed a constitution. But he was Pashtun and wanted to build an authoritarian, unitary state structure. His coup had been backed by the PDPA (People's Democratic Party of Afghanistan), the Afghan Communist Party. He immediately established firm ties with the Soviet Union. During the regime of Daoud Khan, Massoud, after involvement in a military uprising in the Panjsher Valley against Daoud, along with other members of a party called Jawanan-e-Musulman, or Moslem Youth, were forced to flee with their professors to Pakistan to avoid repercussions of their anti-communist statements.

The Prime Minister of Pakistan, Zulfaqar Ali Bhutto,

welcomed these Islamic fundamentalists. In 1975 he commissioned the Pakistani intelligence service, the Frontier Corps (later known as ISI), to create unrest in major cities and strategic points in Afghanistan. By forcing the government to spread its forces, he paved the way for the 1978 coup. To launch this plan, Bhutto recruited and trained a group of Afghans in the Bala-Hesar of Peshawar, in Pakistan's Northwest Frontier Province. Among these young men were Massoud, Gulbuddin Hekmatyar, and other members of Jawanan-e-Musulman.

Massoud's mission for Bhutto was to create unrest in northern Afghanistan. It served Massoud's interests, which were apparently opposition to the Soviets and independence for Afghanistan. Later, after Massoud and Hekmatyar had a terrible falling-out over Massoud's opposition to terrorist tactics and methods, Massoud withdrew from Jawanan-e-Musulman. He joined Rabani's newly created Afghan political party, Jamiat-i-Islami, in exile in Pakistan. The Soviets had put Taraki's regime in as their puppets, and they started to try to spread communism into the countryside. Massoud began organizing active resistance to their efforts. Some speculate that it was his resistance that provoked the Soviet to invade Afghanistan in December 1979. Quickly thereafter, the Pakistani ISI undertook the formation of *tanzeem*s, political parties, in Peshawar who would help oppose the Soviet hegemon - with covert US aid.

Massoud, who had been appointed a Jamiat commander in Parwan and Kapisa provinces, returned to Panjsher in the winter of 1979. He went into battle but nearly died from a leg wound before he ever began. His already tiny force had dwindled to ten men with only mulberries to eat. "All the people had left us," Massoud recalled. "We joined hands and promised ourselves that we would either liberate our country or die here, but we would never leave." His fierce commitment inspired an unbreakable bond among his followers.

Massoud's capture of the important emerald mining area of Dara-e-Khanj in late 1981 gave him an extensive and unprecedented financial resource. The presence of emeralds there had just been a rumor until the 1970s, but once rediscovered, the mining developed quickly. According to the Associated Press, 10 September 1982, and Radio Free Afghanistan, Massoud's yearly income from the Dara-e-Khanj precious stone mines reached $100 million dollars. (That report most likely referred to a retail value in Europe or the US and not the value of unfinished material in Afghanistan. But still..) That was enough money to support a war effort. So Massoud was well aware of the potential the gem trade held to generate money, and improved methods and new finds could increase that yield considerably. Knowing this, he had consented to see us.

In 1982, Massoud signed a truce agreement with the Soviets at their request, which resulted in two cease-fires of six months each. Some said Massoud only fought when he had to and preferred to negotiate. Others said he was tired of seeing his people killed. We know the Soviets agreed because they couldn't seem to control the North once Massoud united it - his leadership was too powerful. He wanted to create a Supervisory Council for an autonomous region under his control. He created Shora-e-Nazar, a coalition of the many-party, regional commanders. Then, aided by Western intelligence experts, he began forming an intelligence network that kept him aware of the activities of other Afghan commanders as well as Soviets in the region.

Apparently his two cease-fires with the Soviets had caused some grumbling among the ISI and CIA supporters.

Was Massoud going soft on Communism? Or was he just not an ideologue? Maybe he just had a different agenda. Maybe he just wanted peace and a chance at democracy for his people. Naturally, the CIA and ISI were too cynical to buy that line. Massoud's military success and the love of his people caused a lot of hatred and envy. His strategy of not starting a battle until forced to upset the ISI and Hekmatyar but served him and his supporters well during the years of resistance.

In fact, Massoud continued to wage war with the Soviets and with great success. He was regarded as a tactical genius, and no one could move him from his territory in Northeastern Afghanistan, centered in the Panjsher Valley. There were 100,000 Soviet troops occupying Afghanistan now, fighting against seven US-backed rebel factions. In 1985, the US sharply increased its covert support for these Mujahideen, providing both high-tech weaponry and expertise, all funneled through Pakistan's ISI to Gulbuddin Hekmatyar. Some estimate that the US gave more than $2 billion worth of guns and money to the now 15 Afghan rebel factions during the 1980s, the largest US covert action since World War II. But Massoud never got the same share as the others. He was too busy fighting Russians and building coalitions in the North to go to Islamabad or Peshawar, where the spies, politicians and journalists could be found. Much more went to Hekmatyar, who spent most of his time in Peshawar stockpiling weapons and money. One source quoted him as having claimed he could fight for 25 years without ever needing supplies!

Gary on trail at 12,000 ft. in Badakhshan, Afghanistan

Chapter Seven
The Lion of Panjsher

1988

I don't know how long I was in that blessed, shock-induced oblivion, but it wasn't long enough. Even my physical state of shock wasn't enough to ease the pain, first throbbing like a locomotive, then sharp as a razor's slice. I could make out the sound of the others coming to my rescue. They pulled the quivering horse forward off of my leg and struggled to drag me by my shalwar kamese away from the precipice and back up the mountain to the trail. In the cacophony of tongues, I heard someone asking what they could do for me. I heard my voice tell them, "Just let me rest a few minutes, and then I will try to walk." Miraculously, the horse, bearing only some superficial abrasions, stamped in relief, fully alive. Except for the pain raging throughout my body, I too seemed whole. I asked Guy to please bring me the orange pain pills from my first aid bag. (It's funny how one remembers to be polite at moments like this...) I gulped some down, and slowly a strange clarity enveloped me.

We were at a decision point. I was hurt, but I didn't know how seriously. I was at risk for infection and, in the worst case, even losing a limb. We were in Afghanistan but far from anything resembling civilization. There would be no medical help until we reached Massoud – three days and several mountain passes yet to negotiate. We stood at the place where the Karakoram and the Hindu Kush come together, some of the densest and highest peaks in the world. The Dorah Pass, our best path, was at 14,972 feet of altitude.

Behind, the Pakistani guards remained a threat, and they would certainly cause us serious problems when they realized we had slipped past them. No doubt they would act out their anger and embarrassment. We would all risk physical abuse depending on their individual temperaments and proclivities. And there was no one to rescue us. There was only one solution – we had to press on.

I cringed in pain as my companions helped me onto my horse. My body soon responded to the painkiller as we rode through Dorah

Pass and down into the valley between Dorah and Tope-Khana. We stopped in a *chai-khana* for tea, and the pills lifted me to another world, full of fantasies of old lovers, as if my life were passing before my eyes. I faded off into another realm.

L-R: Horseman, Paul Costello, guide, and Gary at Dorah Pass

I awoke to Guy's urging, "The horses are ready, and we need to start." My hip and leg raged anew as I stood up then faltered. I ate the warm *nan* he handed me and drank the hot green tea. I reached for another pill. Guy shook his head gravely but said nothing. Our companions were talking earnestly with another traveler whom reported Soviets just ahead in our path. Our guide had gone ahead to survey the situation and found more travelers coming in our direction. They warned that the Soviet troops had occupied an outpost about ten miles ahead. We could not risk going that way. This was a war zone, and in wars, even innocents get hurt. And the Soviets would not see us as innocents but probably as agents of their enemy Massoud. To continue, we would have to climb over Tope-Khana Mountain. It would be too steep for the horses to carry riders. We would have to do it on foot, Afghan-style, holding onto the horse's tail as he rose up the steep mountainside. And if he should falter...

Paul and Guy – and I – had doubts that I would be able to endure the climb. But if we split up and I went back with a guide, the journey would be pointless, and I might walk into the arms of the waiting Pakistani Army.

A half an hour into the climb, they were already out of sight. Alone, I slowly climbed step after step, like some exhausted pilgrim. I looked ahead. I was nearing the top of the mountain. I heard sounds like gunshots in the distance but thought they were only in my muddled imagination. When they persisted and were getting closer, I lurched forward behind a sizeable boulder. As I fell, I spotted someone running in my direction, wearing a typical outfit and a Chitrali cap. I thought he might be one of Massoud's men. Following my instinct, I showed myself. *Salom-o-alaikum.* My assumption was correct.

We had no language in common. Interpreting his hand signals, I understood my friends had met him and were waiting in the valley on the other side of the mountain. With his AK-47, he pointed to the Soviet troop position saying, "Ruski! Ruski!" Then he pantomimed how they had shot at him as he had topped the mountain. Fortunately, he knew the best way of circumventing their vantage, or so I interpreted the meaning of his gestures. I hobbled in the direction he pointed, and an hour later, I rejoined my party, to everyone's great relief and mostly mine. I was thankful for my medicated state. I had been too drugged to register fear, even sensible fear.

Naturally my companions had all rested while they waited, so they were eager to start off immediately, even though they could see I needed a break. I did not want to delay them further. The pills, those miracles in a bottle, were still effectively reducing my pain, so we started back on the trail, down the far side of the mountain. It was easier going down in the company of my friends, for friends they were at this point. I felt warmth towards them and love for the world and the dark and starry night. I had forgotten about the Soviets, but I'm sure I would have loved them as well. As the miles melted away, I gained confidence that I could make it the rest of the way. And when it was time to stop, we carefully chose a place to camp in the flatlands of the valley floor. I was ready for my encounter with the dream dimension. I fell asleep. And dreamed. At four a.m., well before dawn, I awoke to Guy's vigorous tugging at my arm.

"The horses are ready, and we want to start now in case the Soviets are headed this way." The pain was less sharp, now more of an enervating pulse up and down my side. I alternated between riding until my backside and legs ached as much as my flank and walking until I could barely stand. I stumbled and slogged along throughout the day and into dusk. Just before complete darkness enveloped us again, we sighted, out in the distance, a wooden cabin and a crowd of Mujahideen. Adrenaline carried us the last weary mile.

Afghan chai-khana, or tea house, where visitors are allowed to spend the night

As we entered the cabin, the group of men inside rose and extended their hands then motioned us to join them where they sat. There was no small talk. Securely surrounded by these tall, rugged, well-armed soldiers and exhausted from exertion and pain, I was too debilitated to worry about the Soviets.

A young boy came to each of us carrying a long-spouted pewter pot in one hand and a large pewter bowl in the other. He held the large bowl under our hands and poured water over them, offering us a towel after we had rubbed our hands clean in the warm flow. Dinner was never more welcome – goat stew and green tea with *nan*. We ate quickly; then we slept shoulder-to-shoulder on top of our sleeping bags inside the cabin, like Cossacks in a Babel story.

Long before sunrise we started north up the mountain to Varsaj and on to a village southeast of Taloqan called Farkhar, where Massoud had a command post and several storehouses of supplies. Reaching the crest by early afternoon, we welcomed the green pastures and quick, narrow streams as balms to our eyes and our spirits. In this challenging environment, simply making it to a destination felt like just cause for celebration. Longing for respite from a five-thousand-foot descent, we joined three friendly travelers in front of a fire for tea. Later, while washing my face and rinsing my hair in the stream, I looked up into the stark blue sky. All around me lay boulders brightly festooned with yellows, reds, and browns. "The flowers of Badakhshan," my guide said. At this altitude they are not real flowers but lichens – and beautiful nonetheless. Every moment seemed to have a shimmering aura.

Refreshed, we traveled on until five o'clock, stopping in a hamlet composed of small, new-looking wood buildings. Our guide asked some villagers about Massoud's location. This earned us an invitation to spend the night as their guests. Massoud would come for us in the morning. We were finally safely on his turf. I turned to Guy, exultant. "We will soon get to meet the *Lion of Panjsher*, the man we have come so far to see."

"Anytime now," Guy concurred excitedly. We slept contented.

* * * * *

I sat sipping my morning tea. Out of nowhere, two Soviet jeeps sped into the village and headed directly for us. A gigantic man leaped out of the first with an AK-47 and two bandoliers of ammunition across his chest. Wearing a brown Chitrali cap, a wiry, bearded figure stepped from the second jeep. Though his companions were well armed, he wore no gun. He greeted us with a healthy handshake. It was Massoud!

He wore khaki pants and a khaki shirt with epaulets. His boots were black and substantial, probably Soviet. His posture was slightly hunched, giving the impression of medium height. The force of his presence was striking and immediate. His movement was deliberate. His eyes were alert but not at all shifty. His focus was like a laser, narrow and powerful, but he had an air of composure, not a hint of aggression. I might have been depleted or shown any of a thousand other weaknesses in that

L-R: Ahmed Shah Massoud, Gary, and Haron

moment. Instead, some-how his firm strength gave strength to me. I felt as though he would lay aside his own weariness and concerns in order to concentrate on us, as if no one else existed. He seemed to draw power from somewhere else: from the earth beneath his feet and the mountains beyond. I felt an energy I just can't describe – but I knew that before me stood an extraordinary man. It wasn't anything he did or any way he looked. It was whom he *was* that left the impression.

Massoud motioned us into the first jeep. I was relieved to ride in a vehicle instead of on (or under) a horse! Green pasturelands lined the road, and we arrived in Farkhar in no time. Massoud led us into his office in Chaman-e Khostdeh. He indicated we would be able to spend the night there. He introduced us to his assistant, Haron Amin. He accomplished all of this without saying anything. Massoud spoke Dari and French but not English. As an asylum seeker, Haron had spent time in Los Angeles, and he interpreted Massoud's words into smooth, flowing English. He cut right to the issue at hand. We had proposed to survey the emerald-producing areas and to document the mining methods used. Massoud instructed us to review the details of our proposal with Haron. Massoud would then meet with us again to make his decision. Then, suddenly, he was gone.

We discussed our proposal with Haron for an hour. He asked astute questions, anticipating what Massoud would want to know. Then he asked, "Mr. Gary, would you carry a message back to the U.S. Consulate in Peshawar for us?"

Without much thought, I agreed. I act. Much later, after I had assumed this duty, I realized how dangerous it was to risk being caught by Soviets carrying such a missive. I reached out for the several pages he proffered. "This is an account of a seminar held by the various Mujahideen factions in Chaman-e-Khostdeh (Farkhar) Taloqan, Afghanistan under Massoud's leadership. It is not sealed, so you may read it if you like."

Guy and I sat on the office porch and read the handwritten report prepared by a freelance writer as told by Haron. The report was an account of an ambush the day before by Said Mirza, a commander of Gulbuddin Hekmatyar, against Massoud's commanders after a strategy seminar. As we made our way through, it was clearly more than an account of a strategic and tactical seminar for Mujahideen battling against the Kabul regime. It was, instead, a chronicle of a brutal attack on Massoud's home territory in the northeast corner of the country and a setback to Massoud's organization with a high human cost to him. The story, told in the flat prose of a trained intelligence gatherer, was grim and told the savagery of internecine war.

The breach of the cease-fire had cut the heart out of Massoud's command structure, robbing him of commanders with ten years of discipline and experience. With the sole road unsecured, communication and transport between the two major areas of the northeast became impossible. And worst of all, Massoud now had enemies on all fronts, in Kabul and among the previously unified Mujahideen. How must a man in his position feel? I had never had responsibility of this magnitude weighing on me. Even in Viet Nam I had superior officers with whom I could share or pass on my problems. Since Viet Nam, I had been busy living my little life just for myself – my adventures, my gems, my penthouse in Hawaii. The worries I had in my world seemed, now, like child's play.

And then Massoud walked into the room. He portrayed no burden or concern. His focus burned intensely from his dark eyes, as if he had nothing to think about but gems and our training program for miners. We could help him achieve his objectives, so he gave us his full attention. He was starkly aware of his circumstances. We knew that he suffered, in ways we could only imagine, from the human losses, the tactical setback, and the threat to his campaign. But his resolve was like steel,

Ambush Report

Handcarried by Gary Bowersox to US Consul in Peshawar

Ahmed Shah Massoud: The focus of the seminar had been to define new strategy and tactics for the Mujahideen in their battle against the Kabul regime.

The returning commanders and party officials were traveling on the road between Farkhar and Taloqan in July organized loosely into three convoys. The first convoy consisting of two cars, one with Khanabad commander, Moula Wudaud. At 3:00 p.m., the unsuspecting Jamiat Mujahideen were fired upon with heavy machine guns and kalashnikovs from hidden positions in the Taloqan Gorge, which borders a portion of the 45 KM stretch of road between Farkhar and Taloqan.

Jamiat commander Engineer Yacob was in Mullah Wudaud's car as it passed through the gorge several days ago. He was shot three times in the arm and is only able to relate this tale because he managed to escape from his captivity two days ago. He says that his car was following behind Dr. Sham's when suddenly they encountered a barrage of gunfire that killed one of them, and left two others, including himself, injured. According to Engineer Yacob, the driver stopped the car and Mullah Mudaud tried escaping up the hill but was shot dead. The rest of the Jamiat Mujahideen in both stopped cars were surrounded by Hesbi (Hekmatyar) Mujahideen and taken across to the other side of the river.

They waited there until five to six cars of the second convoy arrived. The cars were stopped again in a similar fashion, money and valuables confiscated, and the new hostages were told to join the other captives. There were now approximately 50 to 60 Jamiat Mujahideen being held. They were taken to the small village of Dahane Kushakdan where they walked until after dark when the final convoy of Jamiat trucks, one of them with Kunduz commander Arif Khan, passed through.

Mohammad Akbar, a Jamiat commander was riding in the last car in this convoy, passing through gorge at 6:30 p.m., "Suddenly we heard tremendous gunfire overhead and we had to stop. Our car was surrounded by 25 men, as were the rest of the cars in the convoy. We were told to pass our weapons out through the window and to get out. When we got out they confiscated our money, watches, coats, and even our shoes. Some of our men were hit by the Hesbi Mujahideen with the ends of Kalashnikovs." A civilian truck then came up the road, temporarily distracting the captors, allowing Mohammad Akbar to slip undetected to the back of the truck where he acted as though he was a civilian and was able to escape on the truck when it was ordered onward.

Ghazni, a Jamiat heavy artilleryman, was also in this convoy. He says "after getting out of the car, they were ordered by Hesbi commander Eshan-Sayad Mirza to cross the river where he was standing. Arif Khan, commander of Kunduz, refused to follow these instructions despite being ordered to do so three times. Finally Eshar gave permission for three carloads of Khan's men to be released.

Shortly after being released, they again came under heavy gunfire in which one car was overturned, killing one man and injuring two others. Eventually the two transports of Arif Khan reached Taloqan where the commander initiated emergency procedures and established radio contact with Ahmed Shah Massoud.

Meanwhile at 9 o'clock that night, Hesbi commander Eshan Merzai requested that the hostages identify themselves as *commanders* or *personnel*. After compiling two lists, the prisoners were searched thoroughly. Maulevi Izattulah and Payandah were then handcuffed in front of the group and taken outside, then led down to the roadside, at which time shots were heard and the two were executed.

The rest of the Jamiat Mujahideen were taken to the valley of Nao Khoja, higher in the gorge where they were separated into two rooms – one with commanders, the other with personnel. The Jamiat Mujahideen asked their captors why they were being held as an oral agreement had been made one month earlier. Agreed upon by four groups: Hesbi (Khalis), Hesbi (Hekmatyar), Jamiat and Harakat, which guaranteed freedom of passage for these Mujahideen groups. The captors told their hostages that "promises had been broken and that the oral agreement could no longer be honored."

In Taloqan the next morning of July 10th, a delegation of four Maulevis and elders of the city were told by Arif Khan to go to the gorge and negotiate with Sayad Jamal, major commander for Hesbi in the area, for the release of the captives. The number of Hesbi Mujahideen operating in the gorge area under Jamal approximately numbered 400 men. The delegation upon arriving at the gorge were informed that no further action was planned and were promised that the hostages would be released shortly thereafter.

The Maulevi's and elders returned to Taloqan by 11 a.m. and were allowed to carry back the bodies of the dead. An eyewitness in Taloqan at the time of the delegates return reported that tensions were high in the city as armed Hesbi and Jamiat Mujahideen patrolled the streets and rumors of the strife circulated among civilians doing their last minute shopping.

According to captive Engineer Yalob, the hostages were held until 2:00 o'clock the following afternoon (July 10) without food or water, nor with any medical relief for those injured. Eight men among them were then selected: Engineer Yacob, Sardot, two Khanabad men, Ghulam Ali and Abdul Ahmad, a driver from Peshawar, Sarmallem Tarique and his brother.

The eight men were brought back down to the river under the supervision of Hesbi commander, Sayad Fakhruudin. They were led across the bridge to the roadside where Sarmallem Tarique, major Ishkamesh commander and his brother were shot while the others watched.

Engineer Yacob said that Hesbi commander Sayad Fakh wanted to shoot them but that the Hesbi commander of another markaz, Babuz Shah, objected and positioned his men to prevent further shooting. Dr. Shams, along with the two Khanabad commanders, Ghulam Ali and Abdul Ahmed were then released, while Yacob and Sardat were held under the custody of Babur Shah.

Yacob was held for three days during which time he heard on radio communication established with Eshan Marzal that many of the captured Tarkhar and Baghlan commanders had been shot. Engineer Yacob escaped on July 13 during evening novmaz and made it back to Farkhar where he conducted this interview.

The dead bodies of executed Jamiat members, some badly mutilated, have been intermittently left by the roadside at the gorge where they have been identified by Jamiat and the news, then relayed to Ahmed Shah Massoud. The burned body of Dr. Hussain was found as it floated down the river at Taloqan.

Some of the major Jamiat commanders confirmed dead: Mullah Wudaud, Head of Tarkhar Province; Dr. Hussain-Vice President and Head of Administration of Tarkhar; Sarmullem Tatique, Head of Ishkamesh; Mualevi Izatullah-commander of Ishkamesh District of Sayab; Officer Payendah, Ishkamesh City Commander; Ahmed Padshah, District of Bangee Commander; Jon Mohammad, Commander of Administration in Bangee; Naqibillah, Education Committee Delegation; and Ustad Shahied, Taloqan Intelligence Committee.

The ambush presents a multitude of problems for Ahmed Shah Massoud. First of all the road from Farkhar to Taloqan has been effectively closed, making communications and transport between the two major areas of the northeast, Faisabad and Kunduz, extremely difficult. On the operation level he has lost several of his most gifted commanders, who led a combined force of over 3,000 men, and who had accumulated ten years of war experience as commanders. In addition, Massoud who has always advocated the importance and necessity of Mujahideen unity, has now to divert his attention previously focused on the defeat of the Kabul regime, and deal with this unprecedented internal provocation.

and he knew his purpose. He had started out with thirty followers, only 17 rifles, and the equivalent of $100. He had lost all but ten loyal troops living on mulberries. Like his father before him, he would rise again. And we were there to help him do it. I had heard about the myth, and now the man stood before me, larger even than the legend. Now, somehow, I too knew what I must do.

* * * * *

The next morning I took a clean brown shalwar kamese from my pack and went off to find a private spot a quarter of a mile upstream from the office where I could bathe and change clothes. As I walked back, I glimpsed at Massoud entering some bushes farther upstream for his own bath. At that moment, I was glad to see him as human like me, rather than as some demi-god. But later in the office, he appeared to have come from some fierce burnished other world. There was an aura about him as if somehow he could remain above the vagaries of politics and frailties of men. He oriented his three-by-five-foot prayer rug toward Mecca, and he began to pray.

He rose and approached us. We all stood up from the floor. He shook our hands and asked us to sit. He was calm, focused, and ready to discuss emerald exploration. Haron outlined my plans for Massoud in Dari. We spent more than an hour discussing the potential for employment in gem mining, which would produce wages for his people, as well as tax revenue and foreign currency for his government.

After a time Massoud excused himself, asking us to stay until the next day. We met with him again the next afternoon. The meeting was very formal, but Massoud appeared to be in a hurry. I could tell by his questions that he had given the proposal much thought. I reviewed the particulars of exploration, mining, and plans for future Symposiums. He recalled that shortly after the Soviet occupation of Afghanistan, the Mujahideen had

Massoud writing letter of introduction for Guy and Gary for safe passage and assistance on return trip

begun finding emeralds in the bomb craters created by Soviet bombs in the valley. Massoud's men had been successful in selling these emeralds, so he was very interested in investigating the potential for commercial production in Panjsher Valley.

Massoud said, "I must go. I approve and will support your plans. I will appoint someone to work directly with you. Have a good and safe trip back to Pakistan. I will give you a letter for the field commanders you may meet on the return trip."

Guy and I thanked him for his hospitality, but I knew letters of permission would be of little value, as only five percent of Afghans can read. We gave our pledge to do our best to assist his villagers with their mining. Then, again, he was gone.

We packed and got on the trail before sunrise the next morning. We wanted to cover 15 miles of mountains toward the south and reach Eskazer before dark. Our party consisted of Guy, two horsemen, and me. Paul Costello had stayed on with Massoud's people.

Early the second morning we made our way toward Tope-Khana, majestic in the distance. Between the time we had first crossed this mountain to reach Massoud's headquarters and now, Massoud's soldiers had attacked and defeated the Soviet-occupied outpost. Since the Soviet survivors had fled into the mountains, we did not have to climb Tope-Khana again to avoid them. Instead, it would be safe to travel around the base of the mountain. Safe from attack, that is, but not necessarily from thousands of land mines the invaders had planted to sabotage Massoud's supply route.

Wanting to get through the minefields below Dorah Pass by sundown, we carefully led our mounts on a tight rein. Along the way we saw dismembered body parts of horses that had strayed off the path. I stopped a couple of times to take photos of the mines within two feet of my foot. Guy and our guide asked me to stop because it made them so nervous to see me perilously near danger.

That night we slept in a chai-khana made from a large gray-colored military tent. Twenty cents purchased a dinner of trout, fresh from the lake at the base of the pass. In the morning I looked up and wondered aloud to Guy, "How are we going to climb that mountain?"

"Don't you remember coming down?" he asked me.

Minefields at base of Tope-Khana

No, I didn't.

"You took those pain pills and just floated down in the dark!" he reminded me. We made slow progress up the steep trail. Many times we had to resort to the Afghan technique of holding onto the horses' tails to pull ourselves along. Even so, the ascent cost us such strenuous effort that we had to rest at the top and again on the other side of the pass. We relaxed until dark before proceeding toward Shasidim, where we found the pickup truck Jon Mohammad had promised to have waiting. Eagerly Guy and I jumped into the back. Even though the road was only a two-tire-wide winding path paved with rocks, we were both happy to be riding instead of trudging uphill at the end of a horse's tail.

I have often looked back at the time we spent with Massoud and wondered how he had impressed me so strongly. As best I can describe it, it was the calm intensity of his attention, fueled by faith or passion or something else. I wondered, as well, what I could accomplish if I found my passion. And so I began my search for it, listening more carefully to those internal voices.

The first two posts we reached were unattended. Apparently the guards had not expected visitors and had slipped into their tents for a nap. But ten minutes later the driver hit the brakes with all his weight. Apparently the guards posted just ahead had rolled a huge log across the road to control traffic while they slept. Guy, one of our Afghan guides, and I scrambled out of the back of the pickup truck, lugging our gear with us. We jumped over the log and lumbered ahead as fast as we could on the stone-filled dirt road. We had managed only ten yards when we heard noises from the tent. Fortunately for us, by the time the guards had opened the flap, we were well down the road and lost to sight in the pitch-black night.

We slowed to a walk five minutes later as truck lights shone behind us. After a bumpy ten-minute ride, the truck came to a stop again. The driver leaned out of the window and signaled with his hand that another guard post lay directly ahead. Once again we shouldered our gear and walked down the valley at a 45-degree angle from the road. This time two guides led us to the bank of a 15-yard-wide roaring mountain river. It was so dark we couldn't see the water, but one guide pulled on our arms to indicate that we must cross the stream to avoid being detected.

All four of us linked hands tightly and started into the current. As we reached the halfway point, the water suddenly surged, adding another four inches of depth. Now it was roiling around our hips. In panic, both guides wrenched free of our grip and scrambled back to shore. Just then another swell hit us, taking Guy under. I managed to grab his shirt, but I couldn't prevent myself from being forced downstream. Seizing a good hold on the back of his shirt, he towed me like a water-skier. Then the surge hit us again, rolling and tumbling us both underwater for several yards before I was able to get a tenuous footing on the rocky bottom, even as Guy kept dragging me along. Finally he forced his head above water. This wasn't an easy trick because he had tied his bootstraps together and hung his boots around his neck by the laces, where water filled them like ballast.

After Guy was up, we staggered for the opposite bank and followed the stream for about a mile before crossing back to find the road and the truck. After waiting half an hour without a sign of our group, we figured the driver had gone on without us, so we decided to continue on foot to Garam Chasma.

Guy started to chill in the cool air. Then he began shaking, and as we walked, he shook worse. About 15 minutes later we spotted a large military tent surrounded by horses, goats, and sheep. Obviously the livestock belonged to Afghans traveling to or from Pakistan, so we decided to wake them for help. Coveting the warm clothes one man was wearing, we offered Pakistani money equivalent to US$50. By that time Guy didn't care what he spent. He was getting hypothermia. The men stared at us as if we were crazy – two sopping-wet aliens blue with cold arriving out of the dead of night offering to buy the clothes off their backs for an outrageous sum. But they groggily agreed to sell us one herder's big wool coat. Shaking from the cold, Guy quickly buttoned the coat on his body.

We had been walking for another half-hour when, we saw lights advancing from behind. To keep out of sight, we dropped to the ground on the side of the road until the truck had drawn a little in front of us. Spotting our driver, we began waving and yelling to him, but with the engine noise, he couldn't hear us. So we chased the truck and banged on the door. Finally he realized what was happening and stopped.

He looked shocked. Obviously he had feared us drowned in the stream or captured by the Pakistani army. No doubt Jon Mohammad would have been hard on him if he had lost us. Feeling lucky and grateful, we jumped into the truck and rode into Garam Chasma just as daylight graced the sky.

I had felt deeply inspired by the first Symposium. Now we had the go-ahead and blessing of Massoud to continue our work. In addition, we had permission to start surveying in his territory. Guy and I began planning immediately for a survey of Panjsher and a second Symposium. I realized that the best thing I could give the people of Afghanistan was education on exploration, mining, and marketing gems.

* * * * *

When I delivered the handwritten ambush report to the US Consulate, they thanked me for acting as the messenger but didn't realize that I had read it until I told them so.

"You took quite a risk doing that," said the consul. "If you had been caught, they might have thought you had more to tell. Do you know what you're doing here, Mr. Bowersox? It's a dangerous place."

I tried probing to find out how Massoud's group stood among the freedom fighters being funded through the CIA and ISI in Pakistan.

"It's none of your business. But I will tell you one thing. He's not our guy. We prefer some of the other factions; they are more accessible."

"In other words, he spends his time being the most effective resistance to the Soviets instead of down here schmoozing you guys." I was angry at his smug ignorance and mortified by the well-known support of the US for Hekmatyar and his side-switching clan, the favorites of the CIA.

"Let me give you a bit of advice, Bowersox. Go home and hunt for gems somewhere else. This isn't child's play. And you are in way over your head. Your friend Massoud has read Che and Mao and all those other Marxist types. He has picked the wrong team."

I wanted to respond. I wanted to tell him that reading Mein Kampf doesn't make one a Nazi. I wanted to choke this arrogant, ignorant creep. But I didn't. I excused myself and walked out of his office. Our tax dollars at work, I thought as I left, passing the none-too-discreet Marine guard in front of the Consulate. Our policy in Central Asia was then and continues now to be utterly confused, heedless of local realities, and highly dangerous to us and to others. Sadly, recent events have proven me right … as much as I might wish that I had been wrong.

U.S. condemns killing of mujahids' commanders

US Consulate reacted and released the report as many headlines similar to this Prologue *appeared in papers around the world*

Notation

I returned to the US two months after receiving my leg injury. I was still experiencing periodic pains and numbness in my hip. An examination revealed that I had damaged nerve endings in my hip and leg. The nerves appeared to be healing and nothing more could be done. I experienced pain during the next six months and numbness for the next two years.

*Looking from main valley in Panjsher towards Darun and
Derik emerald mining area*

Chapter Eight
Emerald Hunting in Panjsher Valley

Summer, 1989

A year had passed since being with Massoud in Farkhar. Back then, I had made two commitments to him. First, I promised to visit the emerald-producing areas to assess their potential. Second, I promised to undertake conducting some educational seminars to improve their mining methods and skills. Massoud did not own the mines but charged the miners a 10% government tax. Thus, he was very interested in the mine production and modern methods. I sat at a table piled with books in my Honolulu apartment, fourteen stories above the glittering coastline. I was studying the geography and geology of Afghanistan – a place so opposite from the view from my window. I was preparing to do a field survey of the Panjsher Valley's emerald mines.

Here's an amazing fact: Nothing had even been written about emeralds in Afghanistan prior to some Soviet geographic studies in 1977. Nothing! There were no ancient mines or vast trade in them since the times of the Silk Route. They were a relative secret, hiding in plain sight! This was virgin territory! A decade before, I had planned to explore the new finds of emeralds in Panjsher, urged on by the economic *chargé d'affaires*, Larry Thompson, at the US Embassy and by Prokofiev. But the Soviet invasion complicated that endeavor. Now we had the go-ahead and blessings of Ahmed Shah Massoud to visit and evaluate the emerald mines in his territory and to present a teaching symposium to spur economic development of these mines. Guy and I started planning as soon as we got back to Peshawar, but it still took a year to put the pieces together. Now I was in Hawaii researching for both the survey and the upcoming second educational symposium.

What had previously been mostly a business proposition now had a different focus. By granting us his permission, Massoud had unleashed our enthusiasm. My perspective was shifting. I was spending more time on this project and less on my gem business at home. Rather than hoarding the best gems for my profit, now I thought in terms of how to align myself with that extraordinary man I had met. The best contribution I could offer was education on exploration, mining, and marketing gems, and so I would. New passion was beginning to brew inside me.

I had wondered, during the year of preparation, what this shift was about. Could I change the people's primitive mining standards and methods to modern ones? My reflection turned around this question: how many times in our lives do we meet remarkable people? Does it happen every day when we are thinking about other things? Or is it something rare and special? My brush with Massoud was brief but powerful. I felt his presence and charisma immediately. My first hypothesis was that because I had to travel long and hard for it to happen, I invested our meeting with great significance. I was even willing, in short order, to risk capture as a spy in order to deliver his message to the US Consulate in Peshawar. When I got there, I advocated for him, trying to convince the staff that he was the real McCoy and our best hope in the region. My 'hard travel' theory could explain some, but not all, of my sense of engagement with his cause. However, it did not explain the fierce commitment of his followers and the respect he commanded from others – Mujahideen, journalists, and soldiers – on both sides of the conflict.

I obviously never met Hitler, but I have read that he had a presence as well. I did once rub shoulders with Osama bin Laden. We both happened to be in Green's Hotel in Peshawar. In the worst sense, he, too, is a remarkable man. But I was not affected by his acquaintance as I was by meeting Massoud. Bin Laden seemed passionate. His eyes had a strange skewed quality, like those of a visionary or a madman; he looked like he was listening to some other voice, some broadcast in his head. His thin, six-foot four-inch frame made him look otherworldly, like some saint painted by El Greco. I felt no warmth, no rancor, and no sense of connecting with another human being. It wasn't because he ignored me. We all ignore strangers every day: in the grocery line, in the subway, wherever unacquainted people find themselves in propinquity. No, it was as if one of us was elsewhere. And I think it was he who was absent. He was off somewhere in his head, fueled by his thirst for revenge, plotting some incomprehensible act, and all in the name of Allah. He did not scare me. He had less presence than a spectre.

He wasn't there at all.

I have replayed my hours with Massoud many times in my head. His attention was memorable. Massoud differentiated from Hitler and bin Laden in that he cared about the people. He was a humanist. He was a highly spiritual and very religious man. When he spoke to us, to me, it was as if no one else in the world existed, as if he had no other concern than listening to me, and as if he was totally alive and present in that moment. This sort of attention cannot go unnoticed by its recipient. And there was something else. Meeting Massoud inspired me to do the field survey and the two Symposia in Chitral. I felt nourished by the fact that I was helping and that I was certain of being on the side of the good guys. Willa Cather put it like this: "That is happiness; to be dissolved into something complete and great."

Since my first visit to Afghanistan, I had gathered surveys and maps of its geology and geography, along with those of India, Pakistan, and other parts of Central Asia. This was standard operating procedure for me – before I went anywhere, I consulted maps. Ever since I was a child, maps have had allure for me. I used to look through the Encyclopedia Britannica at the library. And we had an atlas at home with pages smudged by my youthful fingers. It's not that I look at them like you look at your watch to see the time. It's more like they speak to me. They tell stories with their isobars, legends, and scales. Where others might have to labor to read maps, I grasp their information in an instant. I collect old books just for their maps. I had also collected an enormous file of clippings about events during the Soviet takeover and occupation. I was brimming with intelligence and ready for my July trip to the emerald mines.

The Panjsher Valley is a narrow 93-mile-long scratch across the mountains located 70 miles north of Kabul in an area of considerable strategic importance. It contains the Panjsher River, one of the Five Lions rivers, which is a tributary of the Kabul River flowing into Pakistan. In the period preceding the Mongol conquest (A.D. 1220), villages like Panjsher had a population of twenty thousand including bakers, potters, weavers, coppersmiths, jewelers, merchants, and miners who operated silver pits using a few thousand slaves at each site. The years of war with the Soviets had decimated its population, and the remaining commerce was more in arms.

Emerald has long been held as a mystical stone, one that the Romans dedicated to the goddess Venus. Some still believe it has the power to create wisdom and love in anyone who wears it and to make all visions real. Sometimes, I wanted to believe that as well. In 1989, they certainly had the remarkable power to make Massoud's vision real. The Soviets had already left as of February of that year. They left behind some 50,000 dead (1979-1989) not counting those who were wounded, murdered, or killed themselves. But this did not mean the country was at peace. The Mujahideen continued to fight against the government of Najibullah, the Soviet puppet president who had replaced Babrak Karmal in 1986. Najibullah had proposed cease fires during those years, but the rebels said they would not negotiate with puppets – and they gained ground strategically until the Soviets admitted defeat and left. The war continued around Kabul, but Panjsher enjoyed a period of calm. I knew we could bring some economic development to the Valley after ten battle-weary years. But first I had to get there. There was no way to go from Kabul to Panjsher. Kabul was sealed inside a *cordon sanitaire* to keep the rebel forces at bay. It was just as well. I couldn't get a visa or flight to Kabul anyway. I would have to go to Chitral in Pakistan and sneak across the border, as usual. Then it was simply a week's walk and ride over 14,000-foot mountain passes. A cakewalk.

I met Massoud's brother Yahya in Peshawar. He told me that my friend Jon Mohammad would meet me at the Chitral Mountain Inn to lead me into northern Afghanistan. Two journalists would be coming with us – Massoud had a story to tell the world, and he understood how they could help him tell it. He hoped to garner some support from the reluctant American government. From Peshawar, I traveled on the Malakhand road by minibus through Charsadda, one of the areas that had been captured by Alexander the Great in 324 B.C. From there I took the fork of the road leading east to Swat Valley, putting me in Chitral after six hours of travel.

At the hotel, I received a note saying that Tony Davis would come to meet me. I had heard of him and Patrick O'Donnell from other news reporters. When a sandy-haired young man approached me in the garden,

I knew it was he. He looked Australian – medium-height, strong, and fit. Thirty-five, more or less.

"We should not talk here," he said quickly, "but are you ready to go tomorrow night? Jon Mohammad is sending a vehicle to fetch Patrick and me after dark. You should be ready anytime thereafter. I need to be off. Stay close to the hotel so as not to be seen around the village. You know the game," he said and walked away.

He reappeared the next night, and we went to meet Jon Mohammad at the 'safe house' that Massoud kept.

We pulled up to the wooden gate somewhere on the outskirts of Chitral in the Toyota truck. Following two blasts of the horn, the gate opened, and the driver hit the gas pedal for a quick ten yards then slammed on the brakes. We saw Patrick – a pale, slim, blond American of medium-height. He looked like a plague victim. "I've had food poisoning or the flu or God-knows-what for three days." He smiled weakly.

Jon Mohammad came around the truck with his big grin. "You have a special four-wheeled vehicle tonight with a very special compartment," he said mischievously and pointed to a supply vehicle at the edge of the compound. "You must go now."

Tony, Patrick, and I approached the truck where Jon Mohammad indicated a hole in the top.

"You must all fit into the secret hiding place. We will put supplies, ammunition, and melons on top to cover you and hide the hole. Then we will add a thick layer of barbed wire to decorate."

From inside our hiding place, we could hear them loading melons on top of our heads. The space was small ... intimate, you might say. "Please try not to get sick now," we kidded Patrick.

"My stomach has been empty for two days," he assured us, and our laughter echoed in the tiny metallic hold that would be our transport.

Jon Mohammad cautioned us from the outside, "Do not talk, especially near a guard post." I wasn't sure how we would know...

Our ride was not exactly luxurious. We lay adjacent to each other with little room for air and no breeze at all. The Afghan border was far, and Patrick was still sick, unable to stop belching up an occasional sulphurous blast. On the dirt road to Garam Chasma and beyond to the

Jon Mohammad "Express" truck with news reporters Tony Davis on upper left and Patrick O'Donnell behind truck

border, the ride was rough and rocky. We kept joking that it was better than walking. As the altitude increased, the air became thinner and cooler, which was a blessing in our hot cubicle.

At several of the posts, suspicious guards poked into the supplies with their rifles as the three of us held our breath. One even took a melon. But we went undetected, and finally, at two-thirty in the morning we bumped across the border. This brought us to the middle of nowhere: exhausted, cramped, and shivering from the cold mountain air. The driver stopped half-a-mile inside Afghanistan and began unloading the supplies piled on top of us. We climbed out and stretched, elated to be safe. Life was good again.

We said little as we spread our sleeping bags on the ground in front of the truck. My warm cocoon welcomed me, and sleep came quickly. At daybreak I bolted upright, afraid of being kicked by sheep attempting to jump over and around us. I had heard of counting sheep to go to sleep, but I had never counted on sheep to wake me up!

Now riding atop the supplies in the back of the truck, we enjoyed the panorama until we spotted Engineer Atiquallah, the fellow Massoud had appointed to be our guide for the journey, in the distance. Atiquallah, known as *Atiq*, was having tea with the horsemen who had come to meet us. I had gotten to know him two years earlier in Chitral and had dined with his family. As we approached, Atiquallah introduced Haji Shahabuddin and Abu Ahmad, Atiq's 15-year-old nephew, who would be

Eng. Atiquallah

Eskazer where trails converge

traveling to Panjsher with us. The horses would transport us. We rode off up the Dorah Pass, stopping later in the valley below at a *chai-khana* for a lunch of fresh trout caught by the owner. By evening, we rode around the base of Tope-Khana Mountain. With a penetratingly clear sky, the starlight glinted like mirror signals sending messages across the universe. Patrick's health was steadily improving, and our spirits sparked us to talk. It was a peaceful time I will never forget.

The next day's two-hour ride brought us to the Eskazer *chai-khana* for lunch and photographs. Eskazer, with six buildings located at a crossroads, served as Massoud's Jamiat-i-Islami party command post. One trail led to the lapis-lazuli mines at Sar-e-Sang, Jurm, and Faisabad. Farther along, another trail forked up over a mountain pass to Commander Massoud's base at Farkhar. I parted from Tony and Patrick there, but they carried a letter from me to Massoud in Farkhar, which updated him on our exploration plans.

For the next two days, Atiquallah, Haji Shahabuddin, Abu Ahmad, and I continued toward Anjuman Pass.

I had traveled 18 miles during the last 12 hours. The sun was starting to set. On faster horses Atiq and Haji had gained the mountain ahead of me; on the slowest horse Abu Ahmad plodded on the trail behind me. Heading into the sunset alone, the vastness of this desolate

Abu Ahmad on Badakhshan Trail

territory enveloped me with a feeling that I had entered time past and time future and that, paradoxically, everything was standing still for all eternity.

Just as I reached the base of the mountain, the sun slipped behind it, assuring that darkness would come rapidly. I stopped for tea at a two-room mud *chai-khana* 20 feet from the trail. Three men and four boys occupied the teahouse. They stared at my camera and watch, giving me an unsettled feeling, as if they lacked integrity. Then I noted the connecting trail from the south, which is the route taken by Hekmatyar's followers, the Hesb-i-Islami, when they raid Massoud's supply trains. I wondered whether these men were thieves or Hekmatyar's spies poised for an ambush.

Fifteen minutes later, as I finished my tea, I could see Abu Ahmad coming, so I waited for him. According to the map, to reach the top, we had to climb 4,000 feet at a 30-degree angle. The pass was at 14,900 feet; the same one that Alexander the Great and his soldiers had traversed twice between 330 and 328 B.C.

When Abu Ahmad reached me, I said, "I had considered stopping for the night, but the people operating this teahouse are as *crooked-looking* as I've ever seen. Three men and four teenage boys are staring at my camera and watch. Also this is the spot where Hekmatyar's people raid." Abu Ahmad looked nervous and upset. "I wish Atiq had waited for us. Let's continue."

I had hardly started up the mountain when my horse began to

*Map showing Eskazer to Anjuman with route south into Nuristan by which
Massoud's supply trains were attacked.*

sweat profusely Oh no, I thought, as he began loosing his footing. Without him it would be impossible for me to climb up the mountain. Then, as the air became thinner, the fatigued animal needed to stop every two or three steps.

But Abu Ahmad's horse was in worse shape than mine. She began dropping behind. Soon darkness rendered the trail a virtual mystery. About a thousand yards short of the pass, my horse started slipping every two or three steps. Suddenly his hind legs went over the edge of the trail, and then his belly hit the ground with a thud. The wind whipping around me lifted my *patu* (blanket), which I had drawn around my shoulders for warmth, and wafted it down the mountainside. I dismounted, desperately hoping that my poor tremulous horse and I would not follow. For the next hour-and-a-half I led him slowly up the last stretch.

At the top, sat Atiq in a cabin drinking tea with a few other travelers. Tired and upset, I approached him. "Atiq, you deserted us. You knew that Abu Ahmad and I couldn't make the summit before dark. I can't believe you would leave your nephew behind." Atiq just grinned as if to say survival of the fittest.

A few minutes later, I was relieved to see Abu Ahmad entering the room. Pointedly, he came over and sat next to me. The owner of the *chai-khana* handed each of us a plate of trout and nan, which helped to dissipate my anger. After I had finished eating, I leaned back and fell directly asleep. I was awakened at four o'clock in the morning by the sound of horses moving about. By the time the *chai-khana* people had packed ours, we had drunk our tea and were ready to mount. Abu Ahmad needed another horse. His poor old nag was shaking badly. She was so thin that her sides looked like washboards, and she could no longer manage to walk. In fact, I found out later that she died the following week.

We trekked from the top of Anjuman Pass down into Parian Village in the northern sector of Panjsher Valley – a long, exhilarating journey. The wheat in the fertile fields and the farmers waved like a welcoming committee as we passed by. We picked fresh peas from the field to snack on as we walked. We located a friend of Atiq's who had prepared us an elaborate feast. Afghans honor a guest as *a gift from God*. The meal of *palau quabli*, which is a casserole made with local rice, raisins, sliced carrots, almonds, and pistachio nuts, was accompanied by goat meat, nan, French fries, apricots, and grapes. They served fresh, cold mineral water with the meal, and afterwards, green tea with a dish of hard candy, nuts, and raisins. Being typically Afghan, the meal lasted several sociable hours – gracious time for eating, laughing, and telling stories.

We were almost there. In the morning we loaded our gear into the Soviet jeep that arrived for our transportation and set out to complete our journey. The dilapidated *conveyance* was more than 20-years old.

Repairing old Jeep

Unfortunately, it performed even worse than it looked. We had only traveled a quarter of a mile when it rolled to a stop with a broken oil pump. After a couple of local villagers worked on it for over two hours, we tried once again to travel. Five miles farther the tie-rod broke. The rope we jerry-rigged lasted only a few feet; I decided to walk the last 15 miles to Dasht-e-Rewat. Atiq stayed behind with the gear while the others joined me.

According to my map, the two-track path went downhill, but as we soon found out, the path through the last pass led along a fault line. It proved to be a grueling up-and-down scramble that could hardly be called a cakewalk. I had not bathed in seven days. I arrived in Dasht-e-Rewat five hours later, exhausted and smelly with fierce blisters on both feet. The village had only a couple of dozen mud homes still standing, most of which had been at least partially damaged by many seismic events. As I sat down at a sundry shop in the village, a Soviet spy plane and two jets flew overhead. They flew so low that I could see the pilot of the larger, slower plane, and he could see me. The Soviets still controlled Afghanistan, no doubt about that. Five minutes later, I spotted two MIG-24s, probably the same two that had just passed, flying

Dasht-e-Rewat village center

L-R: Atiquallah, Mahmood,and Gary

high maneuvers to avoid Massoud's US Stinger missiles. Here I am again, I thought, in the midst of it all. I let pass any momentary doubts about my decision to come here during a war. My blood bubbled with adrenaline.

By the time Atiq arrived in the jeep an hour later, four Mujahideen commanders, the village Chief, and about 30 other villagers had gathered to greet us. Atiq's older brother, Haji Mohammad Jan, brought me two buckets of gloriously warm water for a shower in a private room with clay walls and floor, where an open pit had been dug for a drain. I was filthy

Main street village market

and itching all over from flea and mosquito bites. When I returned to the main living room, scrubbed and clean, I thanked Haji profusely for heating water for my bath. I knew he had carried it from afar and heated it over the fire himself. In this remote village there was, and is, no electricity, phone service, or running water. Yet here we sat on intricate Afghan carpets eating a full meal followed by tea and hard candy. After dinner I excused myself to my host and his other guests and moved to the opposite side of the living room where my bags were stacked. There I laid out my sleeping bag on the edge of the carpet, punctured the blisters on my sore feet, rubbed ointment on my flea and mosquito bites, crawled into my sleeping bag, and collapsed. I didn't wake up until ten the next morning.

After brunch I cleaned the trail dust from my camera and tended to my other equipment. In the early afternoon the village leader arrived to invite us for dinner. It was a time for sharing, exchanging information on the war, and enjoying a festive time with friends in the midst of their war-torn lives.

We left by jeep for Bazarak to meet Saranwal Mahmood Khan, the Administrator of Panjsher Valley. He would be our guide, the Great

Dinner at Haji Mohammad Jans and Atiquallah's home in Dest-e-Rawat

Oz in this Emerald City. We passed destroyed tanks. Artillery shells and mangled, unidentifiable pieces of metal marred the roadside, reminders of recent inhumanities.

The local official greeted me ceremoniously. He told me I was one of very few foreigners to visit the valley since the war began in 1979. Growing up in Kabul, Mahmood had an American teacher from grades six through 12, so he was delighted to have an American guest. Not having occasion to practice it since, he had forgotten most of his English, so Atiq served as interpreter. We discussed our plans for exploration in the Panjsher Valley.

"Let me show you what we can find there!" he said, proudly. He reached into his shalwar kamese and pulled out a cloth. Unwrapping it carefully, he revealed … a 19-carat and an 8-carat emerald crystals! Here was physical proof of the value of our impending explorations.

He asked me if I would tell him their value, and I hesitated. Such estimates are rarely welcome because owners usually want much more for a stone than it is actually worth in the market, and reality tends to disappoint them. Miners always overestimate the value of rough. Their assessment is generally buoyed by dreams of their ship coming in then carried aloft by their inflated valuation of their own efforts. Whether they got the gem by stealth, force or labor, they feel "I worked for that … it must be valuable." Only with experience and the knowledge of a cutter can a person evaluate unfinished goods. But to appease him, I took out my jeweler's loupe and studied the crystals carefully for some quiet minutes.

"Realistically, by the time these are cut, they'll be half their size or less, so I'd say the larger crystal is worth $10,000 and the smaller one $4,000." I could see by his look that my intuition had been right. He had expected a higher appraisal, but I was not there to play games.

As we left his spare one-room office, Mahmood handed us letters of passage to give to his sub-commanders, instructing them to assist us in our survey of the emerald mines. Beginning at 6,000 feet and going up to 13,000 feet, we would be taking what I called the *heel-and-toe express*. No more vehicles, with or without melons and barbed wire. The Bizmal emerald mine lay up the mountain directly behind the house.

L-R: Haji Dastagir, Atiquallah, and miner at emerald mine

Next to it, Mahmood said, was a one hundred-year-old sapphire mine. I doubted this, as corundum is not found in the same mother rock as beryl. The crystal form of corundum, aluminum oxide, is either ruby or sapphire, depending on color; the crystal form of beryl, beryllium oxide, is the beryl family, which includes emerald and aquamarine. They are from different families. In addition, no one had shown me any sapphire crystals from the mines. He also told me about old silver mines at the northern end of Panjsher Valley. I surmised that those were the mines Marco Polo had described in his writings. As I

Miners with drill

Entrance to emerald mine

Using gas operated road drills results in carbon monoxide poisoning

prepared to sleep, I wondered how a valley so full of riches could be so poor.

We walked to the Bizmal emerald mine, accompanied by Finance Minister Abdul Quyam and Commander Abdul Razig. From them I learned about the politics of emerald mining in this area. In 1979 the Jamiat-i-Islami party had taken over the emerald mines from the Kabul government after a bloody riot. Besides controlling the distribution and sale of the emeralds, they tacked on a 15 percent tax to raise a war chest. A committee of village businessmen determined the tax value.

Emerald mining requires expertise. But emerald mining had only been done in the Panjsher Valley for just over a decade. And it didn't look like mining to me. The Afghans were simply digging holes in the ground and looking for green. They worked individually or in small teams, climbing the steep mountain slopes up to the 9,000-to-12,000-foot level. Trails did not exist, so pack animals could not be used. The miners carried the equipment on their backs. Half the people in the valley had been killed during the war years of the 1980's; most of those remaining were connected with the industry as miners, support services, buyers, or sellers. Emeralds meant survival for them.

I spent the next days reconnoitering the high rocky slopes of the mountains, examining

Emerald mines

the conditions at Derik, Darun, Mokoni, and Khenj mines, evaluating current procedures and documenting my findings with photographs. I was astonished at the number of separate mines and disheartened to see the evidence of overuse of dynamite. Many small chips of broken emerald crystals lay scattered everywhere. Their mining methods were destroying their stock-in-trade. The mountain looked and sounded like a war zone; they used explosive material scavenged from unexploded bombs and even land mines.

Emerald crystals in quartz

Although post-mining land reclamation is a legal and moral duty in the US, in Afghanistan the concept is far more remote than this region itself. It did not occur to them to fill in the holes or to stabilize areas after they mined them. They figured Mother Nature was large enough to cover a multitude of human sins. There was always another slope, another pass. And these people, scarred as the landscape where they labored, had no extra energy for such luxuries.

The working conditions appalled me. The mountainside looked like Swiss cheese, covered with holes of assorted sizes. To see their way in the dark, they used extremely volatile tin can lanterns filled with oil and gasoline and then wicked with cloth – incendiaries with Molotov cocktail potential. One man was boring with an old Chinese road drill, which emitted colorless, odorless clouds of lethal carbon monoxide fumes. The miners obtained most of their

Handful of emeralds

explosives by taking apart Soviet bombs, a risky form of recycling. After blasting, men carried out the rubble on a gurney, shook and sorted it for gem rough, and then threw the overburden down the steep mountainside. There was excessive fragmentation of the land and poor recovery of ore – in short, a great waste of the nation's resources. But despite their mistakes, they were making substantial contribution to the local economy. The emeralds were equal in quality to those of Colombia, the world's largest producer. And there wasn't much other economy to speak of.

Atiquallah, Mohebullah, and Haji Mohammad Jan

Two days after our climb at Khenj, Abu Ahmad and I ran into Mohebullah, a miner who had sold me lapis and emeralds over the years. He had heard I was in the village and came looking for me.

"Mr. Gary, I have some special emeralds for you to see. Come!" He motioned for me to join him under a tree. Sitting down, he pulled out two knotted cloths and untied them to expose a handful of top quality emeralds. Slowly, thoughtfully, purposely remaining low-key, I chose 21 pieces that weighed 76 carats and offered Mohebullah US$40,000, which came to $526 a carat. "Oh no, no," he replied, shaking his head and thus beginning to bargain – the polite, quiet ritual. He countered with a ridiculous $11,363 a carat. Extremely unrealistic, but this is the way of negotiations here. Sales are very rarely resolved at a first meeting. Given the difference between our prices, we agreed to hold round two of our negotiations back in Peshawar. This haggling sometimes went on for years before the deal was done! Two months later, after several back and forth negotiations, Mohebullah sold me three of the better emeralds and others for a total weight of 330.75 carats for $69,457.50 (US$210 a carat). The largest emeralds in this new lot were 73.87, 83.76, and 43.47 carats – quite respectable.

Horseman Mud Waees and his father

In fourteen days we had completed the initial survey and mapping of the mines. "Atiq, I am ready to return to Pakistan." I neglected to mention that my Pepto Bismol, the cure of choice for diarrhea, was running low. Time was of the essence!

"Mr. Gary, Abu Ahmad and I will be staying to mine emeralds in the Bizmal mine. I will find you a horse and guide." He informed me of this change of plans as if it posed no inconvenience to me! The day before I had seen a Soviet spy plane taking photos of the valley. What would I do if I ran into the Soviet army alone? I was distressed over Atiq's abandonment but had no choice but to make the best of it.

Atiquallah told me of his plans to meet with Commander Massoud and brief him on our expedition. I prepared the following letter to be delivered to him during the briefing:

Letter from Gary to Massoud

August 14, 1989, Dasht-e-Rewat

Dear Ahmed Shah Massoud:
I am giving this letter to Atiquallah to be delivered to you. We have completed our survey of the Panjsher emerald mines. Thanks to all your commanders and village people and businessmen, we have gathered many samples for

geological testing and taken many pictures for study and marketing of emeralds. Also we had many questions answered about mining.

I should now be able to prepare the following reports: 1. Organization; 2. Marketing; and 3. Geology and Mining.

During our discussions with Chief Commander of Panjsher Abdul Mahmood, I agreed to locate and establish a supply system for better blasting powder that is cheaper and less dangerous to man and emeralds. Also, I'm going to try to locate a drill of less weight for mining. Third, I will arrange for more geologists and mining production experts to assist with the mines.

I have further discussed with Atiquallah and Abdul Mahmood having a third symposium in Tucson, Arizona (February 1991). At this meeting we will have many mining experts and can discuss many mining plans, blasting techniques, and equipment problems with businessmen from Panjsher. (I met your brother Walhid in Peshawar prior to this trip and invited him to join this meeting.)

Tucson, Arizona, USA, in February has the largest rough and cut gem show in the world with thousands of buyers and sellers from over 50 countries. I have asked Atiq and several businessmen from Panjsher to bring emeralds to sell. Emeralds are duty-free in the United States, and I have arranged with Pakistan that any emeralds not sold can be returned without charge.

For US visa assistance, Symposium, Tucson business booth charges, customs clearance fee, money transfer cost, I'm asking a ten percent commission on any sales. I do not expect to make a profit the first year, but I'm looking to establish a system for the future. The only cost to the Panjsher businessman or Jamiat representative is the cost of his travel and lodging, US customs clearance fee (one half of 1 percent), shipping fees, and personal expenditures.

There are four major advantages to this program: (1) the Panjsher businessman can see what other people in the world are charging for their emeralds; (2) we establish a regular selling system directly with cutters without going through Pakistan Brokers; (3) we improve miners' education by meeting with other gem miners, cutters, and jewelry retailers from around the world; (4) we establish a World Market for the Panjsher emerald.

To date most of the top quality emeralds are referred to us from Columbia because of their two hundred-year history of top quality. I'm going to write some articles and letters attempting to get the Panjsher emerald accepted as equal or better in quality and price.

While collecting ground samples in Panjsher at the emerald sites, we also gathered some metal samples for testing. My goal is to get more than one product to sell from the emerald mines. I'll explain this in detail in my future reports.

In two weeks, I expect to see Tony Davis in Bangkok for the reply to my last correspondence. I have asked Atiquallah to call me in the USA upon his return to Chitral. In the meantime, we will continue our work.

May God be with you,
Gary

I had much to do when I returned to Pakistan and then the US. We would start a marketing program for Panjsher emeralds. We needed to find a new source of blasting powder that would be cheaper and less dangerous to man and emeralds than disassembling Soviet bombs. I promised to find a lighter drill and more geologists and mining experts to offer technical advice.

I proposed holding a third symposium in Tucson in February 1991 where Panjsher businessmen could discuss mining plans, blasting techniques, and other topics with American experts. This was beyond the imagination of my warrior friends! America! Could Mr. Gary really make that happen? Tucson is the home of the largest cut and rough gem show in the world with thousands of buyers and sellers from over fifty countries. Emeralds are duty-free in the US, and I had arranged with Pakistan that unsold emeralds could be brought back without duties. I asked for a ten-percent commission on all sales to cover US visa assistance, seminar costs, Tucson business booth charges, customs clearance fee, and money transfer costs. After all that, I doubted that I would turn a profit in the first year, but the future held great promise in human and financial terms! The only cost to Panjsher dealers or Jamiat representatives would be travel, lodging, customs and shipping fees, and other personal expenses. There were clear advantages to all. We could begin to position Panjsher emeralds in the world market as highest quality. We could avoid paying Pakistani brokers to middle the gems and compete with Columbian emeralds head-to-head. The plan was a drop-dead winner.

That evening was memorably festive. The village chief honored me at a farewell dinner. Sixteen men from the village and Atiq came to the fête. Afghan men have a sentimental side to their personalities. They all wished me well, but at the same time they were sad to see me leave. And in their manly and genuine way, they showed it.

Fazal Khan was the donkey man selected by Atiq

That day I rode for three hours, walked four, and rode again another four, a pattern I continued for the next five days. We stopped occasionally to visit relatives of my guide. Relationships mean everything in these mountains, for life can be short and death sudden. It would have been unacceptable for him to pass so close to their village and not visit. I also remember passing some magnificent streams. The water was so clear I could see, from my vantage on the horse, hundreds of trout, up to 12 inches long, like swimming prisms just beneath the surface, throwing their light in every direction.

As I drew closer to the border, six Afghans from Jon Mohammad's *border running express* unexpectedly presented themselves to me at our tent. They briefed me on the upcoming six security posts, some manned by the Pakistani police, others either by Chitral Scouts or Pakistan soldiers. True to form, each post had its own commander and its own orders as to who should be allowed to pass between the two countries. It was 27 miles to Garam Chasma. We would have to walk around the guard posts in the pitch-black night without lights. If anyone spotted us, they would shoot. They wanted to leave in 20 minutes. And that was the best plan we could come up with!

If pushed to speak by some guard who might surprise us, I was instructed to play *Uzbek* – to say only Uzbek and act sick. The ancestors of the Uzbeks of Northern Afghanistan had migrated from Russia. The present-day people share bloodlines with White-Soviets, so many are light-skinned. They have their own language, which few Pakistanis speak or understand. With my five-month beard and no bath or change of clothes for nine days, I just might pass for an Uzbek!

The rest of the trip back across the border was typical – the whole night spent jumping over walls, wadin through shoulder-deep water, walking twelve miles in the dark of night with only the sliver of a moon to show the path along a narrow ledge. At one point, one of my escorts threw my patu over me and sat on my stomach before I could move. The truck stopped at a guard post. Through the blanket I could see the soldier's flashlight passing over us. The truck started again and then stopped ten minutes later. Still wet from the river crossing, once again we jumped out with bags. This time we had to scale a four-and-a-half foot rock wall of loose cobbles, some of which tumbled and rumbled as we climbed up and over.

Running into a wooded area and along a narrow water channel, we had to guess at the path until the clouds passed, providing dim starlight once again. Walking the mud channel was like negotiating a slippery tightrope in boots. The course of the water was too narrow for my foot; the right side of the water-channel dropped down ten feet into a stream; whereas, the other side dropped off 18 inches to a single foot space against a stone wall. My feet kept slipping as I tried to hurry along the constant curve and slope. Every now and then I stepped off the 18-inch side to regain my balance. A slip to the right could have meant a broken leg. After 50 yards of water hazard, we inched our way across a field and back up the hill. Dogs barked close by as we reached the road and clambered into the back of the truck. Up, down, in, out – we were like a precision drill team of night crawlers. We finally made it to the Mountain Inn. Payment. Haggling for more. Shower. Sleep.

I awoke bruised. But I was home. Well, not exactly home, but it felt just as good. I was back in Pakistan: not arrested, no broken limbs, and knowing more about Afghans, the Panjsher Valley, the emerald deposits – and yes, about myself, than I could have anticipated. Survey done. Mission accomplished! Silver stars all around for valor! I was a happy man!

Haji Abdul Rahim and Haji Bismillah with parcel of
13 emerald crystals purchased by Gary

Symposium attendees' luncheon in Chitral

Chapter Nine
Gem Symposiums

August 1989

A year had passed since promising Massoud I would organize some educational seminars. I took a day off to recover from my grueling but exhilarating month in the mountains. I had to treat my wounds – blisters, bites, cuts and remnants of missing toe nails. After twenty-four hours I was on my way to Peshawar to meet with the faculty for our upcoming symposium. From Chitral, in the north of Pakistan, to Peshawar was a thirteen-hour ride, with two flat tires, aboard the *flying coach*, and old VW minibus driven by an apparent madman.

On the way to Peshawar I opened the large packet of forwarded mail that Haider had been holding for my return. To my pleasant surprise there was a letter from Dezhad.

Letter from Dehzad

Dear Sir Mr. Gary W. Bowersox

I'm very sorry that it is a long time I could not write any letter for you so it does not mean that I forgot you. I was so busy and I had so many problems in my life during 14 years that our country was captured by the Soviet troops. If you remember you had need a visa in 1981 in that time I had finished for you and was sent it by the Exploitation Department to the Afghanistan to the Washington and the Embassy had your address. But you did not come to our country. I didn't know why? After that time I was in Prison and some time I had no job and was in my house. Finally, I left my country toward the Iran (Persian Country) I rent a house right there for my family and then I came back to the southwest part of my country and I participated in Jihad (fighting against

Communism). During the Jihad, I lost my brother and some other close relative and friends.

I think in this year on July you were in our country. Excuse me that I was in Pakistan. I know you asked and you couldn't find me. I take your address from my close friend Mr. Nedaye, Deputy Minister of Mines and Industry. Up to now that I write this letter for you I didn't take any official job, because I'm very tired. But I like to work over the gemstone of our country.

A few days ago I had a meeting with the Republic President around the gemstone of our country. I have mentioned that you have interest in this position.

Mr. Gary our gem stock was inside the Republic House and was sealed by the Soviet troops in that time. Please send me your photo in size 6X4.

Mr. Gary after 2 days I will go to the Iran to see my family. I will stay right there one month and then for 3 months I will be in Kabul and then for 15 days, I will go there to bring my family back to Kabul.

Mr. Gary if you want to come to the Kabul, near the Ministry is Afghan Department store and in Persian is called Froosh-gahi-Buzurgi-Afghan, 2 Floor Mohammad Kasim Satta (he is my brother in law)

November 21 – Yours sincerely
S.H. Dehzad

After reading this letter, I hoped that Dezhad could join forces with me on an Afghan gem and mineral project. We shared a strong desire to help the Afghans rebuild their economy, but I wondered whether I would really ever see him again.

I arrived in Peshawar covered head to toe with road dirt and dust, but they welcomed me anyway … although I noticed there were no embraces. Was it my hygiene after a month in the mountains, perhaps?

For several hours we planned the upcoming Symposium, a balanced mix of lectures, discussions, demonstrations, and movies. We divided up the topics based on our expertise, with one taking Gem Location in Mineral Deposits, another Identifying and Grading. Increasing Mine Production belonged to someone else, but I would handle Increasing Profits through Proper Care of Gem Crystals, as well as Cash Flow and Marketing. We wanted to create jobs and regional development, but we also wanted to use the mineral resources efficiently and to exploit their value for the benefit of everyone involved. The participants would likely be prospectors, miners, geologists, engineers, and perhaps a few collectors, so the curriculum had to aim high but also suit a mixed audience.

With presenters coming from all over the world – Germany, England, Pakistan, and the US, we needed some logistical help in Peshawar and in Chitral. Someone among us suggested using geology students from the National Centre of Excellence in Geology, Peshawar University to assist with organization and translations. Wonderful idea. They translated most of the lectures live in three or four languages simultaneously – Urdu, Pashtu, Dari, and Khowar (Chitrali). And they became the core of the next generation of in-country experts. Our

Symposium Instructors: L-R: (front) Akbar Khan, Dr. Roshin Bhappu, Guy Clutterbuck, (middle) Dr. Eugene Foord, Bonita Chamberlin, Gary Bowersox, (back) Dr. Larry Snee, Andreas Weerth, and Jawaid Anwar

Hands On Instruction and Demonstrations

Instructor AndreasWeerth points out mineral specimens and their quality in photos

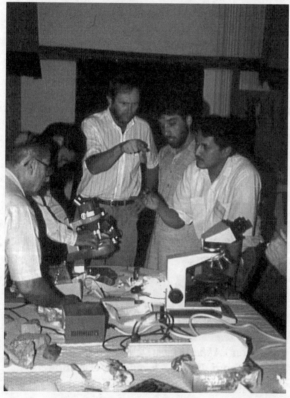

Dr. Larry Snee demonstrating gem identification equipment

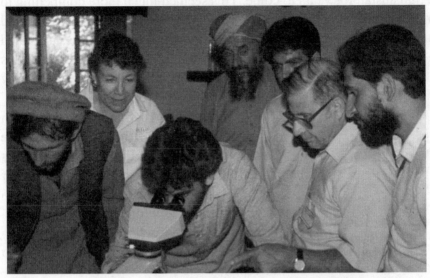

Dr. Roshin Bhappu instructing on use of binocularscope

*Symposium lunch served in courtyard of Chitral Mountain Inn
next to classroom building*

investment of time and money could pay dividends for Pakistan and Afghanistan for years to come. This seemed much more compelling to me than just doing business as usual. We shared a common dream, and uniting to make it happen seemed challenging, yet effortless, as if I had

stopped swimming against the current. This felt like my destiny: building a community around a common set of passions.

More than 30 attendees came from Afghanistan and Northern Pakistan. The invariably smiling and hospitable Chitralis added home tours and nightly music to our agenda. Prince Assadur Rehman invited us to have dinner in the throne room of the castle, which had been closed for several years. No one lived here, and much of it had fallen into disrepair.

Shuja ur-Rehman son of His Highness Saif ur-Rehman, the late Ruler of Chitral

This was the castle in which Surgeon Major Robertson of the British army and his escort of four hundred men were besieged by fighters from Dir and Chitral for 48 days until a force arrived from Gilget to rescue them. The castle was not like something from the Loire or Rhine valley, needless to say. No crenellated walls or damsels in distress: Dungeons? Yes. Dragons? No. Over a wonderful dinner of goat meat, chicken, rice, nan, and a large variety of local fruits, Chitrali Prince Shazada Kushwaqt ul-Mulk and Prince Shuja ur-Rehman regaled us with history lessons and told tales about the photos adorning the

Chitral Castle

Major (Ret) Khush Ahmad ul-Mulk son of His Highness Shuja ul-Mulk, the late Ruler of Chitral

walls of the Chitral Castle-Fort. In some way, I felt we restored their royalty. Here they were, after years of strife and neglect, entertaining foreign visitors in the heart of their traditional home – their Kingdom. That night loosed energies that had lay dormant and stirred pride and interest in history and cultural roots. I was the catalyst, the spark plug that got the machine moving, but the forces were there all along, waiting for this moment to arise. We were explorers, discovering or rediscovering worlds hidden from view.

We also made time to get out of the classroom and see a mine and a gold and antimony refining plant. We toured the Kalash Valleys of Birir, Bumburet, and Rambur. The Kafir Kalash, who number about three thousand, still keep the lifestyle of their own ancient culture and religion. Kalash men often distinguish themselves by wearing a large Chinese pheasant tail feather in their Chitrali woolen caps. The women wear black gowns of coarse cotton in summer and handspun black-dyed wool in winter, but the most

Field trip to gold mine in Chitral area

Residents of Kalash Valley

notable feature of their costume is picturesque headgear weighing between three and four pounds. Made of black woolen material encrusted with cowry shells and buttons.

Legend has it the soldiers of the Macedonian conqueror, Alexander The Great, settled in Chitral and became the progenitors of the Kalash. They surely look Greek, and they enjoy wine, music from drums and flutes, and colorful dances expressing peace, joy, and contentment, not struggle, warfare, and suffering. Later, we visited the ex-rulers' summer palace, overlooking the valley from 8,000 feet (2,462 meters) above sea level, and shared the view over Chitral, plumes of smoke rising, with 25,230-foot (7,763 meters) Mount Tirichmir as a backdrop.

Sometimes the meeting of old and new produced conflicts. The miners desperately needed new and better equipment. In my rational, Western mindset, I set a personal goal to assist them in obtaining this equipment and further training. But the miners could not see the value of purchasing such expensive equipment with their funds. What if it was all buried in a cave-in anyway? Money thrown to the wind, they thought. Worse yet, they had long ago learned the ways of Western foreign aid. They expected someone to *donate* equipment and materials, but without ownership interest, no *skin in the game*, they would fail to properly maintain and care for it. I had seen this dynamic before and the mountains of discarded tools to prove it.

As I promised Massoud, the Symposium was held at my company's expense at the Mountain Inn in Chitral, on August 5 through August 14, 1989. Airfare and hotels for all the Americans were the budget breakers. We also paid all the food and hotel expenses for the attendees and the hired students. Fortunately, my gem sales and events had been going well!

The seminar met the objective of improving the income-generating capacities of individual miners. Everyone who attended expressed satisfaction with the learning they received, and some of us gathered enough information in the visits and sessions to write an article, "The Emeralds of Panjsher Valley, Afghanistan," for *Gems and Gemology* magazine, which would help give us legitimacy when marketing.

The following year, 1990, we held another Symposium in Chitral with an identical agenda but all new participants. During the course of events someone reported that one of last year's attendees had obviously not paid attention during the explosives lecture. Six months after the seminar, he had attempted to open a Soviet bomb with a screwdriver to obtain blasting powder. It opened with a loud noise and a tragic result. We quickly instituted extra lectures on explosives.

GeoVision booth at Tuscon, AZ International Gem and Mineral Show Akbar Khan and Gary

The two Symposiums in Chitral produced a host of positive outcomes. By this time Akbar Khan and I were sharing a booth at the world's largest gem and mineral show in Tucson, Arizona and working

L-R: Sabsuddin, Azzizullah Safi, Zabullah
Nuristani, Atiquallah, Akbar Khan,
and Gary Bowersox

as partners. Other Afghanis and Pakistanis also began coming to Tucson to sell their wares. Thereafter, we found it easier and cheaper to organize symposiums when the participants were already in Tucson. This had the added advantage of being neutral ground for the different tribal people who might be fighting each other at home. We encouraged warring factions to work together in the same room for the joint advancement of their knowledge. They sometimes harassed one another verbally, in some sort of game in which they all understood the rules, but the general tenor was polite and respectful. It certainly helped me on one occasion, when a Tajik courteously recommended that I alter my plans for a trip, as his tribe had planned to attack another tribe in northern Nuristan that week. I changed my plans, and, sure enough, the attack took place on schedule.

I felt good about having brought these people together peaceably for learning and dialogue. Perhaps, I hoped, when they next met, they would have tea and reminisce instead of fight. But I was also mindful of the potential that this vehicle of economic development held for the region and for its leaders. Another goal was to work with Dr. Bhappu, a mining engineer who had spent many years working with miners in Pakistan, to start a formal exploration and mining training program in Pakistan for Afghans involved in gem mining. We further hoped that once the fighting had stopped, we could obtain United Nations and World Bank support for such a project. If gem mining could become a viable industry, the lives of many people on both sides of the border could be changed for the better. That was, in the long run, the point of the Symposium.

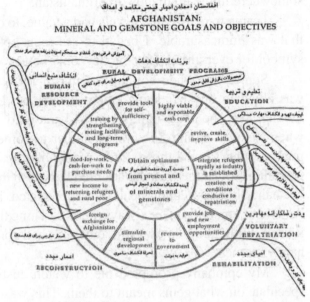

افغانستان : معادن احجار قیمتی مقاصد و اهداف

AFGHANISTAN:
MINERAL AND GEMSTONE GOALS AND OBJECTIVES

And at the time, it looked like things were going in the right direction, both for me and for my Afghan friends. The shifting paradigm inside of me that had started with my first gem rip-off and continued after my losses in Tel Aviv was continuing. Meeting Massoud had impressed me, and I found myself getting fewer thrills from the adventuring aspect of my travels (although I do love a good story!) and more from helping these good people. I was falling in love with the Afghans as other travelers had alluded to in their writings.

I was also learning about myself, not by acting and reacting but by reflecting. I came to understand that maybe my *choice* to go into this business was not really rational but rather intuitive. Let me explain.

Here's the mindset I learned in business school: whether it is height, weight, wealth, the value of a factory worker's finger or a mother's love and care, everything important can be measured with numbers. I believed that back then. I had learned it in the Army's Audit Agency, too. I surrounded myself with people who thought the same way. In retrospect, I suppose my first wife probably looked at me in the same way. She did not know the terms – *future earnings discounted to present value at an assumed interest rate*. But she grasped the concept: I looked like a good earner.

In contrast to this, Einstein said, "Not everything that can be measured is important, and not everything that is important can be measured." These words had started to take on real meaning to me somewhere in the highlands of Afghanistan.

I came to realize that jewels had a value, to others and also to *me*, that was immeasurable. I began to see their potential as a universal symbol for everything. Like money, only better.

Sometimes when holding the mirror for a wife whose husband was about to buy her some emerald earrings, I would envision my mother. Yes, she had a pair, set in 14-karat gold. She only wore them when she was going out with my father to some important social or public event. I loved those times: seeing her dressed-up, smelling her perfume. I loved the way she admired herself in the mirror as she fixed her hair. She was feeling beautiful, appreciated, and even glamorous. And those emeralds were always there, catching the light and throwing it back. Without my knowing it, emeralds had come to represent those happy moments for me.

My epiphany prompted me to watch customers carefully and speculate on what gems meant to them. This was good fun! For some, their meaning seemed linked to the patent attributes of the stones themselves. Gems are solid, often clear, hard, durable, and pure. They are portable and easy to hide.

On the other hand, gems also carry meanings based more on their intangible qualities. They can be security, an escape route from problems or the vehicle to carry us to a brighter future. They can represent freedom. They can symbolize values that don't change over time like endless love. Their prismed aspects can even do the seemingly impossible – bend light itself! And like many small, expensive things – caviar, gold, microfilms of nuclear secrets – their power is evident to the porter and the viewer alike.

Some buyers focus on their hidden flaws. Some are looking for jewels that are underpriced or undervalued. Are they thinking of themselves?

Some men use jewels to bait the trap in order to catch women. Once they catch their prey, they might use jewels to keep them from leaving. They can symbolize control just as easily as love. Just think, for example, of the sense of obligation that can come with an expensive gift. They also represent the power of *women* rather than the power of men over women. In many cultures, women are the keepers of gold and jewels as family savings, dowries, or portable capital. They can be liberty itself. In the beginnings of the Nazi era, many Jewish families bribed their way to safety and freedom with jewels they hid in the seams of their clothes. For them, the jewels represented the lives of their sons, daughters, and spouses.

Jewels can represent a fair return on the investment of a miner's time and labor. Jewels can highlight the miracle that is nature in producing such marvels. Jewels can exemplify the role that man plays in extracting dross and turning it into gold, making rocks into riches.

All of this intrigues me. But what fascinates me most about gems and has caused me to center my life around them is their beauty. The first man who saw a shiny, colored stone and dug it out with a stick did not do it because he wanted to trade in gems or because they had a value in the market or a symbolic meaning. He did it because of the way the stone caught his eye, grabbing the light and bending it. He tried to clean it and then to shape it, revealing more and more of its charms. Then he or probably someone else discovered the effects of rubbing and polishing. Each step bringing out more of its intrinsic beauty. For me, as for him, jewels are one of the most tangible manifestations of sheer beauty in life.

Gems mean all this and more. And little, if any, of all this is reflected *in the numbers*. Gems have been a good and faithful teacher to this boy from Kalamazoo.

Notation

A copy of "Emeralds of Panjsher Valley, Afghanistan" can be downloaded from the internet at: www.gems-afghan.com

1881 map of Kafiristan (known as Nuristan today)

Chapter Ten
A Field Trip to the "Land of Light"

August 1989

The day after the 1989 Symposium closed, I figured it was time to have some fun, which for me was exploring Nuristan. Zebullah arrived by jeep to begin our tour of his country and its mining area. He introduced me to two Nuristani friends who were to join us. He handed me a map that he had drawn on paper. We were to cross the Nuristani-Pakistani border through the Kalash Valley. I anticipated seeing tourmaline, aquamarine, morganite, and kunzite mines. Tourmaline has little lore associated with it in the West because it was not recognized as a distinct mineral until recently. But New Age adherents have latched on to it believing that its pyroelectric, and pryoelectric properties can amplify psychic energy and neutralize negative energies. There is definitely a market for the gem.

I don't know which of these properties was lacking in my life, but I was excited to go see what I could find and what might find me. As I have described, on some level, jewels find their owners and not the other way around! But you must first put yourself in a position where this bit of luck can occur. I can explain.

Zebullah claimed to have permission for our border crossing, which struck me as a unique and interesting change of pace. We stopped at a Kalash restaurant (a primitive stone structure filled with steaming pots of food), and during our meal, I saw that he got into an argument with some local people. When he returned to the table, he announced that we would have to hike up and over the mountains into the next valley without being spotted by the border patrol. Either he did not have full permission or the Kalash people did not want to be party to our expedition, as it might cause trouble with the Chitrali Scouts, the local constabulary. So no more jeeps full of supplies and sleeping bags. We would have to carry these things on our backs.

After twelve hours of exertion, we came upon a shepherd's camp on a high green pasture at the base of the mountain leading into Nuristan. The kindly man and his family of six lived in a one-room mud dome

Shepherd's home in Kalash Valley near Afghan border

furnished with animal skins. Apparently enjoying our company, he slaughtered a goat and prepared dinner for our party. The Nuristani and Kalash languages were new and foreign to my ears, and they soon lulled me to sleep. The next day I would experience another way of communicating using a natural element called…lead.

An early morning climb, sustained by nan and tea, featured grand picturesque vistas, which refreshed my bone-weary body as we started over the mountains into Nuristan. This felt like a package tour. No mission. No edge. Two hours along our way – pa-zing – a bullet whizzed past my ear and ricocheted off an adjacent rock. I cocked my head to determine its origin. Then zing, zing. Bullets started raining down all around me! Chancing a glance down the mountain, I saw the Chitrali Scouts still firing. I struck out running.

"Hurry!" Zebullah yelled, "We must get over the mountain!" Like a mountain goat he negotiated the large boulders that lay everywhere in our path, but I was heavier and unused to such obstacles. They slowed me to a hobble. I thought, "Gary, if you trip, you die." Just when we seemed to have run out of range, the bullets came raining down on us again. We all scrambled as fast as we could clamber, bump, stumble, weave, duck, and leap over the obstacles. But the Scouts were gaining on us. Then, about a hundred yards from the crest, just like in Wild West movies, six armed Nuristanis appeared across the ridge in our defense. The cavalry had arrived in the nick of time! They must have been waiting for us on the Afghan side of the mountains. There was just one problem: we were still struggling to gain the border, and the gunmen were still shooting.

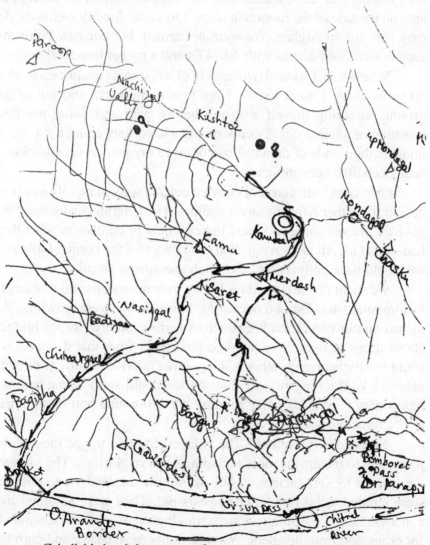

Zebullah's hand-drawn map of our proposed trip through Nuristan

Zebullah shouted to me. "Get behind the rocks! We are going to talk with the Chitralis! They do not want you to cross." Well, even I had figured that much out, even with no tutelage in the language of bullets. Incongruously, Zebullah was trying to bluff his way out of this. He turned and yelled at them, "Surrender! Talk to us, or we will shoot you!" He repeated his demand three times before they stopped. In fact, the Chitralis had few choices; they had trapped themselves in an open area on the side of the mountain some 150 yards directly below us. An easy shot for an Afghan. We were not armed, but our new Nuristani escorts were well-armed with AK-47's and a rocket launcher!

Meanwhile, I spotted two large boulders leaning against each other 50 yards away. Courageously, I ran behind the rocks and fell to the ground, covering myself with my brown patu and doing my best imitation of ancient dirt. Twenty minutes later, long enough for me to imagine thousands of dreadful outcomes to my precarious situation, I heard Zebullah beckoning me.

"Mr. Gary! Mr. Gary!" I crawled out and walked rapidly to where he and five other Afghans stood smiling. The Chitralis had gone. "We gave the Scouts some food and bullets equal in number to what they had shot at us. All is forgiven. You can now cross the border. I told you we would have permission," Zebullah announced proudly.

We spent the next ten days hiking over mountains and glaciers to visit mining sites. On two occasions, however, we were crawling. We inched on our hands and knees across narrow, pure white ice bridges above drops of over three hundred feet. Even from that distance, we could hardly hear each other's shouts over the river's torrent directly below. I kept telling myself that the ice could support me but had momentary regrets about suspending my 220-pound heft on an icicle over a ferocious gorge.

Nuristan is still remote. The villagers have destroyed most of the jeep trails to thwart invaders including local rival tribes. The villages we entered looked ancient. Zebullah told me the mud-walled houses were reputed to be five-hundred-years old. They were adjoined like condos and stacked three-to-four-stories high against the mountainside for protection from invaders. Walnuts, mulberries, beans, and corn lay drying on the flat roofs. I noticed some blue-eyed blondes and redheads

Nuristani sitting on Afghan/Pakistan border near Papapruk

among the population. Even though most of the villagers are poor, using goats and food supplies as currency, they welcomed us into their homes for the length of our stay.

Unlike most other Afghanistan mountain people who sit on the floor, Nuristanis take their meals at simple hand-carved tables with matching chairs. We sat in lantern light listening to their tales of warfare between tribes, which at that time described the Kamdesh fighting the Kyushus. Nuristanis resort to warfare to settle tribal disputes.

Even though Nuristanis are Afghans, they are usually referred to by the name of their region. In 1895-96, when Nuristan was subdued by Amir Abdur Rahman and slowly converted to Islam, the Moslems called the people Kafirs, unbelievers, because they worshiped a pantheon of natural spirits. The idol-hating Moslems proceeded to destroy the ancient Kafir gods, forcibly converting the people by the sword of Islam and renaming them Nuristanis. But one pagan practice lingered another four decades: For the first year after people died, Nuristanis continued to keep them in large open wooden coffins so that they could include them in their tribal councils held on the hillsides, convenient to the recently departed.

The Nuristanis find tourmaline, aquamarine, and kunzite in the large pegmatite fields of Nuristan where we were reconnoitering. Each of these gems has supernatural qualities attributed to it. Tourmaline is said to confer superior knowledge and good health. It also is supposed to make a woman more desirable to men and to stimulate the imagination. Aquamarine is believed to enliven the soul to the beauty

Tourmaline mine in Nuristan

of all nature and bring a deep sense of serenity. People still use it as a stone for meditation. Kunzite, which contains lithium, is thought to increase understanding and flexibility with other people. Supposedly, it has a steady force to promote regularity and fine balance. During my gem events, I jokingly tell customers that kunzite, being lithium $[LiAl(SiO_3)_2]$, is prescribed for manic depression. Therefore, if they're having a bad day, they can lick their kunzite.

Each day we hiked out in search of workers starting mining operations – in Patigal, Merdesh, Kamdesh, Kushtoz, Kamu, Saret, Barikot, and many other small villages. But at the end of the ten-day

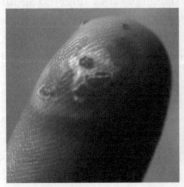 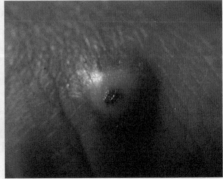

Poison fly bites on finger

Miners digging tunnel at Mirdesh

expedition, I had seen few high-quality gem productions. Being a private people by nature and circumstance, Nuristanis did not care to divulge their production or the exact locations of their mines. The things I discovered were the hardiness of their fleas, the viciousness of their black flies, and the plenitudes and power of their poison ivy.

Having suffered much discomfort, I was pleased to learn that Zebullah had arranged for transportation at Barikot to take me back to

Abdul Majid, a Nuristani gem dealer

Haji Ali Gul, a Nuristani gem dealer

Pakistan. Ten gun-toting Mujahideen joined me in the back of a large Soviet army truck. I was just one of the boys with my turban and dirty shalwar kamese as we crossed the border and returned to Chitral via Drosh. Oh, it was good to arrive at the Mountain Inn. I dusted my fleabites, treated my poison ivy with calamine lotion, and thoroughly rested for a couple of days. Only after all this had I put myself in a position for the strange dynamics of precious stones to work their wonders. I had paid my dues to Nuristan. I had hiked, climbed, crawled, itched, scratched, suffered and was sorely disappointed that the fabled Nuristan yielded so little gemological magic. I was wrong. It was there. It just preferred to come to me rather than the other way around. I had been separated from my hope, and now I lay open for the larger dynamic to take the place of my own, smaller agenda.

Zebullah came to visit me at the hotel, asking if I would like to see Nuristani gems that had just been delivered to the small Chitrali bazaar. We started visiting shops operated by Nuristanis. The quality of the goods displayed attested to my earlier assessment that I had seen little of Nuristan mining while I was in the area. And then a gem made

Nuristan tourmalines

up its mind to make my acquaintance. As we sipped tea in his modest shop, a merchant rooted around in his rag-wrapped inventory and then proudly pulled out a well-structured 42-pound aquamarine crystal he had carried over the mountains himself. What a sight! I tried not to show my excitement and played the tourist. On reflection, I don't suppose that was a credible role. There were not many Western tourists in the bazaars of Nuristan: no one would believe I was there for the cuisine. Nonetheless, with Zebullah's assistance as negotiator (and in exchange for a five-percent commission for him!), I stayed out of sight while he carried messages between the Nuristani and me for four

42-pound aquamarine crystal purchased by Gary in Chitral

days. Finally, on the fifth day, I accompanied Zebullah to the bazaar to make my purchase. Carefully carrying my prize back to the Mountain Inn, I wrapped it in a blanket and placed it in an old Army duffel bag. Later, I hand-carried it back to the US where it sold at an Afghan Connection event in Seattle, Washington. Somewhere in the Northwest, this gem is enlivening souls and bringing serenity. If only that gem could talk!

Another aquamarine decided to come find me, this time in the US. It was the following February when my friend and associate Akbar Khan delivered another treasure from Nuristan – a two-pound aquamarine crystal of superior quality. It was totally clear and as blue as any ocean. From this beauty, a well-known cutter produced many

small, spectacular gems and one grand one – a 169-carat clear, clean, top-colored, museum-quality treasure. This aquamarine, still looking for a home, is worth every penny of its $100,000 price tag…but it, like most high-end jewels, is quite judicious in choosing its owners!

169 carat aquamarine

For this dynamic of being found by jewels to work, we have to either be in a place where man is small and nature is big, so that our plans have little influence over the larger scheme of things, or we must be relatively empty of our own ambitions and designs. We must let the wind of fate blow us where it will. Sometimes when I have gone with the flow, the dynamic has brought jewels into my life.

Here is another illustration of being found by a jewel. I had separated from my wife, the mother of my daughter, in the late 1970's. My nomadic lifestyle, lived by the Rule of Fours, did not leave much time for romance. For four months a year, I was in Afghanistan, in the company of men exclusively. During the four months on the road in my motor home, I would meet people, see friends, stay a few days, and then move on. Only during my four months in Honolulu could I meet potential partners, and by the time I found one I liked and things started to develop, it was time to go. I had considered having some Moslem friends arrange a marriage for me, but I never pursued it seriously.

Once, and only once, did I really know a woman in Central Asia. To protect her, even now I must obscure the facts around our acquaintance. The year does not matter to the story nor the place. Suffice it to say that I was introduced to a bright-eyed, pretty, young woman. She had long, black, shiny hair that reached to her waist. I was quite a bit taller than her. When she stood near me, I could smell the warm freshness of her hair rising from the top of her head, mingling with the scent of delicate skin, massaged with fragrant oils. I noticed this the moment I met her. She seemed to have a glow around her as if she were a source of light.

Mystery woman

She had attended college and spoke English quite well with an accent like that of well-bred Central Asian women. We chatted and laughed, and she shyly averted her eyes from time to time, whether out of true modesty or a time-honored tradition of flirtation I do not know. But she was irresistible, like some gift box festooned with ribbons with rich sweet chocolates inside. But since we met at a diplomatic function, I quickly abandoned any ideas or instincts to try to get to know her better. I had no designs on her, no plans, no expectations. I left the reception quickly, uncomfortable about being tantalized merely by her proximity, and went back to my hotel.

I reflected as I got ready for bed. Was it just the isolation of my solo lifestyle or was she really as compelling as I had found her? I thought of her beautiful, white teeth, perfectly aligned, which I glimpsed just before she covered her laughing mouth. "C'mon, Gary," I thought, "now everyone you meet is remarkable…." I mocked my naïve optimism and reached for the light switch.

Then I heard a knock at my door. I threw on the hotel bathrobe and went to the door, ready for anything from an intruder to a mistake. Slowly I opened the door. She stood there. Alone. Quickly she pushed past me and closed the door behind her.

"I must not be seen here," she half-whispered.

"I know that…but what are you doing here?" My senses were on high alert. I felt stirred by her scent, but my instincts sensed that something was not right. A set-up? Planting drugs? Was she some Mata Hari?

"What on earth are you doing here?"

"I was afraid I wouldn't see you again. I didn't know when you were leaving, but I did know where you were staying."

"There aren't very many secrets in this town are there?" I was beginning to relax, sensing no immediate danger. Yet even her presence here, if a male relative of hers or a policeman discovered it, could get me in trouble.

In the hours that followed, I slowly got to know this surprising creature. She hid when room service brought a pot of tea I requested. We shared that and talked. And talked more. We laughed. She told me stories about life in the city, growing up there, her family, a thousand things, and nothing at all. But I was in the thrall of this bewitching woman, so atypical in her boldness. Before I knew it, we heard the 4 a.m. call to prayer.

"Where do you live? Won't your family notice you're gone?"

Suddenly the real world intruded into our private space, our bubble of conversation built-for-two.

"No. My parents are dead. I live with my brother, and he is away from the city, as he often is in these times." So maybe she knows loneliness too, I thought. "It wouldn't be safe to leave now. Gary, may I stay here?"

She slid closer to me on the divan and looked up at me. I could feel her sweet breath on my face. "This doesn't feel right," I thought. Then I bent and kissed her. Act first. Then react. Her tongue found mine, and she pulled me to her. I picked her up, easily and carried her to the bed. The rest of the night was a blur of tender play and dozing, warm bodies adjacent: hers brown and soft, mine white and rough.

No, she was no ordinary woman. I learned her story in pieces, but when she told it she was quite straightforward, not shy at all. I was not her first lover. There had been another, a faringi like me. He had been a Brit, and their lovemaking was fumbling and awkward but brimming with passion. He had left, posted home. Their parting was terrible. I don't know if she loved him or he loved her, but he left nonetheless. She told me it had been a long time since he left. She now inhabited a strange netherworld, aware of her own passions but unable to pursue them with anyone local. She didn't find them interesting anyway, she said. Too traditional. Too stifling. But, she told me that when she met me, she felt a connection immediately. She decided to come to my room.

That night, she said something I'll never forget both because it was memorable and magical but also because I never saw myself as a stallion or Don Juan. Even though I think she meant it, in her awkward English, the phrasing sounds comical. She said to me, "Gary, I want you to show me the American ways of love."

And sadly, I'm afraid I did. Her words, which did not sound prophetic at the time, had a different ring later on. The American way. Love 'em and leave 'em.

Our passion unfolded and opened like a blossoming rose. I was juggling my schedule just to stay where I was, not thinking past the next time that we planned to meet. Nothing else seemed important, and the hours in between our dalliances were interminable, which left me time to reflect. I was starting to see things more clearly and felt awful.

I might be falling in love with this woman, but I couldn't tell if it was infatuation or something deeper. I was very concerned about the problems it would cause with the authorities and some of the fanatical people in this city if our relationship were to be known. Our meetings could be dangerous for us, yes, but also for her and her family. There was nowhere we could go on a date without causing a stir. We were forced to slink around, never able to be seen together outside of my room. She was interested in me in a serious way and perhaps wanted me to take her away from this world to that dreamlike Emerald City that was America. But America, wonderful as it is, is not a dream. She would be very alone there with no community.

We spent four nights together – the first one and three others in subsequent weeks. Yes, I showed her the American way of love – connecting, then separating, always yearning for something permanent as the mountains in a world as ephemeral as a wisp of smoke. I ended it. She was so brave! She had seen suffering in her life, even though she was privileged, and she knew that our pains were small compared to the pandemonium around us.

After arranging for my shipment of gems, I left the city. I have few regrets in life, but this romance was one, not because it happened, but because I didn't have the courage or power or faith to sustain it. I'm not certain I would have been able to, in any case. We were caught up in the dynamic of the time, visible like a pattern in a fractal, both in the whole and in every part: coming together, then splitting apart. But she remains the one that got away: the jewel that found me but that I didn't think I could afford.

September 1989

After my 1989 walk-about in Panjsher and Nuristan, I rested and reviewed books in the library of my friends Dr. Giraud and Carolyn Foster in Baltimore, Maryland. Giraud, a doctor at Johns Hopkins University Hospital, collects antiquities and old books. After having met them in Pakistan the previous year while they were searching for gems of antiquity, I had agreed to speak to a group of gemologists invited to their home upon my return to the US.

When I got to the Fosters', I felt as bedraggled as any explorer of any century I had ever read about. I thought that his students might have passed an entire semester of med school after treating my ailments. I was suffering from a severely upset stomach, and my skin was a mess, covered with seeping poison ivy infections, swollen red spots from fleabites, and open wounds from poisonous black fly stings. Of the three *plagues,* black flies turned out to have been the worst by far. Their punctures swelled into large bumps that turned into itching blood blisters. Giraud schooled me on the possible results. If the black flies lay eggs in the bites, they may also introduce elephantiasis, resulting in irreversible enlarging and hardening of body tissues when parasitic worms block lymph ducts. I felt lucky to have come out only with permanent scars. Giraud kindly administered antibiotics for my weeping wounds and ordered R&R in his library until I recovered.

Even as I was convalescing, my eyes widened as I read Henry Yule's translation of the tales of Marco Polo, especially his comments about the rubies of the area. On maps dating to 1271, I pored over terrain Polo and I had both traveled. Though I was far from healed, I had already begun to yearn for my next Afghan adventure.

Nancy Dupree Report

In her book *An Historical Guide to Afghanistan*, Nancy Hatch Dupree, a well-known scholar on Afghanistan, has this to relate about ivy:

Nancy Dupree

Alexander the Great, when on his way to India in the fourth century B.C., prepared to besiege the city of Nysa when a delegation from the city arrived to implore him to leave them free for, they said, their city had been founded by the god Dionysus [the Greek God of wine]. "If you wish proof that Dionysus was our founder, here it is: this is the only place where ivy grows." (Arian) Interestingly, modern botanists surveying in Afghanistan have discovered that ivy does indeed grow naturally only in the Nuristan area.

Intrigued, Alexander and his companions went into the mountains, made wreaths of ivy, drank of the local wine and "lost their wits in true Bacchic frenzy." Alexander not only left these people free but also invited the young men to join his army for the Indian campaign. They did, and proved their fighting quality with distinction. When Alexander was forced by his soldiers to return to Babylon, however, these stalwart warriors preferred to return to their mountain home. Many so-called "Greek" motifs and customs found in the Nuristani culture may well date from this experience.

Ms. Dupree reports nothing about the results of Alexander's contact with ivy.

Exposure of Secret Contact Between
Ahmed Shah Massoud and Americans

"... A second man who is working for Ahmed Shah Massoud was a retired American major who reached Panjsher Valley as an emerald buyer. He organized a mineral seminar in the northern area of Pakistan. This American is working for an American agency said the sources."

Chapter Eleven
Trouble in Namak Mandi

Summer 1992 – Peshawar

After the successful symposium and my trip to Nuristan, I left Afghanistan and returned to the US. My business demanded that I pursue my gem business interests there, from which I had been distracted. I also remained committed to my projects with Massoud. I wanted to spend four months in Afghanistan each year, six months on the road in the US doing Gem Hunter appearances and selling gems (of which I had an ample supply!), and two months in Honolulu, where my friends and daughter lived.

I liked my rootless life as an American nomad. I had everything I needed in my motor home and would make the rounds visiting friends and associates all over the country. I was warmly welcomed everywhere and never stayed long enough to wear it out. I would map out my course to hit all the important industry events and to visit my best customers.

In Afghanistan, dramatic events continued. The Mujahideen continued their war against Najibullah. Despite the 1988 agreement which had resulted in the eventual Soviet withdrawal in February 1989, fighting between government forces and the rebels escalated, fueled by arms supplies coming from the US and USSR. Finally these two superpowers, in an attempt to bring about a cease-fire, agreed to halt all arms shipments as of January 1992. By April 1992 the Mujahideen, with the aid of the Kabul government's own secret police, seized Kabul and chased the puppet, Najibullah, away. In actuality, he lived under house arrest in the UN compound until he was lynched by the Taliban in 1996! In June they declared themselves an Islamic republic and installed Rabani as President, and a ten-member Supreme Leadership Council of guerilla leaders came together. Massoud was a member of the Council as was Gulbuddin Hekmatyar, his long-time rival and favorite of the ISI and CIA. (Remember that name: I'm sure he will figure in the future of the country – and not in a positive way!)

This was the time to forge a united nation. But the force of history is undeniable, and a nation cannot be built on shifting sands. The country had a long history of violence among different ethnic groups. Iran and Pakistan had been meddling, providing money and arms to their favorite leaders among the Mujahideen forces. Conflict between Mujahideen factions escalated instantly into a civil war with 100 killed and 1,000 injured in four days of conflict. This dance of us-and-them thinking would continue until the arrival of the Taliban in 1996.

Kabul was not a place to visit during this period – but I was going. On the way I stopped in Peshawar where I went to visit Akbar Khan. What I saw there should have convinced me of the futility of going anywhere near Kabul. But as I often say, it's a thin line between courage and stupidity.

I instructed the rickshaw driver to take me directly to the Namak Mandi district of Peshawar. Early this July morning, I was looking forward to my appointment with Akbar, my now-partner and very close friend. We had paired up after the Chitral symposium in 1989, and he had come to Tucson every year to man the booth with me at the world's largest gem and mineral event every year since. Akbar Khan had been in the gem business in the Peshawar area since childhood and was now a co-owner of an exporter of gems from Pakistan and Afghanistan.

What a relief to step under the cool breeze of the fan in Akbar Khan's office. But the look on his face puzzled me. He reached for something in his desk drawer, and turning *The Daily Pakistan* newspaper in my direction, pointed to an article.

"Did you see this – April 25, 1992?"

I reached for the paper and looked at it, then handed it back, "Even if I had, I can't read Urdu."

He waited as Mohammad Jan, his office assistant, placed fresh brewed tea in front of me. Then he began to read aloud, "Exposure of Secret Contact Between Ahmed Shah Massoud and Americans." After a few seconds, I cried, "Stop! They're talking about me!"

I reached for my pen and notebook. As he began to translate, I wrote what he said:

> *These contacts began through a French lady doctor and*
> *a retired American major. The American major reached*
> *Panjsher as an emerald buyer who is working for an*

American secret department. Commander Ahmed Shah Massoud has already a precious stone shop in Paris, which had been organized by his brother. Direct and indirect exposure between Ahmed Shah Massoud and the American major and one French lady doctor is from 1980. Direct sources informed The Daily Pakistan paper that a French lady doctor reached Panjsher by Konar after 1980. She opened a clinic. In this clinic she treated the injured Mujahideen. The staff of her clinic and home were Persian-speaking people. Ahmed Shah Massoud selected this staff.

The source was informed that some American agencies contacted Ahmed Shah Massoud through this lady doctor, and they sent several things to Mujahideen via Chitral and Nuristan to include TVs. A second man who is working for Ahmed Shah Massoud was a retired American major who reached Panjsher Valley as an emerald buyer. He organized a mineral seminar in the northern area of Pakistan. This American is working for an American agency said the sources. The sources also informed this paper that one agent from the secret police, SAVAK (former Shah of Iran secret police), is also working with the Mujahideen. He has contacts with Americans. Some Iranians in Panjsher Valley killed this agent.

"Great!" I said when Akbar had finished. "Now they have me involved in spying! Living in this part of the world is not good for my reputation."

Being thought of as a spy could be a curse or a blessing. And I was sure that the more I denied it, the more people would believe it. So I decided to refrain from reacting further. Putting the spy accusations behind us, we started to talk business when I heard glass shatter.

Earlier, as I had walked into the main bazaar, I noted a large group of Sunni Moslems in agitated conversation. I guessed they were Sunni from their facial features. I figured they were heated up about some new conflict with the Shiite Moslems (Shia). But I was late, thanks to Pakistan International Airways (PIA) flight delays, and so I hurried by the brewing trouble.

Now, peering out the window to determine the cause of the shattered glass, we saw a group of Sunni Moslems milling around faster and faster like a swarm of bees. Their murmurs, ever louder, were turning to a dull roar in the hot morning air. I felt a twinge of intuition – this did not feel right. As quickly as a summer storm appears, pandemonium erupted. They seemed to be attacking a storefront, ripping at the metal security grate with their bare hands. We could feel the tension like hot air hitting you when exiting an air-conditioned building. I felt a strange, electric crackle in my nerve endings. I was transformed into an instinctual animal that I had not been since ... Viet Nam. We stood spellbound. A hush fell for a few short moments. Then, in seconds, we watched a mob of some two hundred individuals gather, as if we were watching an approaching tornado. The players were taking their places for some exotic, violent dance. And we had box seats.

Police armed with tear gas guns appeared at one end of the street. At once, they shot 20 rounds of shells into the mob, which responded with a deafening protest even as they tried to escape. Then the strangest thing happened. With tear gas choking the air, the police, having done their part and taken car of the situation, left the scene.

The show, blessedly short, seemed to be over. Akbar proposed a cup of tea and busied himself lighting the small stove. But this turned out to be our intermission refreshment. About 20 minutes after we had finished our tea, the performance began again. While we had been enjoying a cup of tea, the crowd had regrouped. Yelling louder now and milling more feverishly, the agitators started breaking into more of the Shiite shops across the street. Wielding long poles, they pried off the pull-down metal security doors. Once they had gained entry, they passed the goods from hand-to-hand along a line of compatriots stretching to the middle of the street. Ah, the sweet rewards of righteous action! Some were content to loot goods and slip away. But most of the mob began piling merchandise, as well as furniture and broken signs, in the center of the street. Akbar and I stood at the steel-barred window again, staring down at the mayhem as the loot rached mountainous proportions. Four unarmed policemen arrived, but they seemed rather perplexed as to how to proceed. After a minute they moved away.

As the mob grew, it became more violent. Out of nowhere, I

spied a Caucasian man with a camera at the end of the street. He was running fast, not away from the crowd but toward it. At the same time, he was pulling a microphone out of his case. To my horror, he began filming the riot. Suddenly a Sunni who saw what he was doing hit him on the head with a stick. Then another joined in the beating. Six more men rushed forward and grabbed the man. We watched helplessly as they lifted and carried the struggling victim, like ants carrying a wounded fly, down the street and out of view.

The police riot squad, fifteen strong, reappeared at the opposite end of the street. They stormed in behind plastic shields, bearing handguns and tear gas grenades. This time the mob did not scatter but started toward the police squad, throwing bricks and yelling until the police backed away. Right before our eyes, Akbar and I watched ten men push down the door of a gun shop next to our building. Within a few minutes we heard shots, and the police disappeared. Now the rioters were free to set fire to the furniture and signs piled in the middle of the street. Some grabbed the burning boards from the bonfire and hurled them into other shops along our side of the street.

Akbar Khan hurried to telephone both the fire and police departments. I don't know what we expected them to do, but we could not

Riot in Namak Mandi as seen from Akbar Khan's office

even get through to them. By then the street people had thrown burning wood through the second floor window of the office next door. Bam! Bam! Bam! We could hear ammunition exploding in the gun shop, and smoke started curling into the office where we stood. Crash! Crash! Now the crowd had turned angrily toward the bank across the street. Smashing windows, they forced their way inside.

Rioters breaking into a bank

As the smoke began to billow, Akbar tried again to phone the police. There was no sense in remaining but no safe way out. Better to try than to stay here and burn, I thought. We started for the door. On the way out I grabbed my briefcase and a set of clothes from my suitcase. I reached the stairway only to find 15 people ahead of us also trying to escape. Residents from the other offices in the building came streaming into the hallway. The first five people through the door drew fire. They fell back in, and we caught them as they fell. Fortunately, no one was hit, but we had to force the massing crowd back so they could squeeze back into the building. Akbar and I retreated to his office, now filling with dense, acrid smoke. What to do? We had a bad choice – die from smoke inhalation or die from bullets.

Desperately I called Andreas Weerth, a friend who had been purchasing mineral specimens in Pakistan for over 20 years. After six attempts to dial, the phone rang at the Pearl Continental Hotel some two miles away. "May I speak to the German, Andreas Weerth?" I shouted.

Three eternal minutes later, he replied, "This is Andreas."

"Andreas, what news do you have on the riots?"

From behind me, I heard Akbar say, *"WE ARE THE NEWS"*

Rioters on the run

Andreas laughed as he overheard Akbar Khan. "I can hear shooting around the hotel, and the police have positioned two armored vehicles at the front door."

"Thanks, Andreas! That is not the news I wanted to hear," I said. "You certainly aren't a great help."

Andreas laughed.

Then I said, "I'll see you as soon as we can get out of Namak Mandi."

"Alive, I hope." Andreas hung up.

Now we had no choice but to evacuate. As we ran down the stairs, we heard sirens getting louder and closer. By the time we reached the front door, five armored vehicles were pulling up outside, and more than 50 uniformed soldiers with AK-47s had circled around them to provide support. About 30 riot police stood on the frontline lobbing tear gas into the crowd. In the back of this parade roared two fire trucks. Our timing was impeccable. As the assembly reached our building, we exited briskly and aimed ourselves in the opposite direction from the crowd, our eyes smarting.

The two-block walk to safety seemed interminable. I was hunched forward, my nose and eyes dripping buckets. I jumped into a rickshaw and headed fast for the Pearl Continental Hotel. Akbar Khan preferred to head for his village 15 miles out of Peshawar. What a relief to check into the Pearl! The Hotel never looked so good, even through red and runny eyes.

That evening, over a Chinese dinner, Andreas and I rehashed the day's events. Ours was an odd anniversary: just three years earlier the Soviets had flown over us in the tribal area west of Peshawar dropping bombs. We agreed we probably had a few more years' leeway before our business competitors would dare enter our territory!

In any event, if I could manage to survive Peshawar's civil unrest for the next few days, I would be off for the Jegdalek ruby mines via Kabul, which by now was even more dangerous.

Notation

The next morning I disbelieved what I saw – the Caucasian cameraman whom I had witnessed being attacked and carried off came limping toward me in the lobby of the Pearl Continental. He told me that he worked for the BBC. The Sunnis had bruised him badly, but from appearances at the scene, I feared they had beaten him to death. I felt extremely fortunate that we both had escaped the mob and the fire.

Sunni vs. Shia

To an outsider, Sunni-Shia scrapping seems as senseless as sibling rivalry. Aren't they all Moslems with the same God and same Holy Book? But like some siblings, they have long been engaged in a bitter fight about who is the rightful heir. The Sunni principle is that Mohammad's successor, or *khalifa* (caliph), should be elected. This position might be some surprising artifact of democracy but more likely reflects a desire to avoid entrenching a dynasty. This conflicts directly with the Shiite belief that Mohammad's successor, in both the caliphate and as religious head, should be a member of his household and the first among them to accept Mohammad as the Prophet. By their calculation, it is Ali who should have assumed the mantle of power upon Mohammad's death. The split developed in the first generation after the death of Islam's founder and went to the heart of all subsequent questions of legitimacy of doctrine and dogma in the faith. In Pakistan and Afghanistan, *The Party of Ali* is represented by the political groups of the pro-Iran Hesb-i-Wahdat and Harkat-i-Islami, and their Imams are both political and religious authorities (as are the Ayatollahs of Iran.)

In Afghanistan, as in Pakistan, the Sunnis represent 75% of the population; the Shiites are about 24%. Most of the Shia minority are *Hazara*. Members of this tribe are the progeny of long ago intermarriages between the Mongols and local tribes. They are an underclass and often work as menial laborers. Most of them live in the highlands of central Afghanistan, around Bamiyan, near the exploded Buddhas, and on the west side of Kabul among the mud houses in the outermost districts like Bajie. Because they are from the same religious denomination, they have maintained direct ties to Iran since the early 1700's. Easily identified by their Mongolian features, the Hazara were persecuted by the

Taliban, who are Sunni. Mass graves of Hazaras who were killed as little as a month before the fall of the Taliban are still being found today, according to UN sources who are investigating these murders. The only other group of Shias, who reside primarily in the Wahkhan area of Northern Pakistan, are *Ismailis*, followers of the Agha Khan.

The roots of the Sunni-Shia rift date back hundreds and hundreds of years; injustice and death have been amply meted out on all sides. During the old *Great Game*, British intelligence officers ensured that Afghan kings remained weak and dependent on Britain by fuelling feuds among the tribes. The Brits were too smart to pick a side in a civil war. In doing so, they would have risked becoming the enemy to anyone their ally had ever fought. Our foreign policy in Central Asia has fallen into this trap. By aligning with Pakistan, a notoriously corrupt, major drug-running nation, we have brought about a host of unintended consequences. Of course, we aligned with Pakistan because of its role in balancing the geopolitical power of India, which has had a leftward keel at times, according to our State Department. I had best leave this discussion for another day! But know this: long after the British colonial policies ended and long after the US has left Afghanistan, the internecine battles will continue as they are now.

Massoud Takes Kabul

The contest for Kabul ended on April 28, 1992, at least a phase of the struggle resolved in favor of Ahmed Shah Massoud. To bring order in the embattled city and establish a stable Afghan government, he moved into the capital late in the night with ten thousand troops. Richard Mackenzie, an American journalist who rode with the convoy, reported that it

... consisted of jeeps, one hundred tanks, and truckloads of Mujahideen fighters. ...

[Massoud] stopped to pray just outside the city of Kabul. Hesb-i-Islami (Hekmatyar) forces fired two shells at the convoy as it prepared to leave its northern Panjsher stronghold, but there was no damage. Massoud sent a decoy convoy down one road to Kabul, where it was known the rebels were dug in, then set off down another route with about 30 tanks, numerous armored personnel carriers and other vehicles in a line over three miles long. After 14 years of civil war he entered the capital of Kabul in triumph, the ultimate prize that cost more than one million troop lives and over a billion dollars. The allied militia fired volleys into the air to welcome him.

On June 28 Mujaddedi handed over power of the Leadership Council at the Presidential Palace to Professor Burhanuddin Rabani. Professor Rabani was installed as President of the Islamic State of Afghanistan.

Leading up to Massoud's triumph were layers of gamesmanship by major and minor powers in the world and factious politics among the tribes of Afghanistan. The financial drain and political embarrassment associated with the Soviet intrusion into Afghanistan so undermined the Communist Party, the KGB, and the military that they led to the downfall of the Soviet Union itself, which in turn precipitated enormous changes on the Afghan scene. Political and social upheavals in the Soviet Union had brought Mikhail Gorbachev and Soviet President Boris Yeltsin to power and weakened Marxist control of Afghan policy. The old Red Guard of the Red Army and hard-line Stalinists, who strongly favored the continuation of the ruling Marxist regime in Kabul, lost their grip over military and political affairs.

Meanwhile, the US had gambled billions of dollars in military aid to Pakistan, which Saudi Arabia had matched dollar for dollar with aid to the Mujahideen in their conflict with the USSR. At the time of the ragged withdrawal of the Soviets, Pakistan had its own plans for Afghanistan. Pakistan's leaders wanted to secure Afghanistan for themselves as a rear guard in the event of war with India. As president of Pakistan, Zia ul-Haq wielded absolute control over the distribution of Saudi aid money. Through the ISI, the Pakistan government set into motion a small anti-Western faction headed by Gulbuddin Hekmatyar, loyal to the Pakistani military dictatorship. Perhaps in hindsight, given the current political situation in Southwestern Asia, at the time of the Soviet withdrawal the US should have taken a stand for the future of the Afghan nation-state – but it did not, so the local factions struggled against each other to gain dominance.

On May 4, 1986, Dr. Najibullah replaced Babrak Karmal as President of the Republic of Afghanistan in a Soviet-backed action to make a PDPA government more acceptable to the citizens.

The Geneva Accords were signed on April 14, 1988. This bilateral agreement between Afghanistan and Pakistan, guaranteed by the USSR and the USA, called for a phased withdrawal of Soviet Union troops from Afghanistan to begin in May 1988 and to be completed by February 15, 1989. As promised, the last Soviet troops departed on February 15, 1989. The government headed by Najibullah, however, didn't collapse as the Mujahideen and the Pakistan government had hoped. In early March 1989, the Afghan interim government, formerly the seven parties, organized and launched the battle of Jalalabad, where they planned to set up a government on Afghan soil on the road from Peshawar to Kabul. Dissension and distrust among the Mujahideen group leaders prevented taking Jalalabad for their alternative capital to Kabul and thereby strengthened Najibullah's position.

In August 1991, an abortive coup took place in the Soviet Union, which rendered the Communist Party defunct. Six days later, Sibghatullah Mujaddedi, President of the Interim Government (AIG) of Afghanistan, received an invitation from Soviet President Boris Yeltsin for talks to bring the Afghan crisis to an honorable and principled end.

By mid-April 1992, as the Mujahideen were closing in on Kabul, the Soviet Union replaced President Najibullah with a council of Afghan Army officers and political associates in the Watan Party. A powerful group of Afghan military commanders – the Afghanistan Army Chief of Staff General Mohammad Asef Dilawar; along with General Mohammad Mouman, his 17th Division Commander, General Nabi Azimee, his Kabul Garrision Commander; and General Baba Jhan, his Begram Airport Commander – agreed to assist Ahmed Shah Massoud in taking control of Kabul. Also Rashid Dostum, a powerful militia leader from the Uzbek area of Northern Afghanistan, who had been an important element in the success of Najibullah, made a deal with Commander Massoud and Najibullah's senior figures in government.

A cooperation accord founded an Islamic Jihad Council of government militia and Mujahideen forces between Abdul Wakil, the Afghan Foreign Minister, and Commander

Massoud. Their exclusion of Hekmatyar's Hesb-i-Islami faction shocked the political-military establishment in Pakistan.

Pakistan's Prime Minister Nawaz Sharif held hotly contested meetings with the ISI chief, his other ministers, and the Mujahideen in Peshawar and the Hesb-i-Islami faction, headed by Hekmatyar, who was deeply loyal to the Pakistan military dictatorship. Hekmatyar's troops started firing mortars into Kabul. Najibullah took refuge in the UN compound after being stopped by General Dostum's forces from boarding a United Nations airplane at the Kabul airport.

On April 24, the Afghan army and the Mujahideen took Kabul peacefully, and throughout the city the various factions staked out zones of control. An Afghan coalition formed an interim government in Peshawar: a 50-member Leadership Council agreed to be led for the first two months by Professor Sibghatullah Mujaddedi, as *caretaker* Interim President of the Islamic State of Afghanistan. This council comprised 30 commanders, ten *ulema* (religious leaders), and one nominated member from each of the ten major Mujahideen parties. The goal of the council was to transfer power to an interim government headed by Jamiat-i-Islami's Professor Burhanuddin Rabani, who was to serve four months while preparations were being made for elections. The Cabinet positions were to be equally divided among the parties.

Pir Sayed Ahmed Gailani, leader of the National Islamic Front of Afghanistan (NIFA), challenged the caretaker agreement. He refused to join a government with Hekmatyar, a Hesb-i-Islami, as Prime Minister. At the same time, Abdul Ali Mazari, representing the alliance of Iran-based Shia parties, declared the council unacceptable because his group was not represented at all.

Next, Mujaddedi promoted Dostum, the ex-communist Uzbek, to the rank of full general in an official ceremony in Mazar-i-Sharif. All the Mujahideen groups disapproved, as did Ahmed Shah Massoud, the newly appointed Minister of Defense; so Dostum's forces became unruly and then violent in the Kabul area. They began confiscating property from the Kabul residents, even automobiles. And there were many cases of rape reported, rumored to have been committed by Dostum's troops.

Miners drilling in marble for ruby crystals

Chapter Twelve
Ruby Hunting at Jegdalek

The gem cannot be polished without friction,
nor man perfected without trials.
– Chinese Proverb

Summer 1992 – Kabul and Jegdalek

On the morning of July 23, 1992, my birthday, I arrived at the Peshawar Airport for a flight to Kabul. Bitter sectarian street fighting was raging there between the Shia of Hesb-i-Wahdat (Abdul Ali Mazari), backed by Iran, and the Sunni of Ittehad-i-Islami (Sayyaf), backed by Saudi Arabia. Just two days before, they had agreed to a cease-fire, but anarchy and lawlessness still reigned. Faction-driven armed soldiers ruled the Kabul streets while Hekmatyar's forces continued to bombard the city with rockets from the outskirts.

I was traveling with Abdul Hakim, whom I had hired as a guide and interpreter. I felt fortunate to be in the company of this handsome five-foot eight-inch Pashtun who had earned his engineering degree at Kabul University. We had booked an eleven o'clock flight, but at eleven-thirty the airline announced that it would be delayed until one. Shortly after one o'clock we watched our plane overflying Peshawar. An announcement asked passengers to wait for further news. At two we were told another plane was to arrive in Peshawar at three-thirty. In true Middle Eastern fashion, the flight finally arrived at 4:10. We boarded immediately with 30 other people, mostly Pakistani, and finally arrived in Kabul at 5:10. I had just spent most of my 52nd birthday in the Peshawar airport.

The Kabul airport and terminal had not fared well in the rocket attacks during the Soviet occupation. In their efforts to defeat the Soviets, the Mujahideen had been attacking the airport for years. All that remained of the terminal was the partial frame of one building. What a mess!

Hakim located a taxi driver in an old Soviet-made car. We applied at three hotels only to learn that they had been appropriated as barracks for soldiers from the countryside. Then we went to the Intercontinental Hotel on a westside hill, where I had stayed many times between 1972 and 1980. Although a tank stood guard outside, to our surprise the hotel seemed empty except for five employees and five guards. The area beyond the lobby appeared dusty and very dirty throughout. The desk clerk told us that the soldiers had been ordered to leave two days ago and that rooms were available for $100 a night "American money."

"Wow, that's expensive," I said, knowing that I was being ripped off.

"Those are our orders from the government," the clerk held firm.

"Okay, I will take a room for one night," I replied.

"I will locate my relatives and sleep with them," Hakim interjected. Then he added for the clerk's benefit, "Tomorrow we will stay in a private home."

As I handed the clerk one of my three new US$100 bills, he told me, "The elevators are broken. Food will be available in the dining room after seven o'clock."

"How many people are staying in the hotel tonight?"

"Oh! We have two other guests," he replied.

Kabul Intercontinental Hotel

As I was dragging my bags up the stairs to my room, a tall, slightly grayed Pakistani was coming down. "*Salom-o-alaikum,*" I said.

He replied, "*Wali Kom Salom.* Are you British?"

"No, American. My name is Gary."

"I have heard your name before. I am Sameen Khan, law professor and advisor for Ahmed Shah Massoud," he replied.

"Would you like to join me for dinner?" I asked.

Promptly at seven-thirty I entered the dining room to find Sameen already sitting at a table. He stood and we shook hands as a waiter approached. "We only have chicken, rice, nan, coffee, cucumbers, and water at a cost of $5 a person."

"How did you know what we wanted?" I smiled. He smiled back and headed for the kitchen.

I asked Sameen to tell me about his work and bring me up to date on current events in Afghanistan. He proceeded to give a very interesting 40-minute lecture before the waiter returned with our dinners. Over our unsavory meal I asked several questions about Ahmed Shah Massoud and Mujaddedi, the past president of the Seven Party Alliance established by General Zia ul-Haq, as well as the history of Afghanistan. He answered them all in full detail.

After dinner, Sameen retired to his room and then returned to knock on my door with a signed copy of his book, *A Strategic Doctrine for Pakistan.* I thanked him for the evening and said goodnight.

Ten minutes after Sameen's departure the lights in the hotel went out. In the distance, I could hear automatic rifle fire getting closer and closer from two directions. Then rockets started landing near the hotel – KABOOM! KABOOM! KABOOM! With nowhere to go, I decided to stay where I was. I watched out the window from across the room.

Sameen Khan,
Barrister-at-law

On this night Kabul reminded me of the *Late, Late Show* I had experienced in Viet Nam in the '60s when I served as a Major in the U.S. Army. Some of us used to sit on the roof of our hotel in Saigon to watch the war off in the distance by following the phosphorous tracer bullets piercing the humid night air.

This time, after an hour, the firing ended as quickly as it had begun.

The next morning the desk clerk informed me that there had been a battle between some of Massoud's soldiers and the Hazaras (Shiite Moslems) over Massoud's control of their district of Kabul. There was no further damage to the hotel building, but two of the guards had been killed, and the tank used for security at the front entrance had been captured and driven away by the Hazara troops.

Just as I finished talking with the clerk, Hakim showed up with a taxi. He said Commander Abdul Mahmood, who had been the commander in Panjsher during my first visit, was waiting to see us in his headquarters in downtown Kabul. As the two of us walked into Mahmood's office, my friend from Panjsher, Mohebullah, approached and greeted me with a smile and hug. Mohebullah, a 5'4" dark-haired, light-skinned Tajik, had been selling gems to me for several years.

"Commander Mahmood is in a security meeting over last night's fighting in which several soldiers were killed," Mohebullah informed me.

"Being that the Commander may be occupied all day, Mr. Gary and I will attempt to locate Commander Anwar Khan and find a new place to live," replied Hakim.

"Kabul is very dangerous right now," said Mohebullah.

"We are only staying long enough to arrange permission and transportation to visit the ruby mines at Jegdalek," I reassured him.

"Please tell Commander Mahmood that we will return later today," added Hakim.

At Commander Anwar Khan's office we were invited to have lunch while waiting for him to arrive. Two hours later Anwar arrived full of smiles. He greeted us warmly, "I am very happy to see you and to get this ruby project started."

"Life certainly isn't dull around here," I commented.

"It is not only the Hazaras. We are having many problems with the Hesb-i-Islami. Hekmatyar, the leader of the Hesb-i-Islami, is finished as Prime Minister this morning, and we expect fighting to start. You will have to go through Hekmatyar's controlled area to get to the ruby mines. It will take a few days for me to clear and arrange transportation and security. I suggest you take Commander Mahmood's advice on Kabul, as the city is under his command. I will contact you as soon as I can make arrangements for you to travel to Jegdalek."

I thanked him and told him we would return to Mahmood's office. When we got there, Mohebullah informed us that Mahmood had made arrangements for me to move into his headquarters in a room with six of his soldiers. He wanted to meet with me at five o'clock that afternoon, so Hakim and I returned to the Intercontinental Hotel to pick up my bags.

Back at his office Mahmood was waiting for us. He said, "Commander Ahmed Shah Massoud says that he would like to see you but that he has too many problems at the moment. Hekmatyar has threatened to attack Kabul. Massoud suggests that you go on to Jegdalek and visit with him upon your return to Kabul."

Commander Sher Mohammad

"Thank him for his hospitality. I realize how busy Massoud must be with all these security problems. I'll stay out of the way until we are cleared to travel." We exchanged handshakes, and I went to the assigned room.

For two days and nights I stayed in the room, reading novels by Robert Ludlum and falling asleep to battle sounds ten miles away. On two occasions, for five minutes each, the guards outside my room exchanged open fire with someone on the street.

At eight a.m. on the third day, Hakim returned. "Commander Anwar wants to see us immediately. He has made arrangements for us to go to Jegdalek! Bring all your bags!" Fifteen minutes later we arrived at Commander Anwar Khan's office.

A new face greeted us. "I'm Commander Sher Mohammad from Jegdalek, a relative of Anwar Khan's," he said. "Anwar left full instructions for me to escort you to Jegdalek because he was called by

Massoud to come immediately."

Sher Mohammad, with his newly started beard, looked like Arafat in size and stature, though his features were smoother. I felt uneasy. Here was a man I had never met before who was about to escort Hakim and me through a war zone to Jegdalek. If Anwar had been present for an introduction, I would have felt more comfortable. Even a note would have helped. How could I be sure that this Sher Mohammad was really the man Anwar had selected?

Turning toward us, Sher Mohammad said, "We will take a taxi to the military depot where a vehicle and guards are waiting for us. We will be leaving immediately for Jegdalek."

At ten we arrived on the outskirts of Kabul at a military compound previously used as a Soviet headquarters. The taxi came to a halt inside the compound. An armed guard looked at us and said, "You are to take the four-by-four Toyota."

Just then two other guards with AK-47s approached us. They climbed into the back of the Toyota driven by Commander Sher Mohammad. After an hour of bouncing over craters in bombed-out roads, we reached our first guard post, which Hekmatyar's soldiers controlled. To our surprise

Hekmatyar's Guard Station between Kabul and Sorobi

they invited us for tea because, as it turned out, one of our assigned guards knew them personally. I was a bit nervous, but we accepted. They even allowed me to take some photos.

On our way to Sorobi we passed many destroyed vehicles and buildings along the road. In some places the Soviets had scorched the earth, leaving nothing growing. We stopped near the edge of town on the Kabul River at what once had been King Zahir Shah's rest house. During the 1970s and '80s the KHAD (secret police) had used it as their headquarters. A sadly dilapidated building of thick clay walls distressed by hundreds of bullet markings was all that remained.

After lunch Sher Mohammad veered off the road into a streambed, which was to be our route to Jegdalek. I learned later that Soviet land mines had rendered the road too dangerous to traverse.

After three hours we arrived at the Jegdalek mountaintop command post. Eighteen of Massoud's Jamiat-i-Islami soldiers greeted us. They had been anticipating that we would bring fresh food from Kabul. All too soon we were to discover the meagerness of their rations.

There was trouble to the east, where Hesb-i-Islami soldiers occupied the other end of the valley. If they started firing during our survey of the mines, we would be caught in the middle between the Hesbi and the Jamiat troops. The commanders of each side had agreed between themselves to cease hostilities for the time being, but often a ceasefire is an agreed-upon fiction.

Our host invited us to sit on an old Afghan carpet, where he served us tea and fresh mulberries. In the distance we could see the ruby mines, approximately two miles away. To stretch our legs, we took a long walk down the mountain into the rubble that had been Da'Gary, a village that had been named long before my appearance on the scene.

At dinner, I realized that the six-inch dark brown slabs hanging like bats from wooden sticks around the campground were meat. After the soldiers had soaked the dried beef in water for a day or two, they overcooked the strips and served them with rice, nan, and tea. We ate in the open at nine o'clock. The meal was almost palatable.

For the evening's entertainment each soldier provided us with his version of war stories. Over a thousand troops commanded by Anwar Khan had held off Soviet commando units for 14 years to protect the mountain on which we were bivouacked. These men proudly related these events to us. As the stories began to repeat themselves and our eyelids began to droop, our hosts set up army cots for us. The cots looked rickety, so I smoothly offered, "I can just sleep here on the ground."

The commander came back flatly, "No! We have many snakes, scorpions, and spiders."

Earlier, I had seen several large spiders. Just then, one of the soldiers turned on a flashlight as another soldier hit a two-inch scorpion with his sandal.

"OK, I'm convinced! I accept the cot."

The next two days I spent surveying about half the ruby-sapphire mines. We were told that the other half belonged to the Hesbi people, who would not welcome us at this time. So we gathered surrounding host rock and corundum samples, both rubies and sapphires, from only the western half of the deposit area. Some of those samples I later delivered to Drs. Larry Snee and Gene Foord at the U.S. Geological Survey in Denver, Colorado and to Dr. Jim Shigley at the Gemological Institute of America, in Santa Monica, California.

In addition, I listened intently to the stories of the miners. Some, such as Jamal Khan, Sher Mohammed's brother, had spent over 20

Looking from Mujahideen command post across Village of Da'Gary to Jegdalek ruby mines

years in the mines. They told of many rubies they had discovered and sold. Seeing the doubt on my face about the quality of their finds, within two hours over 20 miners had brought out their personal hordes.

Warmankai ruby mine

Then we started to negotiate in earnest. Of course they aimed at the sky, naming r i d i c u l o u s sums of two to three hundred percent above real value before immediately dropping their prices. When we reached a serious price level, the men started checking with their partners by holding hands underneath a large cloth or turban so I could not *hear* their debate. Each finger held by a partner represents a hundred or a thousand. For instance, if one partner holds four of his partner's fingers, he means either four hundred or four thousand, depending on the level of negotiations. Usually, most deals take more than one bargaining session. My record for length is more than ten sessions spread over a four-year period.

When the session ends without agreement, the parties have two choices – to end the negotiation or to seal the gems for a later round. In most cases the seller wraps the goods in paper or cloth and binds them with tape. The would-be purchasing party then initials the packets until negotiations resume at an agreed-upon time and date.

On this rare occasion, however, during only two bargaining sessions, I purchased over US$12,000 in ruby and sapphire specimens. The best of the lot was one well-formed ruby crystal of 174 carats. Most of the gems were from 5 to 20 carats. I gave the miners my last two US$100 bills and agreed to pay the balance to Jamal when I returned to Peshawar. Later, someone explained to me that before my visit the miners had been granting extended credit to Pakistanis. Often times, those merchants returned as late as the next year or more to make good on their promise to "pay soon."

I made my purchases without knowing of the problems to come.

At eight o'clock the next morning a truck from Kabul arrived at Jegdalek. The driver informed us that the situation around Kabul was heating up. He recommended we depart as soon as possible. It took us all of 15 minutes to pack and get underway.

We had only been on the road 30 minutes when Sher Mohammad and I simultaneously spotted a large Soviet truck blocking the road

Gary standing between Jamal and Mir Waees Khan at Jegdalek ruby mines

with 20 armed Mujahideen soldiers standing in the back of it. Sher Mohammed appeared very nervous at the sight. "Hesbi?" I asked.

Sher Mohammad answered tersely between his teeth, "Yes."

Just then a tall man of about 50, sporting a long beard and AK-47, walked directly from the Soviet truck over to my open window. He looked at me and said, "You OK?"

"Yes," I said.

He shook my hand and said to Sher Mohammad, "I know of Mr. Gary! You may pass."

One lot of rough ruby for sale

As the soldier, a Hesbi leader, ordered his vehicle to move out of the way and let us go through, a happy, relieved look swept over Sher Mohammad's face. Although I had not recognized the Commander, I was happy we were safely on our way again.

We arrived in Sorobi two hours later. Here, Sher Mohammed grew noticeably nervous again at the sight of so many armed men in the village. He stopped the vehicle at one point, got out, and started

New trench mine at Jegdalek

Miners searching for ruby crystals

questioning some soldiers. As we sat in the vehicle watching intently, they led him behind a building. Much to our relief, he returned ten minutes later with another man who drove us to the deserted KHAD Headquarters building.

Once again Sher Mohammad stepped out of the jeep to talk with some soldiers. I walked inside the KHAD office and leaned against the wall to update my diary and wait uneasily. It was one long hour later when Sher Mohammad walked through the door.

"I have some bad news," he said immediately. "The Hesbi started attacking the Jamiat in Kabul last night. Today they are lobbing rockets into the airport and other areas. This puts us in a very bad position. The Hesbis control Jalalabad to the east, and outside of Kabul to the west fighting has started. Somehow we must travel 30 miles and get to Kabul as fast as possible!" Then we would be with Massoud, Mahmood, and their troops.

My earlier doubts had been misplaced. Obviously Sher Mohammad was taking his job of protecting Hakim and me very seriously. It would have been far safer for him to leave us in Sorobi and return to his relatives' home. I trusted his judgment as he explained our

Negotiating prices with ruby miners during tea time at Jegdalek

choices and related his decision.

We all looked at one another for about ten seconds and then simultaneously sprinted for the truck. We did not need any orders to evacuate. Sher Mohammad's hands gripped the steering wheel as if to squeeze juice out of it, and he pressed the gas pedal to the floor. We roared off at 60 to 70 miles an hour over a road with bomb pits less than every 50 feet.

Soon we discovered that no one was manning any of the guard posts on the way to Kabul. Both Jamiat and Hesbi soldiers had disappeared. We passed the Hesbi gate where we had stopped for tea on the way to the mines. The post was deserted, but this time the closed gates had been rammed and broken open by vehicles passing through them without stopping. Thirty minutes later we caught sight of Kabul in the distance.

As we approached the outsirts of Kabul, we met mass confusion in all directions: people running for cover and vehicles and tanks traveling at record-breaking speeds in the opposite direction. Hesbi green flags waved wildly from their perches, and 8x10 photos of Hekmatyar stared through the windshields. These were obviously Hekmatyar's troops. Thank heavens they were totally ignoring us!

By the time we reached Kabul, rockets were hitting close by, and all around tanks were answering fire, behind us and on both flanks. As we reached Kabul proper, we confronted a barricade. The guards flagged us down, demanding to see our travel papers and IDs. After scanning them, they waved us on into the city.

We went directly to Commander Anwar Khan's office to report on our trip. At the door of the office his assistant said, "Commander Anwar Khan has been promoted to the Assistant Director of Defense."

Anwar called from the next room, "Please come in; give me your report from Jegdalek, and tell me what you saw on the road today."

We had barely started telling him about our return trip when the phone rang. He answered it, slammed it down, and rushed toward the door, commanding, "Stay here tonight. I will have some food brought to you and the guards I am leaving behind."

Hakim and I looked around the house and found that we could heat water for a shower. This would be our first bath after living in the mountains for four days. It was my first *HOT* bath in two weeks. Afterwards, Hakim said, "I would like to go check on my relatives and see about our plane flight out of Kabul."

"I'll be okay," I told him. "The sooner we fly out the better."

Hakim had only been gone an hour when I began to hear heavy artillery about a mile away. It lasted three hours and then stopped abruptly.

The next morning Hakim called to say that he was going to the airline office and would check in with me later. Toward evening he called again to say that he was waiting at his home for word from the PIA (Pakistan International Airways) office. He said, "I will call or visit you as soon as I have some information."

I occupied myself during the next two days writing a report for Commander Anwar Khan and posting my diary. On the third day, still waiting for travel permits, Hakim and I visited with Dr. Mir Mohammad Mahfooz at the Ministry of Mines and Industry Office. He gave us permission to search their library on the south side of Kabul for literature and reports on gem mining. Before we could get to the library, we found out that the reports had been destroyed by rocket fire between the soldiers of Massoud's Jamiat-i-Islami and Hekmatyar's Hesb-i-Islami. As I told Hakim, "It is one thing to blow up the reports, but each night the rockets are getting closer to my bed!"

The previous night one rocket had hit in the yard and shaken the house. KABOOM! I jumped out of bed and ran for the archway in the center of the house. Six guards and I all reached its solid safety at the same time. Having only room for four people, two bounced off the wall and made for the closet. We all laughed nervously. The next night I slept in my tennis shoes, ready to sprint.

On August 5th, a messenger arrived at the house to inform us that Hakim and I had been selected to fly to Pakistan on an Ariana Airways flight the next morning at eight. At 8:50 that evening a guard and I were listening to the BBC news when the announcer said that Hekmatyar had threatened to blow up the airport and all planes the next day. I visualized my plane exploding and my family holding my memorial service! Fifteen minutes later Hakim showed up. "Did you hear the news?" he asked. "Let's take some guards and head for Pakistan by road."

"Wait a minute! Yesterday you said that was too –"

"I know," he cut in, "but this situation keeps getting worse and something will happen at the airport tomorrow."

Just then Anwar arrived. "Hakim is right. The road is probably your better choice," Anwar advised. "I will send four well-trained trusted guards with you until you get to the Hesbi frontlines. Then two will get lost and the other two will follow you to the border. Mr. Gary, with your American passport and Hakim being Pashtun and from Kabul, I'm sure you will get through."

At five o'clock on August 6, 1992, once again I disguised myself as a poor Afghan traveler. I hid my papers and glasses in an old worn cloth bag and dressed in the dirty, smelly, very wrinkled clothes that I had worn at the ruby mines the week before. On my feet I wore old sandals rather than my tennis shoes. The night before, Anwar's guards had cautioned me not to speak any English until we had reached Pakistan.

Hakim spoke both Dari and Pashtu. I could only understand a few words of each, but I said in English to Hakim, "What about your accent?"

He did not reply.

Our guards spoke only Dari, a form of Farsi also spoken in Iran, whereas, the Hesbi speak primarily Pashtu, the language of the Pashtuns, the largest tribal group in Afghanistan.

At the last minute Hakim decided that we should travel in an old bus with other refugees to Jalalabad. From there we would hire a four-by-four for the one-hour trip to the border of Pakistan. We agreed not to talk during the journey. This meant ordering no food or drink and avoiding contact with other people.

Nine of Anwar's armed men drove us to the bus station on the south side of Kabul where fighting had been in full force the previous night. At the station, among some 20 vehicles, ten had drivers yelling the name of our destination "Jalalabad! Jalalabad! Jalalabad!" Obviously, they wanted to get out of Kabul as much as we did.

Hakim and I rejected the first two buses because they were more than half full and we wanted to sit on a seat in the back row. We boarded the third old bus with hundreds of bullet holes in its sides. Forty refugees wearing burkas and turbans piled in behind us. Hakim and I sat sweating in the middle of the very last seat. Two of Anwar's men with rifles under their patus (blankets) sat on our flanks.

Sorobi was to be our first stop. As we crossed what was now the battlefield, we saw many destroyed vehicles and new rocket pockmarks everywhere, the result of fighting and rocket attacks since our return from the ruby mines just eight days ago. I noticed that the first ten guard posts we had passed then were still deserted, including the large post outside of Sorobi where the Hesbi commander had stopped us on our previous trip.

A few miles from Kabul, Anwar's guard next to me yelled, "Stop! Stop!" to the driver. The bus slowed and one of our guards jumped through the open window. The guard inside tossed the weapons to the guard on the ground, who stashed them in a mud hut on the side of the road. The guard on the ground then climbed back through the window, and the bus began to move once again.

Two miles down the road, fully-armed Hesbi troops, stationed at a roadblock, stopped us and surrounded the bus. They looked under the bus and in all the compartments. The driver reluctantly opened the door so two guards could enter. They began from the front frisking each passenger for weapons, which, of course, ultimately would include the four of us on the back seat. No one spoke a word as each person stood up to be searched. By the time the guards had made it halfway, they appeared to tire of their fruitless task. I was greatly relieved when they neglected my bag at my feet. Only Hakim and I knew that in the bag was the ruby rough I had purchased at Jegdalek. If they had seen those stones, they would surely have confiscated my $12,000 investment. In Afghanistan there is great reason to practice a poker face. Finally the guards exited and ordered the driver to continue the 44 miles on to Sorobi. Hakim and I took full deep breaths again.

Five more times we had to stop for searches before we finally reached Sorobi. Each time armed guards boarded and looked under a few seats in the front of the bus before departing and permitting the driver to continue.

After six hot dusty hours the old Buddhist caves on the outskirts of Jalalabad came into view. Here again, guards stopped and searched the bus at the city limits. Jalalabad is a real city with a population of over thirty thousand. Many of the three- and four-story buildings had been destroyed during the last two years of heavy fighting. We saw many armored vehicles. When we arrived at the bus station in the center of the city, there were some 20 buses similar to ours.

Hakim leaned forward in the seat and said in Pashtu, "Where can we get transportation to Pakistan?"

One man leaned back and whispered. Hakim glanced at me with a slight grin. Then he caught the eye of our guards who were now without their guns. He motioned for the three of us to follow him. One at a time we exited the bus. In single file we walked four blocks, passing many shops with food and drinks. We did not dare stop even though we were feeling parched from breathing the dusty air. People milled about in the streets among vehicles and horse-drawn carts. Everything seemed to be in continual motion, yet the road was almost completely choked with traffic.

Looking across the street, we saw five Toyota pickup trucks. Standing near each one, the driver was yelling, "Peshawar! Peshawar! Peshawar!" Hakim shot me a pleased look. Here was our transportation to Pakistan.

We rapidly walked to the first pickup. For three minutes Hakim negotiated the price with the driver, but to me it seemed like 15 minutes as we stood waiting. Hakim then motioned with his hand for us to jump into the back. The four of us squeezed onto built-in seats with seven other passengers. Within three minutes we were on our way to Pakistan!

The driver only stopped once along the way for prayers. Hakim signaled for me to get out with the others. As each passenger selected his place to pray, I stepped behind some trees along the road into a slightly wooded area. When I heard the others returning, I walked back to the truck with them.

About a mile from the border town of Torkham, one of the men seated on the opposite side of the truck, looked at one of our guards and said something in Pashtu. Our guard pretended not to have heard him. Instead, Hakim, seated next to the guard, leaned forward and said,

"Yes?"

Hakim later told me that the man whispered some useful advice, "I have made this trip many times. If we give the first border guard ten rupees from each of us (US$0.40), he will clear us without an inspection. The problem is you and your friend look too rich. You and your friend should get out when we slow down on the Afghan side of the border and leave your two other friends with your bags. This way they will look at us poor passengers and not bother us with an inspection."

I looked at Hakim and drew in a breath indicating the risk. He picked up on it. Did we want to trust our guards with my bags? After a second thought I shrugged my shoulders and motioned Hakim with my hands and eyes – go for it! The people in the truck, including our guards, probably did not have any idea of what rough ruby looked like or how valuable it was. Hakim gave me thumbs up. About 40 yards from the border Hakim motioned for me to jump out with him and leave my bag of rubies behind. Mentally this was difficult, but I jumped.

We then melded into a group of about 50 other people walking toward the border. In our dirty clothes we matched the movements of the crowd. There were over two hundred people standing on both sides of the border, either waiting to cross or waiting to meet someone. Hakim motioned for me to precede him through the large gates.

I was about five yards inside Pakistan when an uniformed guard called out to me. "Haji!" he cried. A Haji is a Moslem who has completed his pilgrimage to Mecca. Hakim took my arm and stepped between the guard and me. The guard asked Hakim several questions about our journey, our Afghan tribal affiliation, and why we were crossing into Pakistan. Then the guard, satisfied with Hakim's answers, motioned for Hakim and me to continue into Pakistan.

After walking another 50 yards, we located our pickup. Hakim and I jumped into the back. As we drove away towards Peshawar, I said to Hakim in English, "After all these years of being smuggled in and out of Afghanistan, I finally have full permission, yet I'm still smuggled. I really should go back and get my passport stamped."

"It would just be a problem," said Hakim.

"OK. I hope my friends at Special Branch (police) in Peshawar

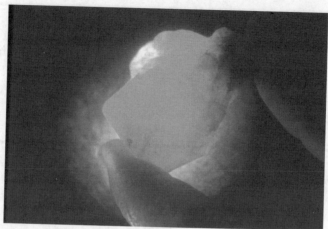

174 carat rough ruby crystal

can solve my no-entry problem." I looked toward the front of the truck to see the other passengers staring at me.

The guard seated on my right pointed at me and said in a loud voice, "American!"

Instantly, all the passengers smiled and started laughing out loud, as if it were a hilarious joke. We all joined in the laughter. What a tremendous relief knowing that we had made the eight-hour, hundred-mile trip through hostile territory without being noticed or stopped. Furthermore, I had cleared the headquarters area of the opposing Hesb-i-Islami faction with 13 pounds of ruby valued at $30,000 after being cut in the US. And I still had my prize 174 carat – very large for a ruby crystal!

Authorization Letters

Four months after completing the survey of the Ruby mines, the following letters were received from Anwar Khan, Sher Mohammad, and Jamal Khan authorizing us to proceed with our program.

Jamiat-e-Islami Afghanistan

جمعیت اسلامی
افغانستان
ریاست (حیات ت عراک)
امریت (جهد دیس)
نمبر   (   )
تاریخ   (   )

No...................
Date...................

Mr. Gary W. Bowersox
President
GeoVision, Inc.
P.O. Box 89646
Honolulu, HI 96830
U.S.A.

Date: 29 December 1992

Dear Mr. Gary

This letter is your authorization to proceed with the program outlined in your September 30, 1992 report on the ruby and sapphire mines of Jegdaleg, Afghanistan.

I look forward to working with you and your staff on this report

Best regards,

Anwar Khan
Commander Jegdaleg

Jamiat-e-Islami Afghanistan

جمعیت اسلامی
افغانستان
ریاست (حیات ت عراک)
امریت (دیس)
نمبر   (   )
تاریخ   (   )

No...................
Date...................

Mr. Gary W. Bowersox
President
GeoVision, Inc.
P.O. Box 89646
Honolulu, HI 96830
U.S.A.

Date: 29 December 1992

Dear Mr. Gary

I would like to assure you that we will take all necessary steps to make save and effective your gem mines survey program in Jegdaleg area during July 1993 which we had discussed in our meetings during July 1992 and you have outlined in your September 1992 report on the ruby and sapphire mines of Jegdaleg, Afghanistan.

I look forward to working with you and your staff on this project.

Best regards,

Sher Mohammed Khan

Commander Jegdaleg area

Jegdaleg, Afghanistan

Approved by:
Anwar Khan

Jegdaleg, Afghanistan

Jamiat-e-Islami Afghanistan

جمعیت اسلامی
افغانستان
ریاست (حیات ت عراک)
امریت (دیس)
نمبر   (   )
تاریخ   (   )

No...................
Date...................

Mr. Gary W. Bowersox
President
GeoVision, Inc.
P.O. Box 89646
Honolulu, HI 96830
U.S.A.

Date: 29 December 1992

Dear Mr. Gary
This letter is your authorization to use Wormankai mine site during your July 1993 Symposium program that we discussed in our meeting during your July 1992 visit to Jegdaleg ruby and sapphire mines.

I would like to assure you that we will take all necessary steps to make save and effective your program in Jegdaleg area.

I look forward to working with you and your staff on this report.

Best regards,

Jamal Khan
Wormankai mine site
Jegdaleg, Afghanistan

East

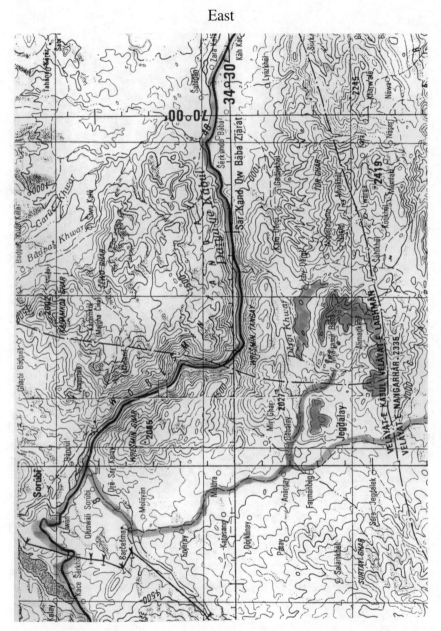

Map showing Jegdalek ruby mining area and the routes leading to the area

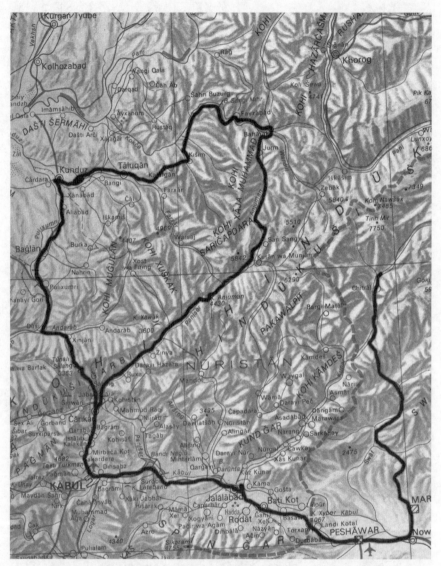

Map showing 1979 expedition to the lapis mines

Chapter Thirteen
A Trip to the Lapis Mines

Summer 1993

Every time I looked at Marco Polo's map, my Gem Hunter heart started pounding. And every time I read Ollie Olufsen's seductive words, I knew I had to find the "ruby" mine called Kuh-i-Lal! (Yes, "ruby" is in quotation marks...I will soon explain why.)

Marco Polo traveled in Afghanistan in the late 1200's

Of these stones (balas ruby, or spinel) of fine quality and great value, they are embedded in the high mountains, but are searched for only in one, named Sikinan. In this the king causes mines to be worked, and through this channel alone, they are obtained; no person daring, under pain of death, to make an excavation for the purpose unless he obtains his majesty's license. Occasionally the king gives them as presents, as they are not procurable by purchase from others, and cannot be exported without his permission. His object in these restrictions is, that the rubies of his country should maintain their high price, for if they could be dug for indiscriminately, so great is their abundance that they would soon be of little value. (Yule 1903 on Marco Polo's trip in the year 1271)

Beyond the Northwest Frontier of Pakistan to the north lies Badakhshan (which the Greeks called Bactria and the Persians called Balkh). It lies adjacent to the Wahkhan Corridor and the *roof of the world*, the Hindu Kush and Pamir Mountains. Major geological trauma has been occurring over millions of years as two crustal plates collide. The tectonic action has created many peaks over twenty thousand feet high that are still growing at two meters a century.

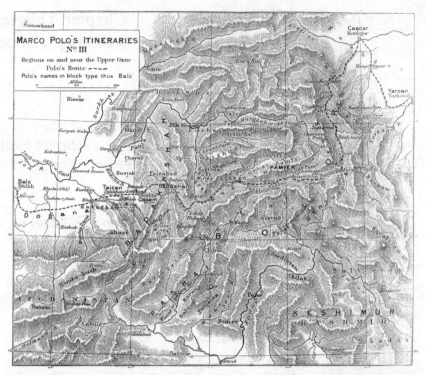

*Marco Polo's map showing ruby and azur (lapis) mines as created by Yule in the
1800s from Marco Polo's dictated travel notes*

The area had been a primary trade route for Siberian and Indian
goods on their way to Persia. Old tales abound of the exotic nature of
these far reaches, secreting Yetis, humanlike snowmen, and untold gem
deposits. Alexander the Great led his troops through here on his way to
India. As a result, the area took on Greek culture, making for an
interesting and ancient mix of influences.

Over the years, I had conducted research at the Library of
Congress, the London University Library, and the Peshawar, Pakistan
Museum-Library, as well as other libraries around the world, in order
to understand the history and geology of this area. I found writings of
other people who had visited this ancient mine, but I saw nothing of
recent vintage. The old reports whetted my enthusiasm, like this one
from A.D. 950 by Istakhri:

> *They are got in certain rocks among the mountains*
> *and in the search for them the people dig great caves*

*1872 map of the country of the Upper Oxus (Amu Darya)
showing the lapis (azur) and ruby mines*

underground, just as is done by the miners for silver. There
is but one special mountain that produces them, and it is
called Syghinan.

Others who mentioned the mines included Ephinstone in 1815,
Colonel Alexander in 1826; Captain John Woods in 1841, and Danish
explorer Ollie Olufsen in 1896.

That was enough evidence for me! By 1993 it was time for an
expedition to look for the lost mines. Khudai Nazar Akbari, my friend
and guide, and I planned a six-week trip for July and August. We planned
to cross over into Afghanistan through Dorah Pass north of Chitral,
continue due north to Ishkashim, and then follow the Amu Darya (the

Oxus) River to the spinel mine at Kuh-i-Lal. We found extraordinary
… but wait, I'm getting ahead of my story.

Khudai was born in 1960 in Parandeh Valley, one of the side
arteries branching off the main Panjsher Valley. The eldest brother of
six brothers and three sisters, he moved with his family to Kabul in
1977. In Kabul, UNICEF had hired him for two years, from 1978 to
1980. After the Soviets invaded Kabul in December, 1979, he had
returned to join the Mujahideen resistance movement for four years.
Afterwards he moved his family to Peshawar and started working for
the Norwegian Committee as a field translator and administrative officer.
For eight years he had been escorting people in and out of Afghanistan.

Khudai was waiting for me at Green's Hotel. Immediately we
began to gather the necessities for the trip. We would take nothing extra
because we would have to carry everything over the high mountain
passes. When we reached the Chitral Mountain Inn, Haider and Prince
Shuja both informed me that we were not going to be allowed to enter
Afghanistan the way we had planned. The Chitrali Scout who visited
us at Shuja's hotel went so far as to record my name in case I attempted
the trip without permission. The next day I returned to Peshawar. I

Looking towards Afghanistan through the Khyber Pass from Pakistan

already possessed a legal visa for Afghanistan, and Khudai did not require one; however, Pakistan officials usually refuse visitors egress from that area into Afghanistan. The only *official* entrance into Afghanistan from the Northwest Frontier province of Pakistan was through the Khyber Pass.

It took ten days to get permission to travel 174 miles through the Khyber Pass and on to Kabul. I had to get letters from the Peshawar Special Branch of Police and a visa from the Afghan Consul, who required letters of recommendation from an American-sponsored organization with offices in Peshawar. Bureaucracy! I went immediately to Nancy Dupree's office at the Afghan Resuorce Information Centre. With her help, it only took five more days to get my visa.

Khudai was at the Flying Coach bus stop waiting for me. He stood amid the brightly-colored buses and vans whose drivers were hustling and hawking all potential passengers to choose their vehicle. We transferred our bags and our bodies into a Volkswagen minibus for the dusty, dry ten-hour sojourn to Kabul. The temperature had reached 100 degrees when we left Peshawar. Appropriate to the conditions, we passed several camel trains swaying toward Peshawar carrying supplies.

After a fifteen-minute stop at the Torkham border of Pakistan to get my exit visa, we picked up our heavy bags and carried them through the border gate between Pakistan and Afghanistan. Once we had crossed, Khudai negotiated with a ragged man in his '30s to put our bags on his homemade wheelbarrow and take us to the Afghan visa building. Upon arrival I handed my passport and Afghan visa to the uniformed guard. He stamped my visa page and wished us a good journey. So far, so good.

Khudai left me to watch the bags while he walked up to speak with the drivers lining the road. They were all sitting in their ever-present two- to thee-year-old Toyota four-by-fours. He negotiated a fare for us to do the first leg of our trip in the back of a pickup to Jalalabad. The temperature was in the high '90s Fahrenheit as we crossed the barren desert land, and the hot breeze sucked the moisture out of us. Travel was slow because the Mujahideen and Soviets had nearly destroyed the paved road with their bombs and land mines. Negotiating around a bomb crater every hundred yards or so ate up the hours.

Kabul

Once in Jalalabad we transferred our bags to a minibus for the 90-mile ride to Kabul. The badly damaged road was not the only major problem on this leg of the trip. Between Jalalabad and Kabul we were stopped five times by armed bandits! These young soldiers of fortune, mostly members of the forces of Massoud's enemy, the Hesb-i-Islami (Hekmatyar) group, pointed AK-47s at us and demanded money. In each case it took our driver five to ten tense minutes to negotiate a price. I was very concerned for Khudai. His Tajik facial features might have made him a target for the longtime enemies of the Pashtun Hesb-i-Islami's. Fortunately, no one singled him out. In addition to robberies, I had heard many stories of kidnappings and shootings along this road since 1982.

We had a letter of permission to stay in the Norwegian Committee's home in Kabul. They had been funding and building schools in Afghanistan. Now tired and dirty, we were looking forward to clean accommodations. We hired a taxi and gave the driver directions to the Norwegian Committee house. As we approached, we could see over the high fence that the large white cement building showed many scars from rocket attacks. Only a third of the windows remained in their frames, the rest having been blown out.

Khudai knocked on the wooden gate and we waited. After recognizing Khudai through a crack in the wood, a less than five foot, very skinny man with thinning gray hair opened the door. He hugged Khudai, shook my hand, and said, "Welcome." Then he picked up two of our bags and headed for the front door.

There were at least ten very large rooms in this two-story house. The man's family of 15 had spread out to occupy all the space. They served us tea and a late lunch during which they vacated two of the rooms for us. The women wore bright-colored Western clothing and did not cover their heads inside the house. Three of the daughters, who taught school, spoke English fairly well. They had never been north, so they had no advice for us; however, they told us about Kabul and the problems the war had brought. Late in the day we tried to contact Dehzad, my friend from the Ministry of Mines, or his brother-in law at his shop in Kabul. To my disappointment, his brother-in-law informed me that Dehzad had left for Iran one week before my arrival. Once again, like ships in the night…

The next morning, we had to go to three different bus stops before locating transport to the southern part of Panjsher Valley. Some four hours later, our pockmarked old bus punctuated with bullet holes delivered us to Rokha. When we disembarked, however, we noticed an eerie paucity of people and nothing that looked like machine or animal transportation.

Khudai left me resting on my patu beside a stream while he went off to locate a ride for us to Khenj, a mining village farther north in Panjsher Valley. Before long two herdsmen in their '30s walked up to within 15 feet of me. They nodded and said, "*Salaam.*" I answered, "*Salaam Alaikum.*" Without more ado, one of them reached for the first of four goats they had been leading on a rope. He picked it up and flipped it down on the grass with its head facing Mecca. Then swiftly, with a large knife, he cut deeply across the goat's throat as it attempted to break free and held it tightly until there was no life left in its body. He followed the same procedure with the remaining three. Apparently, he used this spot every day to butcher goats for his shop. I always say that Afghan food is *food without the mystery* because before you eat it, you see the animal killed and the meat barbecued. I had heard many stories of how Afghans had treated enemies in the same manner. At least for this man, a blood bath was just a part of daily life. I hoped this was not an omen of things to come. My grim thoughts were lightened by Khudai's appearance, but he said, "I cannot locate transportation."

After thinking for a long minute, I decided to start walking towards Khenj. Khudai would stay behind, and if someone came with transportation he would catch up with me. Otherwise, I would reach Khenj late at night and return with transportation early in the morning for him.

I had gone about two miles when I spotted a helicopter in the trees near a stream. Whose was that? Massoud's? I approached across the open unplowed field toward a guard with an AK-47. I waved and smiled broadly before going closer to him. When he smiled back, I thought it was safe to move within five feet of him before pointing at the helicopter and asking, "Massoud?"

The guard shook his head as if to say, "No."

"Speak English?" I asked the guard.

The puzzled look on his face told me he did not.

Then I pointed to the helicopter again, saying, "Commander Massoud?"

Once more he shook his head.

I handed him a business card from my pocket and said, "For Commander." Then he nodded his head up and down and smiled as I turned and walked back to the road. I had walked almost another mile when I heard a car horn. Maybe it was Khudai.

The horn beeped louder as it approached. Beep! Beep! Beep! The driver kept insisting until he was within ten feet of me. I stepped off the road to let the old black Soviet car pass, but when the driver drew within five feet of me, he stopped. Then he motioned for me to get in. I didn't recognize this man, but it beat walking!

Immediately the driver swung the car off the single lane dirt road onto the field and proceeded in the opposite direction. He turned to me, smiled, and pointed ahead, "Massoud," he said. I was doubtful. What would Massoud be doing here? We drove for approximately a quarter of a mile then turned off the road between two bombed-out brown mud homes. He stopped the car and motioned for me to get out. Leading me to a wooden door, one of very few left on any of the houses, he pushed it open and gestured to enter. Inside, a young man seated on an old Afghan carpet stood up quickly and said "*Salaam. Chai* (Tea)?"

"Yes, *tashakoor* (Thank you)," I accepted.

The man left me sitting unattended in the room for almost 15 minutes. He most likely had gone to boil the water. The room was totally unfurnished except for one carpet and a broken-down old lamp table that looked as if it had been repaired several times.

When he returned, he bore with him tea, nuts, and hard candy. I was halfway finished with the tea when the door opened and Massoud entered, smiling! He looked very tired. I stood up to greet him, and he gave my hand a strong shake. After motioning for me to sit down, he sat next to me. We were alone. I knew he did not speak English, but evidently he understood a fair amount. Adding gestures and my meager Dari, I told him we were on our way to Khenj and that I had left Khudai down the road with our bags. Then I told him that we planned to look for gems in Badakhshan along the Amu Darya. Massoud seemed excited about that prospect and thanked me for the symposiums and the field surveys I had already done. "Please continue. Your work has been important to me and to my people. We are coming closer to our dreams every day, thanks be to Allah." He looked directly into my eyes, and my instincts told me he meant it. I felt very good about receiving his nod of approval for this trip and his thanks for my prior efforts. Sometimes that's all it takes. And here he was, the Defense Minister of the country, out being a field commander instead of just playing the political games in Kabul. He always preferred to be on the front rather than far from his troops. Perhaps that is why he had become the most powerful leader in the country.

Massoud then walked to the door and called outside to his driver. Three minutes later the driver appeared with a knotted rag. When Massoud untied it, his gem samples spilled onto the carpet. Although there were many stones, I was very disappointed at the poor quality. Yet somehow, this comforted me. This man was not taking the best for himself, even though he could have. He shrugged, smiling when I told him his samples were of low quality.

Massoud asked, "*Parlez-vous Francais?*" But I do not, so we continued our cobbled-together conversation about his crystals for another 15 minutes.

Massoud looked at his watch and motioned that he needed to leave in the helicopter. Then he asked, in a version of English, "What do you need?"

"Nothing," I replied.

"I will have a car take you to Khenj."

"*Tashakoor*," I thanked him in Dari.

He wrote me a short note to carry with me in case we needed assistance, shook my hand, and walked out the door as quickly as he had walked in.

The young man returned. He courteously motioned for me to finish my tea. Five minutes later, I heard a car drive up. I walked outside and stepped into my tennis shoes that I had left by the door, as is the custom in this part of the world. Then with hand signals I related to the driver that I needed to pick up Khudai and our bags. He started the engine. As the car approached Khudai, he jumped up from his relaxed position. He was astonished when I got out.

"Where did you find the car?" he asked.

"Oh, as my guide could not provide transportation, I went to the top man," I kidded him.

"Who was that?"

"Massoud, of course," I answered casually.

"You saw Massoud?" he asked, clearly not believing me.

"I had tea with him," I added, "I told him that I had this lazy guide who could not come up with transportation, so I left him sleeping along the road." I started laughing.

Khudai's eyes opened wide, and then he shook his head and laughed. This Mr. Gary was just teasing him. We packed the car and arrived in the village of Khenj's bazaar in about 50 minutes.

Our good fortune continued. When we arrived, we immediately met Abdul Rahim, an emerald miner and wholesaler, from whom I had purchased emeralds. He invited us to his home, and afterward he gave us two buckets of hot water each to dump over our heads as a shower. We slept clean and well that night. The next morning we climbed 4,000 feet to the top of the mountain behind his house to inspect the emerald

Abdul Rahim,
emerald miner

mines. Most of them were simply holes – five feet high by four feet wide – dug into the hard gray shale. The longest tunnel we visited projected about 40 yards straight into the mountain. White tents dotted the rocky slopes. Men stayed up there to mine all week, descending to their villages only on Friday to attend religious services and visit their families.

I entered one mining shaft just as a nearby miner was setting off a charge of dynamite. There was no warning whistle in an effort to clear the area. Talk about an earthquake! I was terrified! No need for a disco here. Rock-and-roll is a mining perk, I thought, and extensive training in mine safety is definitely in order. I recorded video footage of the dynamite blasting in the mining area. OSHA would have winced at the danger it posed to the miners. They probably would have shut down such an operation.

We started the trek back down the mountain, slipping continually on the loose shale. Being Afghan and accustomed to running down mountains, Khudai and our host left me behind to meet the challenge at my own pace. By the time I had skittered and slid to the bottom over shale-strewn slopes, Rahim and Khudai had gathered a large pile of apricots. We sat next to a stream enjoying our treat and looking at the emeralds Rahim had gathered during our trip. I could have munched on two dozen apricots by myself, but from past experience I knew that more than six would necessitate Pepto-Bismol. After eating the meat of the fruit, we cracked the pits open with a small rock to savor the almond-like nut inside.

In Parian, at the northernmost end of Panjsher Valley, we planned to find horses to continue our journey; however, since the end of the war with Russia, most horses were pastured in the highlands during late summer. We had to wait three days and pay double to get three horses brought down to us. We also requested a donkey as a pack animal, but we never did lay eyes on that donkey.

Horses were necessary to cross the 14,900-foot Anjuman Pass to reach the so-called *ruby* mines. I suspected that these mines might prove to yield spinel, one of the so-called *great pretender* gems, not rubies.

Two of the most valuable and most famous *rubies*, both of which were thought to have come from these mines, have subsequently been found to be exactly that. One is the 170-carat *Black Prince*, which figures prominently on the front of the Imperial State Crown of Great Britain, perhaps the best known crown in the world. It had been in the Royal Family for many years: In 1415, King Henry the Fifth led an army against the French at Agincourt. For protection, he wore the famous Black Prince Ruby in his helmet. It is impressive, fluorescent and the size of a small egg.

The other is the 352-carat Timur Ruby, named for Timur the Lame. Also known as Tamerlane, it is in the private collection of Her Majesty Queen Elizabeth II. It is even larger than the Black Prince and bears the names of six of its former owners.

We started for Anjuman Pass as the sky was starting to show the faintest morning light. Each time I climb this peak, it seems to get higher, and each time I reassure myself that this will be my last. Khudai and I felt weak and out-of-breath as we neared the top. The weather was pleasant but slightly windy and cool. By four p.m. we had achieved the highest point on the pass and were ready to negotiate the steep backside switchbacks toward the first village.

A narrow trail leads down the mountain and around three lakes teeming with King Zahir Shah trout. Stopping by a lakeside chakhana, we feasted on an afternoon snack of fresh-caught fried fish, which definitely compensated for the hard -scrabble climb and readied us once more for the road.

I have always been fascinated by the village named Anjuman. I cannot help wondering if Alexander the Great would notice any changes since he walked this same path in 334 B.C. From horseback, I could almost touch the homes on either side of the path. I was tempted to search their walls for graffiti in Greek. They could

The children of Anjuman Village

be entered by way of crudely carved old double-wood doors that served both people and animals, for that is how people lived then... and how some still live today.

At the *chai-khana* an hour later, Khudai and I were so tired that we ignored the rice, chicken, and tea laid out on the floor on a cloth, Afghan style. We stretched back from the oilcloth and fell fast asleep. The next morning, I took an exhilarating dip in the stream to wash my body and my clothes at the same time. The next quarter of an hour I spent cutting away the dead skin on my feet and placing moleskin over my blisters and missing toenails.

Thankfully, the trail flattened out for miles, and the iron-rich red clay on the mountains contrasted with the brilliant young green-colored wheat growing on either side of us.

By late afternoon we had reached the Eskazer junction. As we reached the bridge crossing the wide, sky-blue snowmelt rushing downhill, we saw about 20 people near the *chai-khana*. We dismounted and proceeded to walk our horses across the bridge. A tall man approached us wearing a clean *shalwar-kamese* and a hunting coat with pockets for ammunition. He introduced himself as a Jamiat-i-Islami commander. I took the note Massoud gave me from my pocket and handed it to him.

He then had a five-minute discussion with Khudai. Khudai turned to me, "There are problems on the trail ahead. Let's order some lunch while I explain them to you." We sat down on the porch of the first building, ordering fish and rice to be served with nan and tea.

"Well, let's have the story," I said.

"Bad news." He shook his head. "Communist troops have gathered at a full day's ride from here. They are killing travelers for their horses and supplies. The commander recommends that we turn back or take the northern trail to go around the bandits."

Very disappointed, I asked, "How long will it take us to go around that area?"

"The commander does not know."

"It's getting late now," I said. "Let's stay the night here and talk to other travelers. We can make a decision in the morning."

Khudai nodded in agreement.

Walking towards the *chai-khana*, we heard the call to prayer, *Allah Akbar, Allah Akbar (God is Great, God is Great)*. Fifteen men in the area joined together as we watched. They spread their prayer carpets and bowed to Mecca, an act they repeat five times every day.

That evening we were joined by other travelers. Four groups had come from Pakstan and two from Farkhar; however, none of them had traveled from the Ishkashim area, where we wanted to go. The next morning brought no further word, and the commander had already gone. Over eggs, nan, and tea, Khudai and I decided on the prudent course – we would go north to skirt the problem. Of course this meant no Kuh-i-Lal this year, but we would visit the lapis mines.

I had packed up and started across the bridge when Khudai came up to me and said, "Am I to be your guide?"

"Yes, that was the agreement," I said.

"I want you to know something," Khudai said. "I have never been in this direction."

I looked at him. "Well, Khudai, I have some news for you. I had no idea we'd be traveling in this area either, so I have no maps."

Nevertheless, three days later we arrived at the Sar-e-Sang lapis mines. We were exhausted from the long, hard, nerve-wracking trip. The horsemen had been hassling us about altering our destination as an excuse for wanting to cut the trip short – on full pay, of course. Finally, we settled with them to spend two days at the lapis mines and then to go on to Jurm where they could return to their home in Panjsher. From there, Khudai and I would depart for Kabul via Faisabad, Taloqan, and the 11,031-foot Salang Pass.

We had traveled to Sar-e-Sang to see top quality lapis – a rich royal blue with or without a sprinkling of gold-colored iron pyrite, or fool's gold, included in rock. Sometimes lapis in light blues and greens is found in veins running through a calcite host. Theory has it that the rocks at Sar-e-Sang flowed together with other fluids in the presence of intense volcanic heat and a high concentration of sulfur at a critical stage. Then finally, the lapis-bearing rock froze in the mountain caves.

The narrow trail to the Sar-e-Sang lapis lazuli mines was steep with many loose rocks on the path. Inside we saw that the tunnels were still black from where ancient miners had built fires of dried brush to

*Lapis mule train from Sar-e-Sang headed for lapis
market in Pakistan by way of Dorah Pass and Chitral*

heat the walls. Afterward they had pressed snow or poured icy water
into the cracks next to the blue veins of lapis. The rapid change in
temperature induced the rocks to crack to allow easier extraction of the
lapis. Modern miners use dynamite.

In 1979, the Ministry of Mines and Industry in Afghanistan had
offered to sell me *50 tons* of lapis before the Soviets exported it to the
USSR as payment against arms shipped to Kabul. They had wanted me
to give them a down payment and deposit the balance in a U.S. bank.
That could have been very risky – for them as well as for me. I lacked
the funds, and I had no way to grade the material and get it home safely.

Here at the source, in 1993, the miners were offering me a second
opportunity to purchase lapis rocks at a low price. Waiting for buyers
were stacks of many kilos. Although I found the prices almost
irresistible, I had not made this trip planning to invest in lapis. It had
been spinel I was after. Besides, I did not know when or how I would
return to the USA, and the lapis would have been bulky and heavy to
transport. Finally, I settled on buying more fabulous lapis crystals in

matrix. Here at Sar-e-Sang I purchased five rare opaque lapis crystals to sell at my events in the USA. An array of royal blue and light blue (*Azmani*) dodecahedron lapis crystals prominently displayed alongside iron pyrite crystals had grown in two large (12" x 10") pieces of calcite. Lapis crystals differ from the usual way that the mineral forms in chunks of lapis rock. When I got back to the USA, I sold the best specimen to the Smithsonian! In addition to a tour of the mines high in the mountains, the lapis miners treated us to fine food and even music on an old wind-up Victrola and 78 records from the 30's.

By our second afternoon at the mines the horses had rested, and horsemen pressed us to leave. Khudai and I had refused to pay them in advance, knowing that if we had, they would have long since abandoned us. We finally agreed that if they took us north to Jurm the next day, we would pay them in full and allow them to return home.

What we did not expect when we arrived at the first *chai-khana* was that they would refuse to go any further. After 15 minutes of arguing Khudai and I had had enough strife. We agreed to settle right then; however, when we counted out the money, the older horseman demanded, "You must also pay me for the donkey you ordered in Parian."

"Where is the donkey?" I asked.

*Azmani (light blue) and royal blue colored lapis crystals in calcite
with a sprinkling of iron pyrite crystals (fool's gold)*

"What donkey? We never had a donkey." Khudai-Nazar flared.

The horseman drew himself up. "It is coming," he replied.

"We are not paying for any donkey that we did not have use of," said Khudai indignantly.

Then, from the other side of the teahouse a mullah (religious man) joined our strained conversation. The horseman filled him in on his side of the story. He said we had ordered a donkey and therefore should pay for it. The mullah agreed, displaying a logic that was incomprehensible to me, some local version of the mysterious *Pashtunwali.*

"Why?" I asked.

"Because these people are poor and need the money," replied the mullah.

"This man is attempting to cheat us!" protested Khudai.

"It does not matter. Your foreign friend is rich and should pay," the mullah told Khudai.

"I refuse to be cheated!" I interrupted. Khudai and I were both hot at this intrusion.

"Be gone!" Khudai said to the horseman.

The horseman's eyes flashed rage as he started for Khudai. I jumped up to defend him, thinking, "This is going to turn into a fight."

Khudai yelled at the horseman, "We will throw you into the river!"

Suddenly, the horseman's eyes changed. Now he looked frightened. The mullah, evidently a practical man, turned his head away from us to indicate that he was no longer interested in supporting the horseman.

"Get your horse packed!" Khudai was still shouting, "We will give you the money when you are ready to leave!"

The horseman headed for the door, and I opened my bag to count out Afghanis,

*Haji Inayatullah viewing
92 lb. rough lapis*

bills featuring the face of Daoud, the ruler following King Zahir Shah. Khudai and I approached the two. We handed the older man, who had argued with us, the exact amount we had agreed to pay in Parian. For the younger man, we added a 15-percent tip for being nice. He shook hands and thanked us, while the older man rode off with his head down.

Lacking transportation, we had to stay the night. Even by the fastest route, the return trip would take at least two weeks by a combination of foot, horse, and vehicle.

But luck was with us! At ten in the evening, four travelers with horses showed up and agreed to carry our bags to Jurm, where we could hire a Soviet army truck to deliver us to Faisabad, the capital of Badakhshan. We had obtained transport with only one day's delay. In Faisabad we caught a ride in the truck of an acquaintance of ours from Panjsher.

The green pasturelands were flat and verdant, and the people along the route were Mongolian in features and dress. On the outskirts of the city of Kunduz, several armed men stood blocking the road. One of them approached the passenger side. As our driver continued moving slowly forward, the soldier jabbed his AK-47 through the open window past my chest, pinning me to the seat. He cocked the trigger and yelled, "Halt!" For the next 20 minutes, we negotiated a price for our release. All the while the men kept their guns cocked, but paradoxically, one also offered us tea. Finally they agreed on a price of US$2 and a package of cigarettes. Eight days later, after many benign stops to load and unload sheep, goats, grain, and fruits, we arrived safely at Jabul-Saraj.

We said our good-byes and hired a car to take us into Kabul. Once again, we stayed the night at the Norwegian Committee house, enjoying their good food and hot water. As the sun came up the next morning, we packed our bags and located a bus. In Jalalabad, we piled our gear into the back of a Toyota four-by-four and jumped in for the ride to the Khyber Pass and the Pakistan border. By eight that evening I was back in Room 101 at Green's Hotel.

Even though Khudai and I were disappointed that we had not yet reached our quest, we unearthed other treasures. We were carrying some unbelievable samples of lapis. But more important, my brief contact with Massoud replenished my confidence in him. Perhaps there had been some lawlessness in Kabul when his forces were there. But he was modest, even shy, unlike the swaggering, self-serving opportunists among the other commanders. I am glad I had a chance to confirm my prior instincts, so that I maintained a positive impression of him during the hiatus.

That's the way adventure goes in Afghanistan. Even when you miss the mark, you can win (…or perhaps die.) Nonetheless, fortune gives us gifts that we can't always anticipate.

On parting, Khudai and I promised each other we would make it to the lost mines next year; well, someday. . . . Reaching the ruby mines or spinel mines, whichever they are, had become one of life's challenges for me. For the moment, I would have to go on dreaming of finding Kuh-i-Lal!

A few more bridges to be crossed

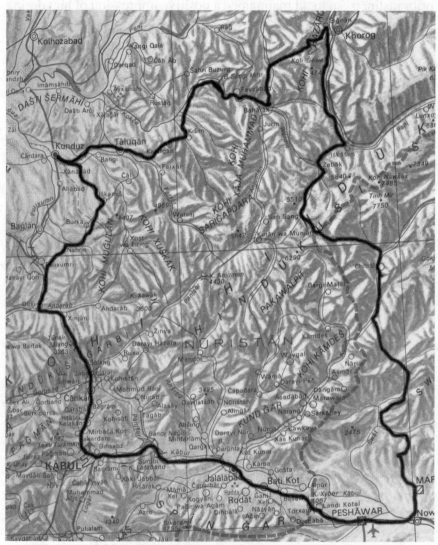

Map of route followed to and from Kuh-i-Lal

Chapter Fourteen
The Lost Mine of Kuh-i-Lal

Summer 1994

There's an old adage that goes like this: It's the journey, not the destination that counts. These words perfectly describe my years of travel in Afghanistan. Six years had passed since I vowed to myself at Dr. Foster's Maryland home to reach the ancient mines of Kuh-i-Lal, The Place of Red Stone. They still beckoned me with all the allure of Xanadu and Shangri-La. I launched myself on a voyage of discovery – and of self-discovery – I was fascinated ! My journeys led me to meet remarkable people in incredible places. Whether I found the mine at Kuh-i-Lal or failed again pales in significance next to the experiences of the quest.

In my obsession, I searched over a hundred libraries and used bookstores in the US, England, and Pakistan for information, but I found few modern references to gems from there. According to Sir Henry Yule, a scholar of Marco Polo's writings, the earliest red spinel recorded had been uncovered in a Buddhist tomb near Kabul in 101 B.C. And as I mentioned earlier, the Timor Ruby and the Black Prince Ruby, now identified as spinels, are suspected to have come from Kuh-i-Lal. Khublai Khan was reported to have paid as much as 170,000 ting for rubies the size of pigeons' eggs from this mining area, located directly northwest of the roof of the world. Other than a few tidbits like these, I gleaned very little from my hours of research.

Rubies, spinels – and even garnets – share a range of pink to violet to red hues. Therefore, it is understandable that before scientists could analyze them chemically, people might have thought they were the same material. Now we know they are not. Rubies are red-to-fuchsia corundum, crystals of aluminum oxide with a trace of chromium, which makes them glow like coals. Spinels are crystals of magnesium aluminum oxide. Although rubies are the rarest and often the most expensive of the four great gemstones, spinels have many virtues to extol. They are usually much less included than rubies; at 8 on the Mohs scale, they are hard, and they present a wide variety of colors,

1841 map constructed from Moorcraft & Trebeck's surveys

including deep luscious highly-saturated reds. So the people of Badakshan would benefit greatly from a spinel mine, especially if I could help them develop their knowledge and markets. I wanted to find that mine, not for fame or glory, but because I knew I could do it better than anyone else. Not many Soviet geographers would be coming this way, and it might be years before anyone else felt comfortable enough in these environs to follow the trail. I had a chance to rediscover the ancient mine and confirm that it contained spinel not rubies. I was the right man at the right time, and this challenge belonged to me.

On a hot summer day in 1994, I checked into Room 101 at Green's Hotel in Peshawar and called Khudai's uncle to leave a message. Then I contacted Nancy Dupree to review the current political situation in

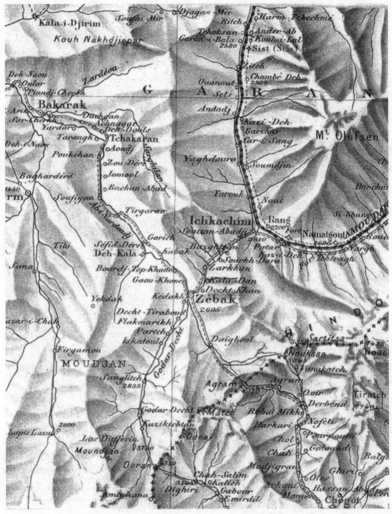

Kuh-i-Lal shown on old map

Afghanistan. During lunch Nancy informed me that Hekmatyar's and Massoud's troops were still fighting each other around Kabul, and the Pakistan government was nervous about its border areas and war supplies. Criminal gangs in Karachi, Pakistan had been purchasing arms such as Stinger missiles from the Afghans. As a result, the borders were tighter than they had been in years, and secrecy was advised. When Khudai came knocking on my door three hours later, he had already secured transport to Garam Chasma and across the border. The good

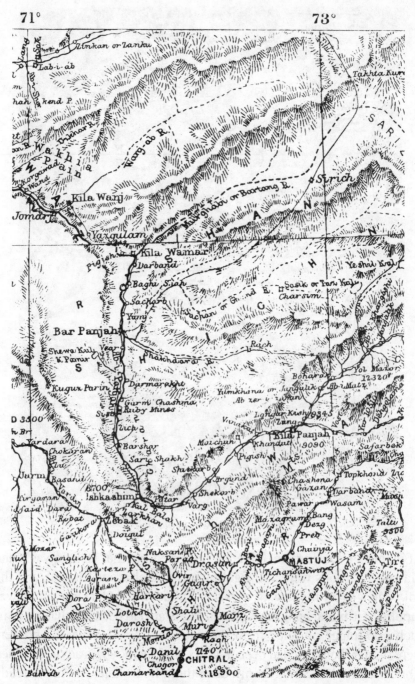

1875 survey map produced from British and Soviet officers (Seat of War in Asia)

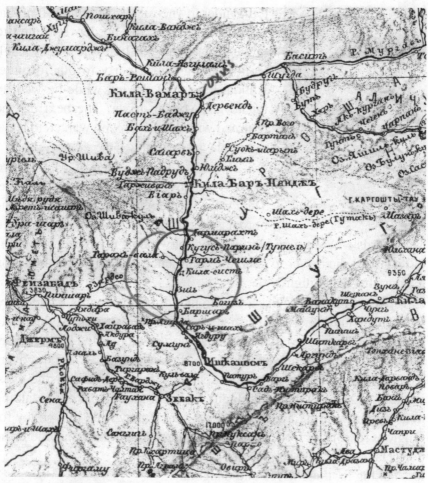

1881 Soviet map showing Kuh-i-Lal

news was that the dirt road now extended into Afghanistan. The bad news was that even if I provided the border guards with my legal visa and money, they were likely to refuse me entry into Afghanistan. Khudai and I agreed to keep our trip a secret and leave in three days.

Two days later, after buying the necessary supplies, Khudai and I began our 13-hour, 190-mile journey to Chitral and the Mountain Inn via the Malakand Pass, Swat, Timargarha, Dir, and 10,500-foot Lawari Pass. Although low by Himalayan standards, Lawari Pass makes up for altitude with 42 drivable switchbacks blocked by snow during the winter months from October to May or June. This time I intentionally did not

Khudai Nazar Akbari

tell Haider, owner of the Mountain Inn, that we meant to cross the border. I wanted to prevent problems for him that might result from making him a party to our intrigue. Khudai left me at the inn while he went to locate the Afghan driver. The next day he returned with the driver who wanted to leave in two days after dark.

I did not like the idea of waiting two days. Too many people in Chitral knew me. They would remember that I had crossed the border several times without being caught. The guards would go on alert if they got wind of my presence. Also I did not trust the driver to keep the confidence. I insisted to Khudai on leaving that same night.

We still had to devise a way to hide from the guards. I had heard from Guy Clutterbuck, a British gem merchant, that some Afghans had smuggled men wanted by Pakistan authorities across the border under burkas, traditional dress of Moslem Afghan women. A burka covers from head to toe allowing only a small mesh screen over the eyes. Pashtun, Pakistani, and Chitrali guards honor the custom of not talking to a woman wearing a burka. I'm not sure if they keep this policy for religious reasons or for fear of the violent response of Afghan men who do not take kindly to a stranger looking at, much less talking to, their wives and daughters.

After an hour of brainstorming other practical solutions, Khudai left the hotel in search of a burka. Unfortunately, I am much bigger than most Afghan women. Khudai returned three times to the bazaar to locate larger sizes. Just visualize his pantomime to the shopkeeper, "She's this large – with his arms stretched wide and high – so I need a gigantic burka." Finally, the fourth trip produced a golden-colored burka that fit tightly and was rather fetching.

Burka

Next came footwear to go with my outfit. There appeared to be nothing in my size 11. In desperation I cut open the back of the largest plastic shoes he could find. It was very difficult for me to walk in my new cute plastic shoes. I definitely did not make a fashion statement.

I was to be Khudai's wife for the night. How ridiculous we looked as a couple – this medium-sized man and his towering mate. I said, "When we reach the border, I demand an immediate divorce."

"Not if I want to keep you," answered Khudai with a chuckle. "Only the man can do that by repeating 'I divorce you' three times."

We could hardly pack for laughing. To enhance the effect, the driver offered to bring his children to ride on my lap. I sat in the middle backseat. We counted on the border guards' not asking me to get out of the vehicle. To insure that the driver did not mention our plans to anyone, Khudai accompanied him home to pick up his children. Meanwhile, I wrote a note to Haider telling him that I was leaving the hotel and asking him to please store my goods until my return. We left by dark of night, avoiding the prying eyes in the lobby of the Mountain Inn.

During the war this road was the superhighway of supply routes. Now, the only ones who used it were a few returning Afghan families trying to avoid Kabul and lapis mule trains. Several miles from Garam Chasma the driver stopped the vehicle. I stepped into a moonlit wooded area and slipped into my burka. Then, how willingly each station opened the gate for us! Only three times guards signaled us to stop. After our driver had chatted with them as if they were old friends, he presented them with fruit. Only on one occasion, did he have to give money to a guard.

At one-thirty in the morning with great apprehension we approached the last guard station on the Pakistan side of the border, the post we feared most. Pakistan Army regulars controlled it: there would be no bribery here. They had been refusing passage to everyone except people of Afghan origin. The driver stopped our vehicle two feet from where a tree hung from ropes to form a gate. I slipped down into the seat to reduce the grand appearance of my golden-draped six-foot frame. The driver's young daughter slept deeply on my lap. I hoped that no one would order me to vacate the vehicle as my tight plastic shoes had broken. Through the small round holes in the burka mesh, I could see three armed guards approaching. Each one carried an AK-47. If they discovered my guise, we would have no escape. I began to sweat inside my burka. The guards were examining the car's contents with flashlights.

Finally, one guard said, "Whose woman is this?"

"Mine," Khudai answered.

"Get out," the guard next to Khudai's door ordered. He obeyed, and the guard searched in, around, and under his seat.

"Come with us!" the guard ordered Khudai.

The remaining guards stood next to the truck doors while Khudai disappeared into a tent. It seemed like hours passed. In the silence the child on my lap continued to sleep. I could barely breathe with worry. Finally, Khudai reappeared. As he and his escort approached the vehicle, I heard the guard say in English, "We have been ordered to look for a foreigner coming this way. We are to assist him with his border crossing."

I bit my tongue and said to myself, "Yeah, right..."

Khudai, being very quick of mind, commented smoothly, "We have seen no one else coming this way." Khudai took his seat. Our driver started the engine and slowly pulled away. Khudai told us, "Two officers inside the tent quizzed me in depth about my personal history. They wanted to know my wife's name and where she was from. I told them Fatima from Kabul."

In brilliant moonlight two glaciers gleamed in monumental contrast to the roadway ahead, littered with donkey carcasses and skulls, rocket casings, and wire, indicating a land mine area. The Soviets had knocked out everything that might help the Mujahideen and the hapless beasts that had been carrying food and war material. We remained silent, honoring the dead around us. Fifteen minutes later the driver turned his head and announced, "We are now in Afghanistan!"

"OK!" I said, very loudly, before I remembered the child still sleeping on my lap.

"Remain dressed as you are until we locate horses," said Khudai. "We do not want other people to see you as a ferangi (a foreigner) and cause a problem for the driver on his return."

"You're just trying to keep me as your wife, Khudai." We all laughed so raucously that the children stirred awake, then turned over and went back to sleep.

At the base of the mountain, the driver stopped so he and I could sleep three hours until sunrise. As Khudai departed to fetch our next transport, I transformed myself back to Gem Hunter in my own hiking clothes and tennis shoes. An hour later our transport arrived – three horses and their owners. The horsemen loaded our gear on the horses. Khudai and I climbed on top of the gear for our ride to Zebak.

Although the land was flat, twice Khudai and I rode into rushing water up to our horses' shoulders. We were thankful for the help of some local people who pointed out the safest crossings. Against such swift currents, a misstep and stumble could have precipitated a full-blown disaster. I wanted to take photos of one ford, but staying on the horse was difficult enough in the deep water. I almost leaped straight up off the load as the icy torrent came rushing over the horse's back, but I controlled myself, opting instead to hold on with both hands while attempting to keep my camera dry.

Once across the river, we soon arrived in Zebak. I pulled out a sealed letter from Prince Shuja to his relative, the King of Zebak. I handed it to a prosperous-looking local man standing near the first village house, and he led us to the king's one-story clay compound. Inside stood a large, shuttered single-story house constructed of clay and wood with a separate guesthouse. The whole compound appeared to have weathered the past fifteen hundred years without change.

An English-speaking man escorted Khudai and me to the guesthouse. After we had unpacked, we were treated to a nice lunch and later in the day to a dinner of beef, rice, and fruit. Unfortunately, we ended up giving as much as we received. During the night, we provided the resident fleas a continuous feast. They danced all over us, reveling from head to toe.

Early the next morning we found that the king's translator had arranged for horsemen and horses. Oddly, during our stay we never saw the king; the reason remains unknown. We were served eggs, nan, rice, and fruit before starting for Ishkashim. It was a leisurely ride through fairly flat pasturelands and rocky streambeds.

By Afghan standards, Ishkashim is a large village located on the western bank of the Amu Darya at the threshold of the Wahkhan

Trail along river starting at Ishkashim going past Kuh-i-Lal to Shighnan

Corridor. Ahead of us lay the Pamir Mountains, a formidable barrier, so high it is said "even the birds cannot cross the summit except by foot." After we had located a *chai-khana* for the night, we paid our Zebak horsemen. Here in Ishkashim we planned to rent horses for the rest of our trip north along the Amu Darya River to Kuh-i-Lal. We were disappointed to learn that the inhabitants had not heard of Kuh-i-Lal. In fact, they reported that anyone rarely returned from a trip to the north. Ominous. For three days, Khudai searched for other horses to rent, but the villagers shook their heads. Finally on the fourth day, he met a young man in his '20s who agreed to lease us one horse. His deal was that we would also buy the horse. I had never before heard of having to purchase a horse in order to rent it! Then the owner hit us with another condition. We had to take his elderly father along! When we asked why, the son would not tell. It was either take this one horse and the old man in the bargain and continue our journey or turn back. We made the deal but soon found out the reason he wanted his father out of the house. The elder had a great fondness for smoking poppies.

He was a tall, thin man in his late '60s who had once served in the Afghanistan Army. I immediately liked his big smile, even though it showed many missing teeth. We left with the toothless old soldier: a

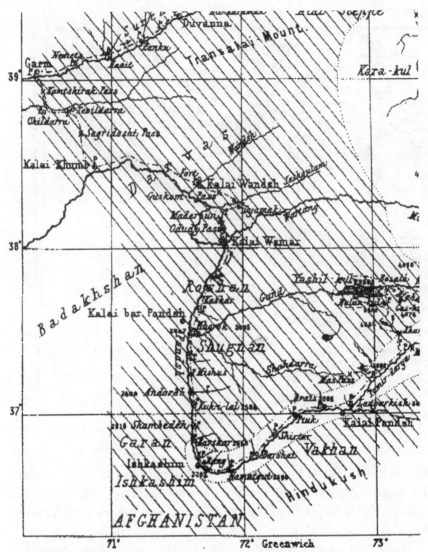

1896 map of the Danish Expedition in the Pamir led by Lt. Ollie Olufsen

party of three with one horse to carry our supplies.

Now we were truly on our own. I had gathered maps and some short stories by a British officer, Captain John Woods and a Danish explorer named Ollie Olufsen, both of whom had traveled here in the 1800s. In my search at the Library of Congress and the British libraries in London, I could locate no information on travelers having visited

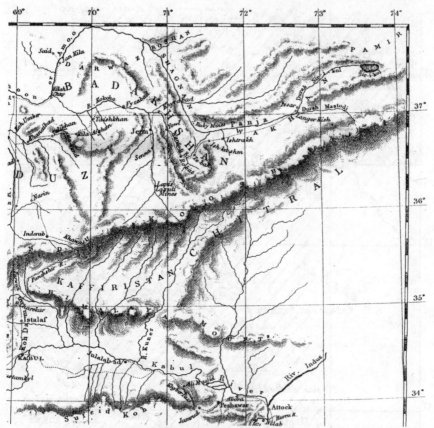

1872 Captain John Woods Expedition

this area in the 1900s. Maps showed the trail simple and fairly straight, yet Olufsen referred to the Devil's Passes One, Two, and Three. We would surely discover what lay ahead while walking the next hundred miles.

For two days we practically strolled on the many flat areas between our climbs over the mountain passes. Smoking poppy seeds made the old soldier alacritous. He could beat any of us up a mountain. By the third day, we were calling him Kaakaa (Uncle) Poppy!

Each evening Kaakaa Poppy and Khudai would walk ahead into a village to ask for food and a place to sleep. Someone always accommodated us. Most nights the village people would join us for dinner or at least for tea after our meal. In this area of Afghanistan the women and children join in with the men in conversation. To my surprise no one expressed interest in my background or in America. The villagers wanted to know about doctors and medicine, information I could not provide. However, I had packed a large supply of balloons which children and grownups alike enjoyed as a novelty. As thank-yous, I took many Polaroid photos. They were popular in every village. To put an end to the photo taking, I had to tell folks that I was out of film.

Giving us food was very generous of these subsistence farmers because every family owns a small plot of land where they grow their food. Rarely is there surplus to sell or to trade.

Our party of pilgrims grew. On our second day from Ishkashim, one farmer suggested that we take his 18-year old son and his horse with us on the rest of our journey. At the end of the trip we would only need to pay what we thought he had been worth. This worked out well, as two days later we passed a village where his uncle lived. There we were able to rent another horse and a donkey. Now, by taking turns, we could each ride for part of each day. Better yet, the young man was very polite, strong, and helpful, especially in mountain crossings where the horses tended to shy and startle.

Eight days had passed since we crossed the border into Afghanistan. Now looking across the Amu Darya River toward the 20,000-foot snow-covered Pamir Mountains was like seeing a Wonder of the World. Onto a lapis sky they imposed massive terraces where small villages seem to have been shelved long ago.

We made a few side trips to search for gems, but most of the time Mother Nature turned us back. At 12,000 feet, the side trails were too steep for climbing, and in many places the path, scarcely half-a-foot wide, skirted a 3,000-to-4,000-foot drop off on the low side of the mountain. Occasionally, the old dirt path had crumbled down the mountainside a thousand feet. Thus, we had to walk slowly, intently keeping our weight on the trailing foot.

With the assistance of local tribesmen we were able to locate three old mine shafts that they said had been operated in the 1950s during King Zahir Shah's reign. They had since been filled in, and garnets were the only crystals of any size we found at the entrances. Many of these garnets were over one inch in diameter, but they were not good enough to cut. Later, however, Dr. Eugene Foord reported seeing very small crystals of spinel, less than one-half millimeter, in the samples that I donated to the U.S. Geological Survey in Denver, Colorado. Therefore, I think that in the future someone may find gem-quality spinels in the area.

Once during our survey, night approached before we could get down the mountain. I decided we should remain at the mine site rather than attempt the perilous path in the dark. But when I told Khudai that I would rather go hungry than have one of us hurt or lost by falling down the remote mountainside, he was upset. We argued for a few minutes before he acceded to my wishes. In spite of burning what little wood we could find, we shivered through the remainder of the night. The next morning the

Gary's foot blisters

villagers were waiting for us at the base of the mountain with a breakfast of eggs, nan, and tea. I've never had a better meal in my life!

As we finished our meal, an elderly man approached us to ask for medicine. He said the baby he was carrying had some disease. Upon inspection it appeared to us that the six-month-old's head was coated with dried blood. We suggested that they wash the child's head. No soap. We suggested that the next time they sell a goat, they save some of the money for soap.

"No! We need that money for poppy," the man answered.

To bolster our drive to find Kuh-i-Lal, and to help us recognize it when we saw it, I reread the commentary by the Danish explorer Ollie Olufsen, who visited the mines in 1898:

"Great numbers of garnets are found in the slate on all mountain slopes in Vakhan (now Wahkhan), Ishkashim and Garan (now Tajikistan). Near the Kisklak of Kuh-i-Lal in Garan are some caves in the rock whence the natives have tried to dig out spinel. They told me that in former times pieces had been found of the size of a hen's egg, but the mines were no longer worked. The caves and the slopes round about them were full of little bits of this mineral, which were examined in Copenhagen. In the caves we found veins of spinel amongst other kinds of stones. . . .The trail is the Devil's Pass one, two and three. The passage along steep paths scarcely half a foot broad, along the border of precipices that go sheer down into the foaming river that roars several yards below. Often there is no other path than the foothold that one may get in the small roughness of the steep precipice of gneiss. Here horse, donkeys, and baggage had to be hoisted with ropes from one terrace to another."

Reading these words, encouraged me to keep going. On the sixth day from Ishkashim we had just finished a long uphill climb when I turned a corner in the trail. There in front of me across the river I saw it – Kuh-i-Lal.

The lost gem mines spanned an area of 100 by 30 yards with the land below scarred by tailings dumped down the mountainside. They lie approximately a thousand feet above the river, which is too rocky and swift for boats and too cold and wide for swimming. At a distance the mine looked just as Olufsen described it. I sat down to gaze at the sight and photograph my long-awaited reality. I was thrilled that this spot on the old Marco Polo map in Dr. Foster's home still existed – and

Ancient ruby/spinel mine named Kuh-i-Lal, which means "mountain of red"

that I had found it. Now, I dared to set a new goal – to dig in these mines. I mused: Would it happen this year? Or would it require as many years as it had already taken for me to reach this spot where I could gaze at the mine from afar? Would I only get to imagine it? Or would I actually get to collect a precious spinel of my own?

As Khudai came up from behind, I stood and pointed across the river.

"Kuh-i-Lal! We made it, Khudai," I said and shook my friend's hand. He nodded and smiled.

I took the Trimble-Scout GPS (Global Positioning System) from the orange pouch fastened on my belt and obtained a reading of 7,700 feet elevation, North 37 degrees, 11 minutes, 05.4 seconds and East 71 degrees, 27 minutes, 18.2 seconds.

"This completes the jigsaw puzzle. We've put all of the pieces together: hints, snippets and guesses mixed with a few facts from all available sources throughout the centuries. And we've found these mines hidden in plain sight here in this rugged, daunting Hindu Kush Range. I wish we could cross the river and go inside the tunnels."

"We will try in a few days at the city of Shighnan," Khudai sagely replied, tempering my desire to leap across the river.

"This is one of the highlights of my life! May we actually walk into the mine one day soon," I exclaimed. For the next 30 minutes we rested, taking many still and video photos with my Hi-8 video camera and my Minolta 700X. We could accomplish nothing else at this spot, so we decided to stop at the next village for the night. At about five p.m. ten villagers with Mongolian features came out to greet us as we approached their houses. According to Dupree's ethnic map (see page 254), they were either of Shughni or Roshani decent.

Wanting to celebrate our accomplishment, Khudai told one of the villagers he wanted to purchase a goat for our dinner. A nice-looking, tall man, probably in his '40s, led us to his home. His teenage sons brought out carpets and pillows for us to sit on. We laid down our packs, took off our tennis shoes, and sat on the carpets under a shade tree. The farmer's sons set a tray of apples and another of grapes in front of us.

Ten minutes later they served hot green tea. That night the whole family of about 15 people joined us for dinner. I passed out balloons to the children and gave them many Polaroid photos of themselves. Everyone was in a celebratory mood. We sat around a lantern and talked about their lives until nearly midnight. Then I leaned back on the pillow and fell sound asleep watching the bright carpet of stars float above me.

At five-thirty the next morning a rooster took his post and crowed. I heard the children talking and playing. Then flies started landing on my face. Still tired, I pulled the blanket over my head and slept for another two-and-a-half hours until Khudai shook me awake saying, "Breakfast is served." As I slowly sat up, I saw a tray of hard-boiled eggs, a pile of nan, and more apples already on the carpet in front of me. Our hosts were just about to serve tea.

Everyone from the night before was present except Kaakaa Poppy. No one at the table had seen him. We took a relaxing hour to eat, letting our breakfast settle and talking about continuing our trip to Shighnan. Then we asked two villagers to locate our travel companion. Twenty minutes later they returned while we were packing the horses and said, "Kaakaa Poppy smoked too much last night! He wants to stay with us today."

This was the third time Kaakaa Poppy had overdone his smoking, so Khudai said to the villager, "Please let him know that we are taking his son's horse on to Shighnan."

I did not want to leave him behind as I had taken a liking to him. However, if we stayed, he would probably start smoking again anyway. Then we would never leave. "Azoo (Let's go!)," I said to Khudai and the farmer's son.

Lucky for us we had eaten a big meal the previous night because we could not find a village to eat dinner in this night. We slept hungry near the trail in a group of trees. I hadn't bathed in five days, and I felt particularly dirty the next morning.

I announced to Khudai, "I'm taking a bath before we leave."

"You are crazy!" he replied. "That is glacier water."

"Sorry, I can't go without a bath any longer," and I followed the fast flowing stream up the mountain about a hundred yards until I located a private place. My clothes were as dirty as I was, so very

Family living along the Amu Darya near Kuh-i-Lal

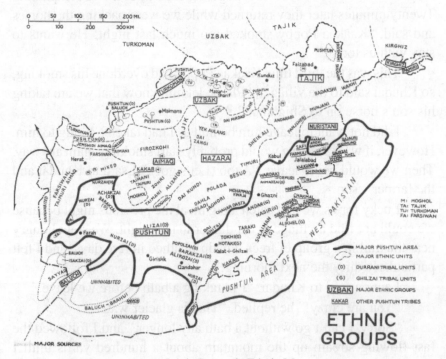

Louis Dupree's Ethnic Map

slowly I inched into the 38-degree freezing water still trying to breathe as the cold blocked my ability to exhale. I soaped my body and clothes at the same time, rinsed and walked back down the mountain soaking wet and blue. I shivered and shook for almost three hours of very cool walking before my clothes finally dried.

As we walked, we shared the apples that the farmer had given us as a going-away present. However, by late afternoon we were famished again. The young farmer's son told us that something edible grew wild in the glacier. We climbed one and found white radishes. Digging up 15, we ate them on the spot. I didn't like them, but hungry as I was, even ice-cold white radishes tasted delicious.

The next night repeated the previous one: no lodging and no food. However, we knew that we would reach the Shighnan area by noon the next day. We were almost too exhausted to eat anyway. The next morning we rose before the sun, ready to go. A long, arduous hike up the mountain lay ahead of us.

By ten, we reached the top and saw farmhouses in the distance. By eleven we hungrily approached the first house. The family invited us in for tea and a

White radishes located in glacier ice

hearty breakfast of eggs, chicken, nan, and apples. We were very grateful to have something in our stomachs, and the family reluctantly accepted our offer to pay for breakfast. Late that afternoon we entered the village of Shighnan. I was in the lead with Khudai and the farmer's son close behind. I immediately noticed that these villagers were not the usual happy people we had been enjoying all along our path. Most stared at us and only a few returned a smile to our "Salaam Alaikum."

Khudai asked several men, "Where is the commander?"

They did not seem to know.

We entered the main bazaar with its eight-foot wide dirt road and wooden shops set wall to wall against each other. From my vantage on horseback, I could almost see over the tops of the shops. Several people moved about in the streets, so we slowed our horses to a walk. Then suddenly, two men stepped into our path to block our way. They spoke to me without smiling. I did not understand them, so I pointed at Khudai. A crowd was already gathering in the street hemming us in. Khudai brought his horse up next to mine.

"You must wait here for the commander," said the man who had blocked my way.

"Where should we wait?" asked Khudai.

"In that shop," he said roughly, as he pointed to a murky shed only five feet from where we sat astride our gear.

We dismounted as directed, tied our horses, and entered the small empty six-by-six-foot windowless shop. There were three cots inside where it appeared people had been sleeping.

"Where is the commander?" Khudai asked the man who had ordered us to wait.

"He will come soon," he barked. "You must wait here!"

The shopkeeper served us tea. As 30 minutes passed, I noticed the young farmer's son had grown extremely jittery. His face was a portrait of naïve anxiety.

I said to Khudai, "The boy is getting nervous. Do you think we can let him take the horse and donkey and return home?"

Khudai agreed, "Let's try!" He stepped outside and talked with the man who had acted like our jailer. Khudai showed him our letters of permission, but they seemed to have no impact. Unfortunately our captor could not read. Neither could anyone else in the bazaar. I could see Khudai hand gesturing and growing exasperated. After five minutes he stepped back inside and said to the young man, "You may leave us and return to your family now."

The boy's expression shifted to a big smile.

"I want to pay for his help, the horse, and the donkey," I told Khudai, "but please stand in the doorway so they can't see me getting money from my bag." I counted out US$40.00 in Afghan money. So many bills made a big stack. After I had replaced my other funds in my bag, I motioned for Khudai to have the young man sit beside me so I could discreetly hand him his pay. Then I motioned him to hide it under his shirt, which he did immediately.

To Khudai I said, "Please ask him to locate Kaakaa Poppy on his return and tell him we're taking care of his horse."

"That is just what I was about to do," said Khudai.

The young man then shook hands with us both and hurried out of the shop door. He roped his uncle's horse and donkey to his own mount and waved goodbye.

The small fly-filled shop felt very warm and uncomfortable when we first entered. Soon it became unbearable, with the shopkeeper and three of us all sitting in the cramped space, swatting the flies that were landing on our faces and arms.

"Khudai," I said, "let's test the situation. Are we under arrest or are we free to roam around?"

"Let me find out," he replied.

Khudai spotted our jailer across the road. Their conversation lasted over 15 minutes during which we witnessed both Khudai and the jailer very upset and animated at times. However, I was used to such discussions with the Afghans; they enjoy heated negotiations.

Finally Khudai walked back to the doorway.

"Here is the story," he said. "Our jailer, or sub-commander, has refused to let us go until we have the approval of his commander. He agreed to move us into their command post down the street by the river. We will have a large room to stay in, and they will feed us. He does not know when his commander will return."

"That's certainly an improvement," I said gratefully.

Then two young men appeared at the door indicating they would help carry our bags. We collected our bags and walked down the street with the sub-commander leading Kaakaa Poppy's skinny horse. The village people gathered to watch us move into our new quarters which I found very agreeable. The men heated water for us to take towel baths, and a friendlier soldier supplied us with a tray of chicken, rice, peas, and tea. He then sat down to talk while we ate.

He explained that he was a commander visiting from Faisabad. He, too, was waiting for the Commander of Shighnan. He further explained that a war was in progress at the border just a few miles ahead between the Tajik Mujahideen and the Soviet Army. The Soviets were there at the invitation of the Communist Tajikistan government. Both parties wanted to control Tajikistan. Each night Tajik Mujahideen from the Afghan side of the border crossed the river on rafts mounted with rocket launchers to attack the Soviets. "Before midnight you will hear the fighting," he warned.

He then told us about the large number of drug dealers in the area. They transport poppies from the local farmers to Tajikistan and Pakistan. Being very poor, most of the villagers take drugs in place of food. The poppy buyers make money while the farmers barely survive.

The bridge between Shighnan and Khorog, Tajikistan had been destroyed; therefore, we would not be able to reach the mine site. But since we were not free to go, it did not matter.

That night the sky popped with fireworks like the Fourth of July in the US. The noise kept us awake until two a.m. It was somewhat comforting to know that the Soviet troops had never yet crossed over to the Afghan side of the border to fight.

The next morning, the sub-commander had no news about our situation and appeared to be in a foul mood. He had no idea how long we would have to stay or whether transportation to Faisabad was available. He had learned that I had taken the houseboy's photo with a Polaroid camera. In a mean voice he demanded that I take one of him, too. After it developed, he held it carefully and left in a hurry.

Ten minutes later, the friendly commander from Faisabad appeared. We suggested that he approach the sub-commander to see if he and Khudai could be allowed to go search out his boss, the illusive commander. We were anxious to get on our way and out of his hair. Three hours later permission was finally granted; together they headed north to find the commander at the war front, Khudai riding Kaakaa Poppy's horse and the Faisabad commander on the borrowed horse of a local man. They stayed away all night. At noon the next day, an elated Khudai returned.

"What happened? Are we free to go?" I pressed him.

Khudai sat down, looking tired. "We were lucky. I knew Commander Basir Khalid. He is a good friend of Massoud's. We are free to go, and the commander gave me a letter for the sub-commander.

He is to find us horses. If the sub-commander cannot locate two more horses for us, he is ordered to give us his own!"

The two of us laughed out loud, and I shook Khudai's hand. He certainly had a talent for getting things accomplished!

Kaakaa Poppy
dancing on the mountain

"You're a good man, Khudai," I said. "Let's leave at daybreak tomorrow." As we were finishing our evening meal, a smiling toothless old face appeared in the room. It was Kaakaa Poppy. We told him of our adventures in Shighnan.

"Bad people here!" he concluded.

At six o'clock the next morning, Kaakaa Poppy showed up with his horse and two others, accompanied by the Faisabad sub-commander. Within 30 minutes, we had packed and left this unfriendly environment without saying good-bye to anyone.

Our energy was soon to be tested. Shebar Pass, over 14,000 feet high, lay directly in front of us. It took Khudai and me until late afternoon to reach the top. The climb was steep, and our horses were good for riding only half the distance. On the mountaintop we discovered that Kaakaa Poppy was back to consuming poppy. Whereas we needed to rest, with bloodshot eyes he began to dance on one leg and sing at the top of his lungs. We lost our breath laughing at the old clown, and I took videos of him in his exclusive *lala poppyland.* Even the camels on the barren slope a hundred yards away stopped grazing to watch Kaakaa Poppy cavort.

By four that afternoon, we were down the backside of the mountain and onto the shores of Lake Shiva, most likely named after the great god, the lord of the beast. Shiva is shown as a phallic symbol, or lingam, many representations of which have been found on Indus culture sites; whereas, the Aryan religion centers on the great deities of the sky and atmosphere, sun, moon, storm, and fire. This was strange to me as we were now in the area where the Aryan race began. According to my GPS, the altitude of the lake is 12,800 feet. Nestled on the very shore

Walking down Shebar Pass to Lake Shiva

of its deep blue crystalline waters was a *chai-khana* where we spent the night after enjoying a delicious dinner of freshly-caught trout.

We spent the next two days wading through streams, hiking, and riding over loose slate, rocks, and rolling hills. Boring except for the poison fly bites.

While I was leading through one valley, poison flies bit me 11 times. The others in our party only suffered a bite or two. I still have the pitted scars from these miniature rattlesnakes with wings. The wounds can take up to six months to heal. The poison eats away the flesh and damages the nerve to the point that there is no pain when medicating with iodine.

Emerging from the Hindu Kush Mountains, we were treated to a spectacular view of orchards and multi-colored poppy fields waving in the slight breeze. It was a spectacular vista well worth the trouble of the climb. Finally we arrived at Barak.

With no vehicles available in Barak, we opted to travel the next 26 miles to Faisabad on horseback. We were so bored and sore that we rode the horses sideways, backwards, and cross-legged, any which way to liven things up and spread the pain around. Just after riding into the Badakhshan capital, Haji, the Norwegian Faisabad Director at the Norwegian Committee house, remembered me from the year before and welcomed me with open arms.

"Stay as long as you want! We have lots of hot water!" he exclaimed using good English.

"Tashakoor! Tashakoor! Tashakoor! Thank you!" Khudai and I replied.

Kaakaa Poppy

Tea was served. Afterward, we recorded Kaakaa Poppy singing. Then he and the Faisabad sub-commander departed. The Commander went to his home in Faisabad, and Kaakaa Poppy began his return journey to Ishkashim. I was sad to see Kaakaa Poppy go. I wondered if I would ever see him again. I would have no way of knowing even if he safely reached home.

Then, Haji gave us the bad news. War was raging in and around Kabul between Massoud and Hekmatyar, and the Pakistan Army had sealed off our planned entry point on the Pakistan northern border at Shasidim. No one was allowed to cross. Only United Nations planes were taking people in and out of Afghanistan.

"Haji, why is the Pakistan Army on the Afghan border?" I asked.

"The U.S. and Pakistan governments have discovered that the Afghan Mujahideen seem to be selling Stinger missiles and other weapons to gangs in Karachi. Also they sold some Stingers to Iran," Haji explained.

"Does this mean that because of U.S. government political pressure, the Pakistan government has closed the border at Chitral?"

"Yes," Haji confirmed, "the border is closed. No one is allowed to enter or exit Pakistan at Dorah Pass."

"That leaves us in a real fix!" I said. "How do we get back into Pakistan?"

"The United Nations is your best bet," said Haji.

"I'm not a government organization," I said.

"Some people from the Swedish Committee will arrive tomorrow. You can inquire about the UN through them."

We spent the next four days weighing our options and trying to figure a way out of our predicament. We made four 20-minute trips to the UN airstrip before we finally got to talk via radio to the UN schedulers located in Islamabad, Pakistan. On the third day they agreed to help me, but two days later word came back that, because I was a private organization, they were not allowed to aid me even though they had room on the next scheduled flight from Faisabad. It was a sad night for Khudai and me!

Now we were down to dire choices. We knew that without proper papers we would not be allowed to enter Iran or Uzbekistan, either of which would be very risky. Even if we climbed over 20,000-foot passes from the Wahkhan Valley into Pakistan or China and managed to survive without winter or mountain gear, we would probably get arrested. And heading for Jalalabad and Pakistan, we would have to cross the front line of the war between Massoud and Hekmatyar's troops near Kabul. What irony that we had rediscovered the lost mines only to realize the precious knowledge might die with us in a civil war. How many of our predecessor explorers had succumbed having had to choose between nature and armed conflict?

On the fifth day, the two of us agreed to make the 360-mile trip to Kabul and study the situation there. At least we knew the route. As in the year before, we were able to locate a Soviet Army truck loaded with goods that was leaving the next morning on its way to Keshem and on to Taloqan. Khudai negotiated our fare. This got us past the worst of the dirt road and riverbed problems. We then went by bus and car from the city of Taloqan to Khanabad.

At Khanabad we heard Massoud's and Hekmatyar's people were fighting each other only 16 miles ahead near Kunduz. After a day in town, we found a minibus driver who agreed to avoid Kunduz by taking us along the back road from Khanabad to Baghlan. Just outside Baghlan we got news of more fighting and changed our route again, going east into the mountains to Nahrin. This way we circumvented the villages of both Baghlan and Pol-e-Khomri. From Nahrin we headed south again, passing through Jabal Saraj and into Kabul.

People on the bus had heard that Hekmatyar had shot a BBC Afghan journalist named Mir Waees in the head at point blank range because he had reported favorably about Massoud. That cold-blooded murder had created such an international outcry among journalists that all warring factions had agreed not to harm or kill reporters. This news hit me hard as I had spent many hours with Mir Waees in Peshawar.

Arriving in Kabul, we again visited the closed Norwegian Committee house. The same caretaker opened the door to us, and after serving tea, he heated well water for our baths. We changed into clean clothes that we had been saving. Just after dinner, rockets began to fall, first with a whistling sound and then a boom. More than eleven thousand people had been reported killed from fighting since the Soviets departed. All the hotels were closed. People were staying in their homes and not going to work.

I asked the caretaker, "How do you live like this?"

"When it hits, it hits!" he said with a philosophical shrug.

I started to reply as another rocket plowed into the house next door.

"When it's near me, it's serious!" I replied, as he scurried from the room.

Khudai left me while he went to check on his family in their Kabul home. He was to get as much information as possible for me to help decide how we might safely return to Peshawar.

At midnight I was leaning out the window watching the fireworks and trying to determine where the hottest fighting was taking place. I heard the whistle of a rocket just before a bright light flashed directly behind me. From my Viet Nam days I knew my life was finished. Then I turned around to see the guard had turned on the flashlight. I released my breath. "Please do not do that behind me again," I said.

He laughed.

Finally, around three in the morning, the rockets stopped, and I slept. At seven a.m. Khudai arrived with his mother, whom I had never met. I still do not know what she looks like as she was fully covered in her burka.

"Let's go!" he said.

"OK with me!" I answered. "But how?"

"Both sides are allowing buses to Peshawar," Khudai said.

"Isn't it dangerous for you to travel in Hekmatyar's area?" I asked.

I was very worried about Khudai because his Tajik facial characteristics, especially his aquiline nose, looked much like Massoud's. Persian and Arabic peoples have Tajik noses, whereas, Pashtuns have more of a Caucasian-looking nose that is slightly rounded at the end. Hekmatyar's people had been out to kill Massoud's people, and Khudai would never pass inspection as a Pashtun. I would be much safer than he would traveling through Pashtun territory.

"Yes, but with you traveling as a foreign journalist and me as your assistant, we have a good story," he said. Before I could respond, he added, "Most soldiers will not bother us with a woman, and I need to get my mother away from Kabul."

How could I deny his taking his mother with him? Obviously she would be much safer in Peshawar – if we made the trip alive. Khudai was a crafty fellow. If he thought this was best for his mother and me, so be it! At the station we boarded a bus to Jalalabad and struggled over people's bags to reach the rear. No one seemed to pay us any attention, but to hide his nose, Khudai kept his face down most of the way.

Upon arrival in Jalalabad we heard that Pakistan had closed the border at Khyber Pass, but we decided to take our chances in a rented four-by-four truck. Our information turned out to be correct. The 15-foot iron border gates were closed.

I walked up to the gate with my passport in hand. "Hello!" I yelled at the border guard standing some 30 yards away. He approached close enough to recognize my American passport. Without speaking, the Pakistani guard opened the gate and allowed the three of us to enter. He pointed to the passport office across the open yard. I started for the office when automatic gunfire – rat-a-tat-tat – rattled the gate. Then eight large trucks crashed through it, their engines whining at high speed and their tires kicking up enough dust to obscure the gate entrance. Kaboom, Kaboom! Acting quickly, we hit the ground as all the border guards, shooting wildly, ran after the invaders. I scrambled to my feet, frantically grabbing my bag, and ran into the passport office, leaving Khudai and his mother outside.

I recognized the man at the desk. He handed me an entry form as another man poured tea. Within five minutes they had cleared me without asking a single question.

Khudai arranged for a taxi, and we zipped through the Khyber Pass and Torkham. Barely an hour later, the front desk manager, Mr. Shuja Uddin, waved us into Green's Hotel, and within minutes more I was once again safely ensconced in Room 101, hardly daring to believe we had made it back to Peshawar alive. Indeed, this successful arrival might have been the perfect ending to my chapter on finding Kuh-i-Lal had that been the conclusion to my adventure.

But my euphoric gem hunter high lasted only three weeks before

I woke up in the US, feverish and weak with my skin and eyes glowing an eerie neon yellow. Hepatitis, of course, from Kabul. I blamed my weakened immune system on the antibiotics I had taken to counteract the fly bites. Although I continued to work my events, I spent most of the days and nights over the next six months feeling exhausted.

About the same time, Dezhad wrote a note with dismaying news:

Letter from Dehzad

September 29, 1994

Dear Mr. Gary:

The bloody fights are continuing in Kabul and we are losing our relatives time after time and we couldn't do anything...just to look at them dying. We don't know when the war will stop.

My son has got the big problem in his life because he could not continue his studying after 2nd class and always I am thinking of this problem and I cannot find any solution except your helping. Mr. Gary according to your humanity that you have, please take my son with yourself for two or three years. He is honest and quiet and I'm sure will not get any problem for you.

Yours Faithfully,

Engineer S. H. Dehzad

Gary's Comments Regarding Dehzad's Letter

I felt very deeply moved at Dehzad's request. Even though he and I had been close, for him to entrust his son's well-being to me, a non-Moslem, spoke both to his friendship for me and his desperation for his family. I come and I go from their troubled scene. The great difference in circumstance is that I can leave whenever I feel worried or threatened, ill or sated; most of the population of that harsh political and economic scene exist in the midst of a struggle almost as old as human history. My loyalty to my Afghan friends makes me regret that I cannot shelter them all.

Although I have continually tried to reach Dehzad through all my contacts, since that letter in 1995, I have not heard from him. I can only hope that he and his son are alive and well somewhere or have gone on to a greater peace.

Notation: Baby's Outcome

We will never know what happened to the baby, but the incident points up a local social problem that links to us on the other side of the world. In this area of Badakhshan, farmland once planted in wheat is now used for growing poppies, which brings substantially more money than a food crop. Meanwhile, food has become scarce. Not only do villagers trade opium but also more and more locals have started using it themselves. By the time children reach their teens, they are already addicted. I have even seen parents blow opium smoke into the faces of crying babies to quiet them and ease their hunger pangs. It strikes me as contradictory and counterproductive that devout Moslems, who eschew alcohol, seem to condone using this powerful narcotic. Afghanistan is the world's number one producer of opium having surpassed Burma in production. They produce 75% of the world's supply. Europe and the US are the biggest markets for their product. We are all joined together in this unsavory business, and the solution will require something from all of us.

The Rise of the Taliban, "Seekers after Truth"

CIA Director William Casey visited Pakistan in 1984 to review firsthand the logistics and systems to train Afghans set up by the Inter Service Intelligence (ISI), the Pakistani counterpart to the CIA. In 1985 the American military aide budget for the Afghanistan situation is said to have doubled. (Saudi Arabia matched US aid dollar for dollar, and rumor has it that Pakistan did not even have to account for the US money.) At that point the world situation pivoted on the tension of the US versus Russia, superpower versus superpower. The US position of backing Pakistan certainly worried me and my friends, and I imagine, many other Mujahideen, but the US considered Afghanistan strategic to obtain oil and natural gas and to counterbalance China's looming presence.

Hekmatyar was slated to turn over his large collection of weapons and ammunition to Ahmed Shah Massoud and President Rabani in Kabul in May 1991, when Massoud and Rabani took control of the capital city at the time of the Soviet pullout from Afghanistan. However, Hekmatyar, backed by Pakistan, continued to battle Massoud for Kabul until Pakistan switched to the Taliban, who defeated Hekmatyar in battle.

Taliban means *Seekers after truth*. The truth seems to be that they are supported by powers more worldly than the mullahs. They emerged in early 1994 from the Sunni religious schools, *madrassat*, near Quetta, Pakistan. Their name derives from the Arabic word for *student*. Originally a small band of warriors from the majority Pashtun tribe, they swelled in numbers as they met with increasing success. Citizens of the southern Afghan city of Kandahar welcomed the Taliban takeover in April 1994. They quickly established order in Kandahar, disarming all factions and the general population. Amir ul-Momineen, Mohammed Omar, a mullah from Kandahar and a former Mujahideen became the Taliban leader of the faithful.

Osama bin Laden

Osama bin Laden, also known as *Sheik Osama bin Laden, the Prince, the Emir,* and *Abu Abdallab,* operates one of the larger training camps in Eastern Afghanistan. Rumors started flying in 1996 in Peshawar of his recruiters enticing young boys of both Afghanistan and Pakistani origin with promises of a bright future to join the Taliban battle for total control of Afghanistan. Fearful tales abounded about soldiers abducting boys from their families and forcing them to fight in battles for Jalalabad and Kabul. The Taliban still command training camps in Afghanistan and Northern Pakistan, many originally sponsored by Pakistan and Saudi Arabia and backed by America.

To discover what sort of history might inspire the tactics bin Laden has employed, political students may want to consider what sharp contrast exists between the biographies of the two leaders of the Afghan game—the Sheik and Ahmed Shah Massoud. It is also fascinating to note the convoluted role the US has played in the fortunes of both.

Bin Laden was born in Jeddah, Saudi Arabia, the only son of his Syrian mother married to his Arabian father, who had 53 children by other wives. As a construction magnate, his father, Mohammed bin Laden, maintained close ties with the Saudi monarchy.

His son, growing to be 6'1" tall, graduated as a civil engineer and business student from Jiddah's King Abdul-Aziz University and married in his early '20s. As a Moslem fundamentalist, he began in the 1980s organizing Arab fighters in Pakistan and Afghanistan. Word in Peshawar was that his projects were sponsored and funded by the CIA. One of these projects was to build an arms storage depot at Khowst, Afghanistan, which was to become a major Mujahideen base.

In 1987 he and his men faced near-impossible odds in the southern Afghanistan province of Paktia. Despite being outnumbered and poorly armed, they defeated the Soviet units. He is said to still proudly show off an assault rifle taken from a dead Soviet general after that battle, the very AK-47 he totes for television interviews. Since returning home to Saudi Arabia a war hero, he is said to have sold over two hundred fifty thousand audiotapes on his beliefs.

Later, he and the CIA representatives argued over the siege of Jalalabad, Afghanistan. Rumors in Peshawar held that the CIA had arranged for bin Laden to die during the fighting.

As a strict learned Moslem, bin Laden did not want "infidel" armies, as he referred to the Americans, in his homeland. He presented Prince Sultan, the Saudi Defense Minister, with a letter proposing how bin Laden and his colleagues could train Saudis to defend themselves and how they might employ equipment from his family's large construction firm to dig trenches on the border with Iraq to lay sand traps against potential invaders.

Instead, the Saudi leadership turned to the United States to protect its vast oil reserves. When bin Laden continued criticizing the government's close alliance with Washington, the Saudi government, which feared his militant brand of Islam, stripped him of his citizenship.

Upset at that affront, the 44-year-old militant joined forces with fundamentalist Hassan Turabi, in Khartoum, Sudan. Responding to that alliance, in 1992 Saudi Arabia froze bin Laden's bank accounts and his $350 million share of his family's multi-billion-dollar empire. He also lost about $150 million in investments when he was forced to leave Sudan in 1996.

Three years later the US government accused bin Laden's veterans of joining the fighting in Somalia, where many US peacekeepers were killed. As a result, under pressure from the US and Saudi Arabia, Sudan expelled him. In 1998 he was linked to the US Embassy bombing in Kenya and Tanzania in which 263 people died. In addition, many think he initiated the Khobar bombings in Saudi Arabia in 1996, the Luxor massacres of tourists in 1997, and the bombing of the World Trade Center in New York in 1993. Fighters believed to be in his sphere of influence contribute to the violence in such hotspots such as Chechnya and Kashmir.

Bin Laden is now on America's Most Wanted List. Many fear that he has stockpiles of nuclear devices, fatal disease bacteria, and lethal nerve gas. As a result, grassroots Islamic militants across the world herald him as a hero and tremendously popular Islamic leader, the more so because he has declared his hatred of America and Israel. Will once distinct terrorist groups such as Hizbollah, Hamas, and Islamic Jihad close ranks with bin Laden? Surely the CIA must fear such a coalition.

Bin Laden continues to lead a life with his three wives, a Syrian and two Saudis, and their 15 or so children. They live in cities near his bases in Afghanistan.

U.S. strikes terrorist sites in Afghanistan, Sudan
By Aimal Khan, Frontier Post
Released: 20 Aug 1998

WASHINGTON (AFNS) – In late-night raids on two continents, U.S. military forces simultaneously struck Aug. 20 at the heart of terrorist organizations believed responsible for attacks against U.S. embassies in Africa.

Neither President Clinton who ordered the attacks in Afghanistan and Sudan, nor Department of Defense officials would immediately discuss the nature of the operations.

"To avoid possibly putting U.S. forces at risk," a spokesman said, "we will not comment on or answer questions about the operational aspects of these missions at this time."

"I ordered our armed forces to strike at terrorist-related facilities in Afghanistan and Sudan because of the threat they present to our national security," Clinton said.

"I have said many times that terrorism is one of the greatest dangers we face in this new global era. We saw its twisted mentality at work last week in the Embassy bombings in Nairobi and Dar es Salaam, which took the lives of innocent Americans and Africans and injured thousands more.

"Today, we have struck back."

He said the attack was launched against "one of the most active terrorist bases in the world. It is located in Afghanistan and operated by groups affiliated with Osama bin Laden, a network not sponsored by any state but as dangerous as any we face."

U.S. forces also struck a chemical weapons-related facility in Sudan. "Our target was the terrorists' base of operation and infrastructure," Clinton said.

The president said he ordered the attacks for four reasons:

– "We have convincing evidence these groups played the key role in the Embassy bombings in Kenya and Tanzania.

– " These groups have executed terrorist attacks against Americans in the past.

– "We have compelling information that they were planning additional terrorist attacks against our citizens and others with the inevitable collateral casualties we saw so tragically in Africa.

– "They are seeking to acquire chemical weapons and other dangerous weapons."

The president added, "Terrorists must have no doubt that in the face of their threats, America will protect its citizens and will continue to lead the world's fight for peace, freedom and security."

In a joint press conference, Secretary of Defense William S. Cohen and Chairman of the Joint Chiefs of Staff Gen. Henry H. Shelton said U.S. forces hit terrorist camps at Khowst, Afghanistan, and the Shifa Pharmaceutical Plant in Sudan, suspected of manufacturing chemical weapons.

At Khowst, targets included a base camp, support facility and four training sites. They are 94 miles south of the capital of Kabul near the border with Pakistan.

"The design," Cohen said, "was to take down the structure responsible for training hundreds, if not thousands, of terrorists."

Both Cohen and Shelton said they were not going to discuss operational details of the strikes because they did not want to jeopardize forces in case more strikes were needed later.

They did say that this round of strikes had ended.

Planning for the attacks, they said, had been under way for several days. Cohen said that meetings had taken place "around the clock to reassure ourselves" that the targets were valid.

January 14, 1999
Frontier Post

PESHAWAR – Four hard-core fighters, including two Arabs close to Saudi dissident Osama bin Laden, have been killed in rocket attacks at Qila Murad Beg, north of Kabul. Pro-Taliban Pakistani sources said here Wednesday that four close associates of Osama, namely Abdul Salam from Tanzania, Abu Ahmad Al-Khaleefi, Algeria, and two

Pakistanis hailing from Dir, NWFP, were killed in opposition's rocket attacks in the outskirts of the Afghan capital a few days back.

The incident occurred when the two Arabs made a wireless contact with the opposition Commander Mullah Taj Mohammad and started denouncing the Tajik commander Ahmed Shah Massoud's policies in the Afghan affairs and urged him to join the Taliban's ranks. Mullah Taj Mohammad, a well-known commander of Itehad-i-Islami (Prof. Sayyaf's group) who has spent a lot of time with these Arabs in Afghanistan and Tajikistan, strongly opposed their views.

Prof. Sayyaf is the lone Pukhtoon Jehadi leader who, along with his group, are siding with the anti-Taliban opposition, largely comprising non-Pukhtoon members and currently led by Tajik warlord, Ahmed Shah Massoud. Mullah Taj, infuriated by the two Arabs persuasion, after locating their position, fired a Soviet-made rocket at their position, which hit the target killing the two Arabs along with two Pakistanis.

To play the "Afghanistan Game" in my own way, by trying to contribute to the lives of the Afghan people, I continue to collect books and to follow the news. In the English translation of A History of Afghanistan, printed in the Union of Soviet Socialist Republic by Progress Publishers in 1985, I located the following information:

Reviewing the events of the 7th and 8th centuries in the caliphate, which affected the fate of the peoples that played a significant role in the history of Afghanistan, it must be noted that the mid-7th century saw the beginning of the division of Moslems. * Standing out among them were primarily the supporters of "true Islam" – the Sunset's, adherents of the Sunna (they hold that the caliphate is an elective office), and also the Shiites (Shiah, i.e., "the party of Ali"). The latter recognize the hereditary right to be imam-head of the Moslem community of the caliphate and supreme political leader of the state – only for Ali (Muhammad's cousin and son-in-law) and his descendants. The Shiites had several sects within the framework of both moderate and extreme Shiism, Ismailism being one of them. This sect has survived to the present day; its followers live in a number of Asian countries and also in Afghanistan and Pakistan in its northern regions.

The third sect, the Kharijites (insurgents) who came out against big landowners, and supported the legal and social equality of all Moslems and their dominating position over the Zimmiyas (non-Moslems). In their view, sovereign power was epitomised in the religious community, while the caliph (who had to be elected) should, in his ac, be activities, be responsible to it. An important aspect of their doctrine is that any Moslem, and any ruler for that matter, imam or calip, should he commit a "great sin" was thereafter considered a Kafir or infidel, and opposition to him was God-willed. This maxim often served as ideological ground for overthrowing a ruler, or for a "holy war," but in actual fact for political struggle, rebellions and insurrections. In the territory of Afghanistan this sect was most widespread in Seistan.

Shiism, just like the Kharijite doctrine, was used by the political, and often social, opposition in the struggle against the Umayyads, Abbasids and other Sunnite rulers.

*The Sunnites are subdivided into four main mazkhabs, named after their founders: Hanifite, Shafiite, Hanbalite and Malikite schools. The overwhelming majority of Afghans are Hanifites, who, as distinct from the followers of the other Islamic doctrines, are more tolerant of other religions and ideologies. Apart from religious law, they allow wide application of the usual local law (adat) and laws of the secular authorities. Many nomad tribes (not only Afghan but also Turkic), in which pre-Moslem patriarchal traditions were very tenacious, accepted Hanifite Islam.

Massoud's Letter to America

During the first week of October 1998 Massoud and his staff wrote a letter in response to the Taliban and bin Laden problems. It was addressed to the people of the United States of America and presented to the United States Senate Committee on Foreign Relations.

Haron Amin, Member of the Afghanistan Mission to the United Nations, passed on a copy of the letter to me with permission to show it and publish it. As far as I know, the press ignored letter.

A Message to the People of the United States of America

From Ahmed Shah Massoud

Defense Minister, Islamic State of Afghanistan
Through the United States Senate-Committee on Foreign Relations

Hearing on Events in Afghanistan
October 8, 1998

In the name of God

Mr. Chairman, honorable representatives of the people of the United States of America, I send this message to you today on behalf of the freedom and peace-loving people of Afghanistan, the Mujahideen freedom fighters who resisted and defeated Soviet communism, the men and women who are still resisting oppression and foreign hegemony and, in the name of more than one and half million Afghan martyrs who sacrificed their lives to uphold some of the same values and ideas shared by most Americans and Afghans alike. This is a crucial and unique moment in history of Afghanistan and the world, a time when Afghanistan has crossed yet another threshold and is entering a new stage of struggle and resistance for its survival as a free nation and independent state.

I have spent the past 20 years, most of my youth and adult life, alongside my compatriots, at the service of the Afghan nation, fighting an uphill battle for God and country, sometime alone, at times with the support of the international community. Against all odds, we, meaning the free world and Afghans, halted and checkmated Soviet expansionism a decade ago. But the embattled people of my country did not savor the fruits of victory. Instead they were thrust in a whirlwind of foreign intrigue, deception, great gamesmanship and internal strife. Our country and our noble people were brutalized, the victims of misplaced greed, hegemonic design and ignorance. We Afghans erred too. Our shortcomings were as a result of political innocence, inexperience, vulnerability, victimization, bickering and inflated egos. But by no means does this justify what some of our so-called Cold War allies did to undermine this just victory and unleash their diabolical plans to destroy and subjugate Afghanistan.

Today, the world clearly sees and feels the results of such misguided and evil deeds. South-Central Asia is in turmoil, some countries on the brink of war. Illegal drug production, terrorist activities and planning are on the rise. Ethnic and religiously motivated mass murders and forced displacements are taking place, and the most basic human and women's rights are shamelessly violated. The country has gradually been occupied by fanatics, extremists, terrorists, mercenaries, drug Mafias, and professional murderers. One faction, the Taliban, which by no means rightly represents Islam, Afghanistan to our centuries-old cultural heritage, has with direct foreign assistance exacerbated this explosive situation. They are unyielding and unwilling to talk or reach a compromise with any other Afghan side.

Unfortunately, this dark accomplishment could not have materialized without the direct support and involvement of influential government and non-government circles in Pakistan. Aside from receiving military logistics, fuel and arms from Pakistan, our intelligence reports indicate that more than 28,000 Pakistani citizens, including paramilitary personnel and military advisors are part of the Taliban occupation forces in various parts of Afghanistan. We currently hold more than 500 Pakistani citizens including military personnel in our POW camps. Three major concerns – namely terrorism, drugs and human rights, originate from Taliban-held areas but are instigated from Pakistan, thus forming the inter-connecting angles of an evil triangle. For many Afghans, regardless of ethnicity or religion, Afghanistan, for the second time in one decade, is once again an occupied country.

Let me correct a few fallacies that are propagated by Taliban backers and their lobbies around the world. This situation over the short and long run, even in case of total control by the Taliban, will not be to anyone's interest. It will not result in stability, peace, and prosperity in the region. The people of Afghanistan will not accept such a repressive regime. Regional countries will never feel secure and safe. Resistance will not end in Afghanistan, but will take on a new national dimension, encompassing all Afghan ethnic and social strata.

The goal is clear. Afghans want to regain their right to self-determination through a democratic or traditional mechanism acceptable to our people. No one group, faction or individual has the right to dictate or impose its will by force or proxy on others. But first, the obstacles have to be overcome, the war has to end, just peace established and a transitional administration set up to move us toward a representative government.

We are willing to move toward this noble goal. We consider this as part of our duty to defend humanity against the scourge of intolerance, violence and fanaticism. But the international community and the democracies of the world should not waste any valuable time, and instead play their critical role to assist in any way possible the valiant people of Afghanistan to overcome the obstacles that exist on the path to freedom, peace, stability and prosperity. Effective pressure should be exerted on those countries that stand against the aspirations of the people of Afghanistan. I urge you to engage in constructive and substantive discussions with our representatives and all Afghans who can and want to be part of a broad consensus for the peace and freedom for Afghanistan.

With all due respect and my best wishes for the government and people of the United States,

Ahmed Shah Massoud

Kabul

Billboard entrance to Kabul, 1994

Chapter 15
The Rise of the Taliban,
"Seekers After Truth"

1988 – 1996

In August 1996, I was again in Kabul, working with the Afghan Government on plans to conduct a number of major gem explorations during the summer of 1997. In a series of planning meetings held over a two-week period, I met with a select group of government officials ranging from the President of Afghanistan, Burhanuddin Rabani, to Dr. Mohammad Yacoub Lali, the Minister of Mines and Industry, and his staff of geologists.

Between meetings, Khudai Nazar, Mir Waees and I drove to Jabul-Saraj, north of Kabul, to meet with Commander Massoud to brief him on our plans and to secure his approval and assistance. Massoud, who was also the government's Minister of Defense, agreed to our plans and promised us the use of a helicopter the following summer to help

L-R: Gary and President Rabani

L-R: Gary, Dr. Lali , and aide

further our geological explorations in the Panjsher Valley. We all had high hopes that our exploration for gem materials would result in new discoveries and productive finds.

As my trip to Kabul was nearing an end, I was delighted to learn that I had been appointed as a consultant to the Ministry of Mines and Industry. My efforts on behalf of the country were being recognized, and the appointment was gratifying far beyond any measure or prospect of future reward. By the time I left, plans for the following summer had been approved, and we were all in general agreement about our goals and priorities. I could even foresee having my own small office in the bomb-damaged Ministry of Mines from which I could help promote our programs for mining and exploration. But, as is so often the case in Afghanistan, fate was about to intervene.

Leaving Kabul towards the end of the month, I hired a driver to transport me to Peshawar to arrange for the shipment of goods home that I had collected there earlier. I then left for Hawaii, having no way of knowing that it would be two years before I could again return.

At the time I left, Massoud and his army occupied positions in and around Kabul and in the Panjsher Valley with a field headquarters in Jabul-Saraj, just north of Kabul. Massoud had set up and held defensive positions in and around Kabul since 1992 when he liberated the city. From 1992 up through the time I left Kabul, he had maintained these positions to protect the capital from the rockets raining from the south, where Hekmatyar's base was located and from the growing threat of the Taliban, who now controlled Kandahar and much of the country to the south, west, and east of Kabul.

Gary and Commander Massoud

In an attempt to provide some clarity to what happened next, I have included a condensed version of what had happened in the preceding years. As subsequent events began to unfold, it wasn't just me who was affected or even Afghanistan as a whole. It was the entire world.

Keep in mind that given the number of competing ethnic groups in Afghanistan and their widely-varying political views, Afghanistan's political situation has been both complex and convoluted for decades. Alliances have formed and dissolved over the years, and what follows below merely highlights and oversimplifies a very complex and multilayered series of events.

In 1979, the pro-communist, Soviet-controlled government that existed in Kabul was starting to meet strong popular resistance. The Soviets, not wanting to lose a *client state* under their domination, invaded Afghanistan in December 1979. This set off a struggle for liberation by seven separate Mujahideen factions that would last for ten years and result in the devastation of much of the country. News accounts report that over 15,000 Soviet soldiers lost their lives in Afghanistan, and the fighting cost the Soviets billions of dollars. Some accounts report as much as $77 billion. Over one million Afghan civilians lost their lives and more than six million became refugees, mostly in refugee camps across the Afghan border in northwest Pakistan. Over one million Afghans were born and raised in the refugee camps of northwestern Pakistan in the ensuing years.

The Mujahideen (or *freedom fighters)* were initially Afghans of

Appointment of Consultant letter
original and translation

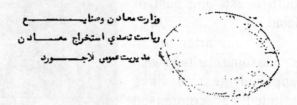

وزارت معادن وصنایـــــــــع
ریاست تصدی استخراج معـــادن
مدیریت عمومی لاجـــورد

GEOVISION INC
MR. GARY W. BOWERSOX
PRESIDENT
P. O. BOX ' 89646
HONOLULU . HI   ' ; 96830
U.S.A

No - 133
Date - 30-05-1375

To whom it may concern

محترم گری باورساکس در مدت اقامت خود در کابل در طی ماه اگست ۱۹۹۶ — سه مرتبـــه
بامتخصصین ورهبری وزارت معادن وصنایع پیرامون نحوه استخراج — صدور و روفـــــروش
احجار قیمتی وسایر معادن افغانستان مذاکراتی انجام داده است • موصوف در خلال ایـــن
مذاکرات اظهار داشتی نمودند که در اینده باکمپنی های مختلف کشورهای خارجی در تمـاس
شده امکانات مساعدت وسرمایه کذاری وکمک های انهار اد رامر استخراج — فروش و بازاریابـی
معادن افغانستان جلب نمایـــــد ؛
چون محترم باورساکس در قسمت فروش وبازاریابی احجار قیمتی مخصوصا• لاجورد وزمرد وزیـــره
تجارب کافی واند وخته لازم دارد • بنا• وزارت معادن وصنایع افغانستان ایشان را مشــاور
اینوزارت معرفی میدارد تاد ر ارتباط موضوعات فوق باکمپنی های ذیعلاقه خارجی — داخلـــی
مفاهمه و مذاکره شده زمینه کمک همکاری واحیانا سرمایه کذاریهای انها رابا درنظرداشـــت
قوانین معادن وسرمایه کذاری در قسمت انکشاف — استخراج — بهره برداری — فـــروش
وبازاریابی معادن افغانستان باالخصوص احجار قیمتی واحجار کریمه معلم وبه اینوزارت حالـی
سازنـــــــــد • با احترام

(انجنیر محمد یعقوب لـمیر)
وزیرمعادن وصنایع

Ministry of Mines and Industries
Department of Minerals extraction
General Directorate of Lapis

No.:. 13
Dated: 30/05/137
8/20/1996

To: Whom It May Concern

Mr. Gary W. Bowersox during his stay in Kabul on the month of
August 1996 met experts and steering committee of Ministry of
Mines and Industries three times relating extraction, export and
sale of Gemstones. During the meetings the above mentioned perso
expressed his interest and promise to contact with different
international companies to find out the possibility of
cooperation and investment and attract their attention to the
sale, extraction and export of Afghanistan's minerals.

As far as Mr. Gary W. Bowersox has experience in the sale and
marketing of Gemstones, particularly Lapis, Emerald and etc.,
therefore, the Ministry of Mines and Industries introduce him as
consultant of this ministry to communicate and discuss the above
mentioned subjects with related national and international
companies. In order to pave the way of cooperation and investmen
on the basis of development, extraction, investment, sale and
marketing of Afghanistan's minerals, specially gemstone and
precious stones in accordance with rule and regulations of this
ministry.

Yours faithfully,

Eng. M. Yaqob
Minister for Mines and Industries

varying ethnic groups and often-competing political factions who took up arms against the Soviets. Hopelessly outnumbered and outgunned by the Soviets, they usually resorted to carrying out guerrilla-style warfare against their common enemy. The various Mujahideen factions were led by their own commanders (or *warlords* as they were generally referred to by Western journalists), and operated more or less autonomously and independently of other factions. In the early days, they relied on contributions of money, food, weapons and other support from other Islamic countries, specifically their neighbors Pakistan and Iran and, to some degree (although indirectly), the CIA.

Unfortunately, but to no one's surprise, serious personality clashes, professional rivalries and political differences among the Mujahideen commanders and their factions soon emerged along the lines of the ethnic and political rivalries that historically existed among the different ethnic groups.

About this time – the early 1980s – Saudi Arabia began providing significant financial support for the Islamic Jihad or *holy war* against the Soviets in Afghanistan. Much of it was funneled through Pakistan. That Islamic call to Jihad led to a growing number of Arab religious fundamentalists from Saudi Arabia and other Arab countries who answered the call and made their way to Afghanistan to receive military training and join in the fighting.

One of these groups produced Osama bin Laden, an enormously wealthy and well-educated Saudi with strong ties both to Saudi Arabia and to his family's origins in Yemen. With huge sums of money at his disposal, bin Laden, a religious zealot, who adhered to an extremist interpretation of Islamic law, eventually built up his own base of operations in southern Afghanistan (al-Qaeda – "the base") and grew militarily strong by inducing growing numbers of Arab and other foreign recruits to join him. In those early days, it was rumored that bin Laden had worked with and received support through the CIA, but as time went on, stories began to circulate around Peshawar that bin Laden believed the CIA had turned on him and set him up to be killed. Thus began his hatred of America.

By the mid-1980s as Mujahideen factions continued their somewhat haphazard resistance against the Soviets, Pakistan, for political reasons of its own, was heavily supporting the Pashtun Mujahideen commander, Gulbuddin Hekmatyar, and his predominantly Pashtun army. Pashtun ties between Pakistan and Afghanistan dated back to 1893, when Britain's Sir Henry Mortimer Durand persuaded the Amir of Afghanistan to accept what would become Afghanistan's eastern border, separating it from what was then British India (and since 1947, Pakistan). This dividing line, which became known as the Durand Line, was drawn by the British with little if any regard for tribal considerations but with the intended effect of splitting long-standing Pashtun tribal lands between the two countries.

By cultivating Hekmatyar's allegiance and creating ties of loyalty to and reliance on Pakistan, the Pakistani Government managed to exercise control over Hekmatyar and thus over the areas of Afghanistan under his control. On the other hand, Ahmed Shah Massoud, who was a Tajik, had no love for the Pakistani government and neither trusted them nor their motives. Nor did he trust Hekmatyar or his motives, and a bitter rivalry ensued between them.

Meanwhile, the CIA was delivering hundreds of millions of dollars in military assistance and funding to the Pakistani Government. Some went towards building up Pakistan's military; some was *diverted* into private hands through their massively corrupt bureaucracy; and some was covertly but intentionally directed to Hekmatyar and other Mujahideen groups in Afghanistan including Hekmatyar's rival, Massoud.

By 1988, major changes in the region, that had actually started somewhat earlier, gave rise to a series of significant events. Early in the year, Russia agreed to withdraw from Afghanistan primarily because the military occupation there had cost them enormous political and economic currency to the point that it was a contributing factor in the eventual breakup of the Soviet Union.

In April, there was a huge explosion at an ammunition dump at Ojhri Camp in Rawalpindi, Pakistan where over ten thousand tons of arms and ammunition were stored. This explosion was believed to have been deliberately set off by unknown agents as a means of covering up corruption. The explosion prevented an audit of arms and munitions that had been illegally siphoned off and were no longer there.

Also, during that same year, Massoud was able to obtain Stinger missiles from another Jamiat commander. The CIA had continued to secretly supply many of the Mujahideen commanders since 1985 but not to Massoud. The Stinger, a highly-portable, lightweight, easily-fired surface-to-air missile proved enormously effective in destroying Soviet helicopters, gunships and other aircraft.

Then on August 17, 1988, an American-built C-130 transport belonging to the Pakistani Air Force took off from Bahawalpur in Northern Pakistan carrying thirty-one passengers and crew including the President of Pakistan, Zia ul-Haq; General Akhtar Abdul Rahman, Chairman of Pakistan's Joint Chiefs of Staff; Arnold L. Raphel, U.S. Ambassador to Pakistan; Brigadier General Herbert M. Wassom, the U.S. military attaché; and eight Pakistani generals and their staff. The purpose of the flight was to view a demonstration of a U.S. battle tank, but three-to-five minutes after takeoff, the plane crashed in a fireball killing all on board. The cause of the crash was widely rumored to be sabotage, and the scant details that eventually were released suggested that nerve gas had been released in the cockpit.

For reasons that have never been clearly explained, this regime-changing crash appeared to be rather quickly and intentionally downplayed by the Pakistani and U.S. governments. The American FBI attempted to conduct a full investigation but later complained in the news that they had been prevented from conducting a proper investigation.

Gary and Zia ul-Haq, President of Pakistan

Whether these events were in any way linked or merely coincidences may never be known, but changes in policies among various governments with regard to Afghanistan continued. The United States began a reduction in arms supplies to Pakistan, and the Soviets began their staged withdrawal, which they completed in mid-February, 1989.

As for the uneasy Afghan Alliance that existed among some of the Northern Afghanistan Mujahideen commanders, they had little voice or control over any private agreements, which may or may not have been made. In the wake of the Soviet withdrawal, the old ethnic political rivalries resumed and civil war broke out.

The now-vulnerable Soviet-backed government of Afghanistan's President Najibullah attempted to end the bloodshed by proposing a government of national unity, but the Mujahideen refused. Afghanistan was caught up once again in internecine warfare. When the Soviets withdrew from Kabul, the city was more or less intact, but the fighting subsequently erupted after Hekmatyar launched rockets in an attempt to control Kabul. After 1992, this resulted in hugh damage to the city.

The next three years were filled with political intrigue and violence. Pakistan was becoming disenchanted with Hekmatyar due to his political and military failures and his inability to gain control of Kabul. Instead, the Pakistani Government and the Pakistan Intelligence Service, the ISI, began heavily supporting a group of Afghan Pashtus living in northwestern Pakistan who wanted to return to Afghanistan and seize control of the government. This group called themselves the *Taliban* and was made up primarily of Afghan Pashtun students who had either been born in or lived in the Pakistani refugee camps in the Pashtun tribal areas of northwestern Pakistan. (In years to come, these same tribal areas would provide refuge for Taliban remnants and for al-Qaeda escapees from Afghanistan.)

The Taliban had taken their name from the Arabic word *talib* meaning *religious student* or *seeker of knowledge*. Taliban students were being educated and trained in Islamic religious schools, *madrasahs*, set up in and near the camps under the approving eye of the Pakistani ISI, with major financial support from Saudi Arabia and other foreign backers. Once in control, their objective was to turn the country into a fundamentalist Islamic state and impose an extremely strict, no-nonsense form of Islam with few real freedoms and harsh consequences for anyone foolish enough to ignore or disobey their authority.

In an earlier chapter, I described how Massoud had taken Kabul in 1992. (See *Massoud Takes Kabul* on page 189.) During and immediately after his takeover, a number of Mujahideen factions, including those of Hekmatyar and the Uzbek leader General Rashid Dostum who had formed their own alliance, all converged on Kabul. On reaching the city, fighting broke out among the factions. The fighting lasted off and on for four years, nearly destroyed Kabul, and cost tens of thousands of lost lives.

It was widely reported in the press that in 1992 and 1993, the civilian population suffered terribly from a wave of looting, raping and killing, which began when certain Mujahideen factions staked out different areas of the city. Massoud's army caught most of the blame for this – as did Massoud himself for allowing this to happen. Pakistan and the Pakistani ISI weighed in heavily against Massoud with an information campaign which sought to blame him and his fighters for these atrocities.

There was little evidence to support the charges against Massoud's faction and plenty of evidence to suggest that the atrocities that did take place were grossly over-exaggerated and almost certainly committed by troops loyal to General Dostrum, a Massoud rival, as well as by another Mujahideen faction, the Hesb-i-Wahdat, a Shia group supported by Iran. At one point in the turmoil of that round of fighting, Hekmatyar began indiscriminately shelling the city, and the loss to civilian life numbered well into the thousands.

With Pakistan's support and with no apparent objection from the US, from 1994 to 1996 the rapidly growing Taliban displaced Hekmatyar both militarily and politically. The Taliban army, such as it was, was a fairly ragtag group with little understanding of military tactics. However, their lack of fighting skills was offset by their sheer numbers and, more importantly, from the steady supply of munitions, heavy weapons and air support they continually received from and through Pakistan.

After a series of successful minor battles and skirmishes, the Taliban succeeded in reaching Kandahar in 1994. Kandahar, roughly

300 miles southwest of Kabul, is the capital city of Kandahar Province in the southeastern quadrant of Afghanistan. This was the same area of the country where bin Laden was operating his terrorist training camps. On reaching the capital city, the Taliban's leader, Mullah Omar, a Pashtun and former Mujahid, set up his headquarters in Kandahar where it remained until the US military arrived in 2001. Soon, almost seventy percent of the country was under Taliban control. Some commanders from other factions joined the Taliban willingly; others allowed themselves to be bought with large sums of cash and still others capitulated in battle.

In May 1996, given the Taliban success in taking over much of the country, Massoud and his bitter rival Hekmatyar were forced into an alliance by President Rabani. It would not last long. When the Taliban began moving on Kabul in September 1996, Massoud pulled his soldiers out of the city and took up defensive positions about 10 (and later 60) miles further north to avoid a battle within the city limits. It was a humanitarian decision on his part to spare civilian lives but also to protect his army. Rabani and Hekmatyar's forces had already fled.

At four o'clock on the afternoon of September 26, 1996, the Taliban Army, supported by Pakistani soldiers on *official military leave* and elements from al-Qaeda, moved unopposed into Kabul with an estimated twenty thousand troops. About thirty percent of these were Pakistani students. They continued north to attack Massoud, but he made another of his famous last-minute escapes and pulled his army back towards the Panjsher Valley. Ex-president Najibullah, the former pro-communist puppet president intentionally avoided to flee Kabul and was seized and executed by the Taliban. His body was strung up for all to see, as a warning and reminder of what would happen to anyone who chose to resist the Taliban.

I was distressed when I learned that the Rabani-Massoud government had fallen, and the Taliban now controlled Kabul. My ties and loyalty to Massoud and what came to be known as the Northern Alliance were solid, and I shared their goal for the establishment of a free and democratic Afghanistan. From what I had learned of the Taliban, I felt it was going to be very difficult to work with them. Time proved me right.

Pakistan believed that a Taliban-controlled Afghanistan would be an ally and give its army strategic depth against India and Iran. Despite its tolerance of Taliban policies and practices of growing poppies for production of opium and abusing human rights, including denying education and work for women, the US government continues to support Pakistan.

Gulbuddin Hekmatyar

Born in 1947 in Imam Saheb, Kondoz province. He is a Ghilzay Pushtun of the Kharuti tribe. He attended the faculty of engineering for two years at Kabul University. He became involved in Afghan politics while he was a student. He became a member of the Moslem Youth in 1970. He was imprisoned in 1972-73. After Daud's coup in 1973, he fled to Pakistan where he joined Rabani and Massoud. In 1975, after the failed Islamic coup, he became the leader of the Hesb-i-Islami Afghanistan (the Islamic Party of Afghanistan). He worked as a saboteur against Daud's regime under Bhutto government's directives. After the April coup in 1978, his party became one of the main resistance forces against the Soviet occupation and the communist government. Hekmatyar was the main recipient of the military aid offered by the Western and Moslem countries to the Afghan resistance forces. After the Soviet troop withdrawal, he allied himself with Tanai, a well-known member of the Khalq Party, and staged a failed coup against Najib's government in 1990. After Najib's fall, Hekmatyar and his party were involved in a bitter and destructive civil war against Massoud's forces over control of the Kabul City. In 1995, Hekmatyar was forced by the Taliban to leave his military posts in Char Asiab, southeast of Kabul. In a deal with his archrivals Rabani and Massoud, Hekmatyar became Afghanistan's Prime Minister in May 1996. His troops were overthrown by the Taliban in September 1996.

7th Symposium Activities

Dr. Larry Snee lectures on the geology of Afghanistan using satellite maps to show locations of gem deposits

Alice Keller, editor of Gems & Gemology, gives opening speech at 7th Symposium on Gems & Minerals of Afghanistan

Derrold Holcomb lectures on use of satellite data for gem exploration

Brendan Laurs, sr. editor of Gems & Gemology, lectures on gem field exploration techniques

Dr. Roshan Bhappu lectures on mining extraction techniques

Chapter 16
Political Hurdles and Roadblocks

1997 – 1998

As the political and military standoff between Massoud and the Taliban continued, I spent the late summer and fall of 1997 planning, organizing and confirming the speakers for my next Symposium – to be held in Tucson, Arizona in February 1998. Funding for this Symposium (as well as all of the earlier ones) came entirely from monies I earned at the gem-selling events which I held each year in cities across the United States.

For the 1998 Symposium, I hand-picked and invited a group of American gemologists, geologists and mining experts, along with my friend Derrold Holcomb, an expert in satellite remote-sensing imagery. I felt that the team of experts I assembled might help to narrow or aid in prioritizing the areas of Afghanistan we planned to explore over the coming summer.

The Symposium, titled *7th Symposium on the Gems and Minerals of Afghanistan*, was held as planned in Tucson on February 4-5, 1998 and was deemed a success due equally to the presentations and expertise

L-R: Jamal Khan, Sher Dil Qaderi, Roohullah Bacha, Gary,
Mir Waees Khan, Khudai Nazar Akbar

United States Department of State

Washington, D.C.   20520

November 18, 1997

Mr. Gary Bowersox
President
Geo Vision Inc.
P.O. Box 89646
Honolulu, HI 96830-9646

Dear Mr. Bowersox:

   Thank you for your letter of November 8, 1997, with the enclosure describing your planned seminar. I have passed the material on to the Consular Section at our Embassy in Islamabad, Pakistan, along with my request that your associates be given all due consideration in their applications for visas to enter the United States. Your Afghan associates should contact the Consular Section at the American Embassy ([92] (51) 826161 through 79) at the earliest opportunity to discuss their applications. The Consular Section's fax number is 822632. You should provide them with letters of invitation that describe the nature of their proposed stay in the United States. They should also be prepared to demonstrate to the interviewing Consular Officer proof of their compelling reasons to return to their country of residence, Pakistan or Afghanistan, following their visit to the United States. Please advise me if there are any problems.

   I also want to thank you again for providing us with a copy of your excellent book, Gemstones of Afghanistan. We have enjoyed both the text and the exquisite illustrations.

   We wish your symposium much success.

                                             Sincerely,

                                             Sheldon Rapoport
                                             Afghanistan Affairs

Sheldon Rapoport, Afghanistan Affairs – United States Department of State

of our guest speakers. Dr. Roshan Bhappu, President, Mountain States R & D Inc., Derrold Holcomb, ERDAS, Inc., Alice Keller, Editor *Gems and Gemology* magazine, Brendan Laurs, Senior Editor *Gems and Gemology* magazine, and Dr. Larry Snee, US Geological Survey all made presentations.

The Afghans present included Sher Dil Qaderi from the emerald mines of Panjsher Valley and Syed Roohullah Bacha from the pegmatite fields of Nuristan. Mir Waees Khan and Jamal Khan from Jegdalek had planned to attend, but the U.S. Embassy in Islamabad refused to issue them visas.

Roohullah professed that he could obtain written permission to work in the areas now controlled by the Taliban. My personal view was to continue to work in all areas to support the local village people and provide them with income. This would include Badakhshan, Panjsher,

Dr. Eugene "Gene" Foord, Ph.D.

Dr. Foord was scheduled to be a presenter at my 1998 Symposium, but shortly before it was held, he lost his long and valiant battle against cancer.

Gene was world-known and greatly respected for his work as a geologist-mineralogist at the United States Geological Survey. He received his Ph.D. at Stanford University in 1976 on the gem pegmatites of San Diego County. At the U.S. Geological Survey, he specialized in evaluation of mineral deposits, mineralogy, crystallography, and pegmatite genesis, with additional work in emeralds. During his remarkable career, he contributed to more than 120 publications on geology and mineralogy.

Gene was scheduled to be a featured speaker at this Symposium, and he had wanted very much to visit the pegmatite areas of Nuristan.

He was a good friend and a wonderful colleague. His friendship and wise counsel are sorely missed.

Nuristan and Jegdalek at this time. I had no intentions of signing contracts or assisting the Taliban government.

By the end of the Symposium we had conducted a thorough review of our earlier research and formulated what we believed would be the best possible exploration plan for the coming summer's expedition. Little did we know that enormous bureaucratic obstacles would confront us every step of the way.

We planned to complete our project in Panjsher and then return to Peshawar. A second trip to Nuristan would be followed by a third trip to Jegdalek. Each trip would be with a different local team. In other words, we would work with Sher Dil and Khudai Nazar in Panjsher, Roohullah and Khaliullah Nuristani in Nuristan and Jamal and Mir Waees in Jegdalek. We would all meet together in Peshawar but not in the field, as doing so could present some political problems. Witnessing these different tribal people working together on the advancement of their gem and

*Dr. Larry Snee and
Khaliullah Nuristani*

mineral industry has made me proud since the beginning of our projects; although, many times you would think it was the last game of the World Series the way they ribbed one another.

The plan we developed called for Larry Snee and me to go to Panjsher Valley with Sher Dil Qaderi in early July 1998. We would begin the first ever geological mapping of the emerald deposits. Brendan Laurs, a field geologist and senior editor of *Gems and Gemology,* and I were going in August for two weeks to survey Nuristan with Syed Roohullah Bacha and Commander Habibullah. During the month of March, I received a letter sent to me from Habibullah via Roohullah confirming our invitation.

Late in the summer I planned to spend some time at the Jegdalek ruby mines with Mir Waees Khan. We planned to gather ground samples which would then be sent for testing to the U.S. Geological Survey's laboratory in Denver.

To induce Larry and Brendan to come with me, I offered to pay their airfare and expenses, which I estimated to be about $10,000, if they would donate their time and talents. They both agreed, but in early May Brendan had a change of heart and decided not to join us.

Before leaving for Afghanistan, I traveled to Washington, DC to meet with the State Department and brief their Afghanistan Desk Officer on our plans. On May 18, 1998, I met with Sheldon Rapoport of the State Department's Afghanistan Desk in his office and told him of our plans to explore the gem mines and collect samples in Nuristan, Jegdalek, and Panjsher. We also discussed obtaining permission for Larry Snee to travel to Afghanistan since Larry, as a USGS employee, needed permission from both his own agency and from the State Department before he could legally enter Afghanistan.

Before concluding our meeting, Sheldon asked if I would stop in Islamabad and brief Jim Novak, the new Political Officer at the U.S. Embassy, on our project there. I agreed and Sheldon later confirmed a meeting to be held there upon my arrival on July 3, 1998. So far so good, or so it seemed at the time. In addition, he stated that there were no objections from Washington, DC for Larry's proposed trip to Pakistan and Afghanistan.

When I arrived in Islamabad on my scheduled flight, I called Novak's office to confirm our meeting. A secretary told me, "Mr. Novak is not available at this time." Being persistent I called again an hour later, and this time Novak answered the phone. I knew he was expecting my call to arrange a meeting on my short Islamabad stopover. Sheldon had asked that I brief him on our projects and receive final clearance for Larry Snee to enter Afghanistan as a US Government employee.

"Gary, my schedule is full at the moment; I'll call you back later today," he responded curtly. That seemed a bit odd, but having dealt with bureaucrats for years, I just gritted my teeth. He never did call and from the tone of his voice, I can't say that I was surprised. Having wasted an entire day in Islamabad, the next morning I left for Peshawar, frustrated by the whole experience.

I had just reached Peshawar and checked into room 101 at Green's Hotel, when someone came knocking on my door. I opened the door and found Roohullah and the Taliban Commander Habibullah, a thin, handsome, six-foot-one Afghan sporting a black, eight-inch beard, standing before me. They were eager to begin our fieldwork in Nuristan and Jegdalek, so I informed them that we would finalize the program once Larry and the six Afghan team members arrived in Peshawar.

Three days later Larry arrived in Islamabad and was met by Sher Dil, Khudai and me. We had taken a Flying Coach from Peshawar to

Mir Waees Khan and Sher Dil Qaderi

meet him. Having already obtained permission from the USGS to proceed, Larry requested and was granted a meeting with Jim Novak for his final clearance into Afghanistan. While they were meeting, Sher Dil, Khudai, and I went to the Uzbekistan Embassy in Islamabad to request visas to enter the Panjsher Valley via Uzbekistan. Officials at the Uzbek Consulate seemed very accommodating and informed us that we could expect to receive our visas in short order.

This initially was to be a backup plan if we were not allowed to enter Badakhshan or go via the Taliban-controlled areas. I vividly remembered my past experiences with border crossing problems.

When Larry returned to the hotel, he was distraught and discouraged. "Novak refused to give me permission to go to Panjsher Valley. I told him that we were being up front about having to enter Afghanistan through Uzbekistan. Then, would you believe, he asked if he could go with us to meet Commander Massoud!"

This was a major setback. I thought that my work in Central Asia had been respected and appreciated by all parties involved prior to Novak. He was new at his post, and this was my first association with him. Unfortunately, he had the final say over whether Larry would be permitted to enter Afghanistan. Had we come all this way for the expedition to be halted by a green functionary?

We stayed over in Islamabad. The next morning Sher Dil called the Uzbekistan Embassy to check on the status of our visas; we were informed that our visas had been *delayed.* A week later they were refused altogether. I couldn't help but feel that governmental involvement by either Pakistan or the US was behind this.

Feeling discouraged yet thinking something would work out, Larry, Sher Dil, and I boarded the Flying Coach for Peshawar. The two-hour ride gave me time to think about possible solutions to our dilemma.

Once back at Green's hotel, I immediately phoned Brad Hanson, the U.S. Consul in Peshawar. I had first met Brad several years earlier when he had been on an assignment there. At the time we had enjoyed several dinners together, and Brad had assisted me in obtaining a visa to the US for Atiquillah, my guide to the emerald mines.

"Brad, I could use your advice," I told him without getting into details. "I need Dr. Larry Snee and Sher Dil to assist me in my exploration trip to Afghanistan, and we've run into an obstacle."

Brad invited the three of us to meet with him that afternoon at his office at the Consulate in Peshawar. When we arrived, Brad ushered Larry, Sher Dil, and me into the private quarters behind his office and ordered tea. At that point I was still feeling optimistic that he would give us the help we needed. Not so!. Putting down his teacup, Brad began to hit on my exploration programs.

"Do you know what you're doing, Gary? Your projects are supplying the funds to purchase war material."

I was taken aback by his tone of voice and his comments but managed to bite my tongue.

"Brad," I carefully explained, "our projects are producing employment for Afghans. And in the future they will provide monies for taxes and foreign currency. It is better than drugs."

I strongly defended our good works, but I felt my words were falling on deaf ears. I also realized that Brad was probably just following orders, but why these orders?

"You know Brad, Dr. Snee has already obtained permission to work in the Taliban area. Are you now telling me that he won't be allowed to enter Massoud's area?"

His reply was an odd mismatch. "Our government has been strictly neutral in the Afghan situation!" he responded.

Really angry at this point, I challenged his contention. "How can you say that, Brad? I was in the State Department Office in Washington to meet with Roberta Chew, Desk Officer for Afghanistan, on June 20, 1997. When we were asked to move the meeting into the office of her supervisor, Mr. L. Caldron, he played a video of the Taliban fighting in Afghanistan. Knowing my pro-Massoud position, he clapped his hands and praised the Taliban as the hope for Afghanistan, saying, 'Massoud's a great soldier but a stupid politician.' That's not being neutral!"

Brad reacted to my statement. He stood up abruptly to end the meeting. Then, in an apparent attempt at diplomacy or to resume control of the conversation, he asked me to come back for lunch soon. I was polite, but I certainly had no plans to call him. I knew that anything he would have to say was bad news for our explorations.

Larry Snee had kept quiet during the meeting, but getting into a taxi he let out a sigh of disappointment, "There seems to be little for me to accomplish on this trip, Gary." He had seen first-hand how the *system* worked – or rather *didn't* work.

"I agree." I told him reluctantly.

"I'll check with PIA to see about a return flight." Larry responded.

"While you're arranging your flight, I'll call a group meeting for later today. That way you can at least brief us on how to collect the field data for the USGS laboratory," I told him.

Pakistan Airlines obliged by changing Larry's ticket for a departure on the next day.

That afternoon we met as a group with Sher Dil and Khudai representing the emerald mines of Panjsher Valley, Jamal Khan and Mir Waees Khan representing the Jegdalek ruby mines, and Syed Roohullah Bacha and Khaliullah Nuristani representing the tourmaline, aquamarine, and kunzite mines in Nuristan. Larry briefed us in detail on how to collect and index the ground samples, obtain and document the GPS data, and photograph our sample collecting. His briefing was very helpful, but we would sorely miss his presence.

After Larry's departure I went to Mr. Naeemi's office at the Afghanistan Embassy in Peshawar to obtain my visa for the Taliban area. Mr. Naeemi stated that I would have to wait a few more days for approval. I was discouraged. In New York City the Afghan Consul representing the Northern Alliance had already provided me a free visa on the spot.

More information was revealed later that night. I had invited Nancy Dupree to join me for my birthday dinner at the Chinese restaurant in the Pearl Continental Hotel. Our conversation quickly turned to the recent refusals I had been encountering with officials.

Nancy hesitantly told me, "The U.S. Ambassador to Pakistan informed me today that your program has been providing money for guns." The Ambassador's remark fueled my indignation and frustration over the past day's events. It was common knowledge that US aid to Pakistan was financing the Taliban. And as for my work, it would be years before our current geological studies would significantly increase gem production in Afghanistan. Currently, in my estimation, mining was providing Afghanistan with a paltry forty million US dollars, and that was from all sources, both legal and illegal, for the entire country. My annual purchases didn't even amount to one percent of the total. I was appalled. My program was the only honest, non-political, non-drug, non-tribal, income-generating employment program in existence for the Afghan population. The Afghan gem trade revenue equaled only a tiny fraction of the revenues received from their illegal drug trade, and current US aid to Pakistan was rumored to be running in the neighborhood of three billion dollars. Nancy's comment confirmed my suspicion that US government personnel were causing my visa problems. At that point, I was thoroughly fed up with bureaucrats and our tax dollars at work.

The next day I posed my dilemma to Roohullah and Sher Dil. We could either put our summer program on hold, or we could work around the government functionaries. While Sher Dil called Massoud's brother-in-law Rashuddien in Panjsher Valley, Roohullah called Habibullah at the Taliban headquarters in Jalalabad.

Within a few hours Habbilullah returned the call.

"Forget the Consulate in Peshawar, Roohullah. You and Gary be at the Afghanistan border at Torkham tomorrow morning. Your permission to meet with Commander Khan in Jalalabad will be waiting for the two of you there."

Delighted over the news, I immediately called Sher Dil and told him to expect me back from Jalalabad in two days.

Dressed as Afghans, Roohullah and I drove through the Khyber Pass without incident. Occasionally a guard stopped us on the road, whereupon, Roohullah, having typed and signed an official looking permission slip, presented it to the guard upside down. Guard after guard accepted the document, nodding their heads in approval without ever turning the letter right side up. Watching each guard carefully inspect the document and knowing he couldn't read gave us a few good laughs.

The Spinzer Hotel in Jalalabad was a one-story, whitewashed, cement building with many gone-to-seed-and-weed gardens. Soon after we checked in, five armed guards visited us. After asking several questions about our backgrounds, they called their commander on our room phone and left. Fifteen minutes later there was a knock at the door. One guard had returned with Habibullah's boss who, with a pleasant smile, introduced himself as the Commander for Eastern Afghanistan. He appeared to be in his late '20s, slightly over six feet tall and in good physical shape.

"It is good to meet you. I have heard of your plans for the ruby mines." After twenty minutes of talk about our past and his problems, the commander asked, "Would the two of you be available to travel to Kabul? I would like to arrange a meeting with the Minister of Mines and Industry."

"I agree, but first I must get a message to Sher Dil, another member of our team, so he doesn't worry about us."

Handing me his satellite phone, he said, "Here." Pleased that the minister would just hand over his phone, I quickly accepted it and dialed Sher Dil's number. Sher Dil was still waiting to hear from Rashuddien.

Before leaving, the commander handed Roohullah a note for us to show anyone questioning our traveling to Kabul. We stayed the night and left in Roohullah's truck early the next morning. The roads were still in disrepair, but we arrived in Kabul without delay.

The Minister of Mines and Industry, al-Haj Moulawi Ahmadjan, apologized repeatedly for my delay in getting a visa. Six months before, he had requested to see me when I arrived, but he had not been informed that I was in Pakistan awaiting a visa. Most interested in our program, he asked me to make a proposal to the Taliban government.

"Before I can do that, I'll have to talk to the local miners at Jegdalek," I said. "Unless they are in agreement and willing to cooperate, it would be pointless for me to submit a proposal."

I showed Ahmadjan my letter from the previous Minister of Mines and Industry. He said that he was already familiar with it.

Ahmadjan asked us to return to his office in two days after we had met with the Minister of Foreign Affairs. During that time Roohullah gave me a tour of Kabul and introduced me to several of his friends. At our second meeting Ahmadjan gave me a letter for the Afghanistan Consulate in Peshawar demanding that I be given a visa immediately and the right to carry cameras and other equipment. He then asked us to return to Kabul as soon as possible.

Because we had planned for a quick trip to Jalalabad and back to Peshawar, Roohullah and I had not taken any extra clothes. My brown shalwar kamese looked bad but Roohullah had dressed in white which was really showing the dirt and sweat marks. Jokingly, I had introduced him as my gardener to some friends. We could have been characters right out of Kipling's short story *The Man Who Would Be King*.

When we got back to Peshawar in Roohullah's truck, Sher Dil informed me that Rashuddien, Massoud's brother-in-law, was coming in two days to pick up Khudai, Sher Dil, and me in a military aircraft. Two days later Rashuddien arrived. He called Sher Dil to have us pack and meet at the Pearl Continental for lunch.

Large and eternally optimistic, Rashuddien, a Dubai-educated Tajik, has a take-charge attitude leavened with a wonderful sense of Afghan humor. He said that he had to purchase some building materials and was scheduling a flight to leave the next morning.

Over lunch, Rashuddien told me that the airport authorities had requested our passports for approval to board. The next morning the airport personnel told us that the ISI had refused my boarding; furthermore, they refused to give us the name of someone to whom we could apply. Even when Rashuddien came up with equipment problems to delay the return flight for two more days in Peshawar, we still could not persuade the authorities to let me go.

Rashuddien returned without any of us on the plane. Sher Dil and

Khudai planned to travel via Chitral and Garam Chasma to Panjsher while Jamal, Mir Waees, Roohullah, and I decided to return via Kabul to survey the ruby mines at Jegdalek.

L-R: Jamal Khan, Abdul Rafi and Gary

The next day I presented al-Haj Moulawi Ahmadjan's letter to Mr. Naeemi at the Afghan Council. Not only did I get a visa and letters to take my equipment, but he also insisted that I have dinner with him at his home that evening. It was a most gracious evening in a Western style and Western-decorated home. I discovered that he had received schooling in California.

Four days later Roohullah drove Jamal, Mir Waees, and me to Kabul. We met with al-Haj Moulawi Ahmadjan in his office. Again he was very congenial. He assigned the Taliban Assistant Foreign Minister Abdul Rafi to join our expedition to Jegdalek.

Roohullah decided to stay in Kabul while Jamal, Mir Waees, the Taliban Minister Rafi, and I went to Jegdalek. We hired a car to get us as far as Sorobi.

Following stream bed road to Jegdalek

Going to Jegdalek from Sorobi turns out to be more fun to tell about than it was to experience. Jamal had hired a driver with a 1920 Soviet jeep. The jeep had two five-gallon cans roped to the top: one was filled with gas, the other with water; both leaked. Plastic tubes ran from the cans to the engine below. I was praying for a fast getaway to escape the fire trail dripping under the front end. When the driver started the engine, the ancient vehicle quivered before inching slowly forward. Although we managed not to explode from our own fumes, a mile down the stream bed the front wheel came off and rolled ahead of us. Laughing outrageously, we stumbled out and sat on rocks while the old driver retrieved the wheel. He fastened it back on with wires and ropes, but before the afternoon was over, it came off again several more times. Then, two miles from the ruby mines the engine overheated, coughed, blew out steam, and fell silent. We walked the rest of the way to Jamal's war-damaged house where we ate and stayed the night sleeping on army cots.

We spent two days walking the perimeter of the ruby mining area and gathering about thirty pounds of rock and soil samples for Larry Snee to test for chromium. Chromium is the trace element that makes corundum red. Strange as it may seem, chromium reacts differently as a trace mineral in beryllium where its presence colors emeralds green. We knew that if the ground samples we collected revealed the presence of chromium, we would probably find rubies or emeralds in the area.

Late in the afternoon and during the evening meals, several miners showed up in hopes I would purchase some of their parcels of very red mixed-quality rubies. During the course of our stay Jamal, Mir Waees and I selected a large number of bright red facetable rubies, ranging from 2 to 70 carats, to take back to Peshawar. During these meetings it was obvious that the local miners wanted nothing to do with the Taliban

32.32 carat ruby carved from 77 carat by Bart Curren and set with diamonds in pendant designed and built by Greg Crawford

Mir Waees with 77 carat rough ruby

officials unless it was to be given permission to continue with their private mining business. They did, however, ask for assistance with geology work.

In mid-August when I returned to Room 101 at Green's Hotel, Peshawar was living up to its reputation as *The Spy Capital* and was overflowing with rumors. On August 7, 1998, the U.S. Embassies in Kenya and Tanzania had been bombed and 263 people had been killed. The U.S. government was blaming Osama bin Laden, who was living near the area I had just visited.

Peshawar was becoming a very dangerous place for Westerners, and it was clearly time for me to leave. I made arrangements to ship my ground samples home, and by August 18th I was on a flight home. Two days later – on August 20th, US warships launched a series of cruise missiles against targets said to be terrorist bases in Afghanistan. At least 21 people were killed in camps in the mountains around Khowst, about 95 miles (150 km) from Kabul. Separately, a volley of Tomahawk missiles was launched against a factory near the Sudanese capital of Khartoum, where the U.S. State Department said that chemical weapons were being produced.

Pakistan lodged a protest with the UN Security Council claiming that the US had violated its airspace and citing as proof a Tomahawk missile that crashed without exploding into Pakistan's southwestern province of Baluchistan. Later rumors stated that Pakistan sold the missile to the Chinese.

As an American, I had great difficulty understanding how the US could justify continuing to back the Pakistan government and, in turn, the Taliban with funding and supplies. Given the rhetoric about drugs and women's rights, how could we as a nation, in good conscience, have supported Afghanistan's rapidly increasing drug production and the Taliban's extremely abusive policies against women? Women were not allowed to work, attend school, or even go outdoors without escort by their husbands or fathers, and without first totally covering themselves. What were we doing supporting this extremist government? I had no plans to present the Taliban with a mining program that would support their cause. I only desired to help the poor, destitute villagers and miners. The same held true for my associates. The Taliban took over control of Jegdalek, but this did not make Jamal Khan and Mir Waees Khan followers of them any more than when we Americans have presidents of different parties. When a Republican president is in power, for example, very few, if any, Democrats change sides or political ideology.

Sadly, it would take another three years and the catastrophic events of September 11, 2001 before the powers that be in Washington, DC would realize their mistake in supporting the Taliban.

"The Lion of Panjsher"
(Commander Massoud)

Dexter Filkins described his aura very dramatically in his story that appeared in the *Los Angeles Times*, April 26, 1999:

An Afghan Lion looks at a Possible Final Stand

FARKHAR, Afghanistan – His troops are outnumbered, his supply lines are thin, and the sweeping hair of the once-dashing warrior is finally going gray. Ahmed Shah Massoud, legendary Afghan guerrilla leader, is making his final stand. As a daring young man, Massoud beat back seven Soviet invasions of his home region, earning the nickname "The Lion of the Panjsher." Twice since 1996, he has slipped away from the Taliban, the fanatical Islamic group that has conquered all but a corner of this rugged land. Now, as the sole remaining rebel commander in Afghanistan's 10-year-old civil war, Massoud is holed up in the barren crags of the country's northeast. He is rallying his troops for one last, desperate fight – for the Taliban assault that is certain to come. "In a very short time they will attack," Massoud said, looking up from a map at his mountain hideaway here. "But always, with the help of God, we have been able to continue our struggle and destroy our enemies."

A romantic warrior in the mold of Lawrence of Arabia or Che Guevara, Massoud, 46, is one of the most colorful – and complex – soldiers of his time. He inspired the Ken Follett novel, *Lie Down With Lions*, and was portrayed in the Sylvester Stallone movie *Rambo III*. Yet he is dogged by accusations that he cut deals with the Soviet army to save his skin. Now in his 24th year at war, Massoud still wears the cocked Afghan beret that gives his weathered face the glint of an artist. He still speaks French and dabbles in architecture. The Americans who worked with him in the 1980s during the U.S.-backed campaign to oust the Soviets from Afghanistan still recall his brilliant battlefield savvy.

"Massoud is the greatest of the Afghan war heroes," said former U.S. Ambassador Robert Oakley, who met Massoud during the Afghan war of the '80s. He was a magnificent fighter and not a butcher. He was a devout Moslem and not a fanatic. He not only survived the Soviets, he beat them.

Panjsher Valley

Chapter 17
Escape from Panjsher 1999 Expedition

July – August 1999

In Afghanistan, life requires great effort and sacrifice, and death seems to press too closely from the shadows. I have lost too many friends and associates prematurely. In addition to those I've already mentioned, in October of 1998 my dear friend Akbar Khan died of a heart attack while he was on a sales trip in Bangkok, Thailand. While still grieving that loss, in November I learned that Syed Roohullah Bacha's Toyota truck had gone off a mountain in Pakistan. He did not survive that accident. During this same timespan, political and military tensions heightened over Afghanistan. The Pakistan Army and bin Laden's soldiers had joined with the Taliban forces to destroy Ahmed Shah Massoud's troop positions and conquer Panjsher Valley, Afghanistan. I was very disappinted but not surprised that neither US newspapers nor the US government criticized Pakistan for backing the Taliban or bin Laden.

We had learned during the 1998 expedition that if we were going to reach the emerald mines of Panjsher Valley, we would have to get visas for Uzbekistan and Tajikistan. Although entry visas to these ex-Soviet Republics were nearly impossible for Americans to obtain, I felt with advance planning and the right contacts we could gain entry.

Tajikistan survives as a separate political entity from the ex-Soviet Union, but the President seems to be an *old school* communist, and part of Tajikistan is still under Soviet control – by choice. Other parts of Tajikistan are under the control or the threat of control by Sunni Tajiks and Ismail Tajiks, the latter group being followers of Agha Khan and the Agha Khan Foundation. Because of continual plays for power, street fighting rages from time to time. Because of recent shootings and robberies of foreigners, especially Americans, the Tajikistan Embassy in Tashkent had warned us not to come to Tajikistan. But our trip through this country was only to obtain transportation into Afghanistan.

Derrold and Gail on helicopter to Panjsher

My friend BeverlyBevington, an artist, accompanied me on the trip to help film the expedition and assist me with the purchase of old beads and jewelry. Derrold Holcomb and his wife Gail Whatley, of Atlanta, Georgia, expressed a desire to join us. Derrold designs software for interpretation of satellite-radar imagery. Gail is a registered nurse working in surgical orthopedics. They were ideal companions for me in the continuing exploration of the Panjsher Valley emerald mines. Derrold's expertise in satellite mapping could be a valuable contribution to the project. Having Gail along ensured a margin of safety against food illness, war wounds, and insect bites, to name a few threats.

Over a period of several months I talked to Haron Amin about plans for the 1999 expedition. Haron was with Massoud in Fahkar during my first meeting with the commander. Assigned to the

Beverly Bevington

Afghanistan delegation at the United Nations in New York City, he maintained continual contact with Massoud via satellite phone. He kept Massoud informed of our plans and, in turn, relayed Massoud's approval

Haron Amin

of our trip to me. However, to prevent the problems of the previous year, we agreed to begin in Tashkent, Uzbekistan. Upon our arrival in Tashkent, Mohammad Hasham Saad, the Head of Mission, would aid us at the Embassy of the Islamic State of Afghanistan.

I had met Hasham's brother Qandooz the year before when he flew with Rashuddien to pick me up in Peshawar. The brothers are over six feet tall with broad shoulders like football players,

Mohammad Hasham
Saad, Head of Mission,
Uzbekistan

good-looking, street-smart Afghans from the village of Bazarak in Panjsher Valley.

Our team arrived at the Tashkent airport with only one other passenger from Pakistan. Her apparel was the traditional zigzag-patterned cloth of yellow and orange further accented by a multi-colored scarf. Her mouth gleamed with gold teeth. The customs agent questioned her about her declarations. A loud and bitter argument ensued. We became a bit nervous, wondering if our camera and film would be confiscated. Soon additional guards arrived to search her luggage while the Soviet voices became louder, which none of us understood. After a 20-minute harangue, the agents permitted her to proceed. We cleared with no such problems.

Once outside the airport, however, without knowing the language, the exchange rate for Uzbek *cym,* or the amount a ride to town should cost, we shied from the mob of taxi drivers vying for our business. Fortunately, we discovered one driver who spoke French, so Gail communicated our destination; but even after 15 minutes of negotiations, we paid twice the usual fare and got less than half the current black market rate on our money exchange. Squeezed into an old Soviet vehicle with the propane tank in the trunk, we had little room left for our luggage.

We had selected several possible hotels from a guidebook, so we set out on the five-lane road to find a place to stay. Why such a wide highway, we wondered, with so few cars on the road? And it appeared that many industrial centers were closed. The first stop was a decrepit hotel. It took only a quick glance around the shabby lobby to send us heading for the door where an elderly European lady punctuated our impression in broken English, "Hotel bad!"

Next we tried the Hotel Tashkent, a six-story building spread over a city block. Apparently, the hotel had been quite elegant in its day. Before checking in, Gail and I walked across the wooden floors and up the stairs to inspect the rooms. I was impressed by the good-looking, young women serving as hall monitors. Upon returning to the taxi, I reported to Derrold, "There was a beautiful blonde on each floor." Later, when we were escorted to the rooms, some not-so-good-looking, older, overweight Soviet women had replaced the younger hall monitors.

We were charmed by the ceiling fans and tall French doors opening onto a balcony overlooking the courtyard. Each room provided a refrigerator and a hotplate along with a telephone, a TV, and a bathroom with a welcome shower. Although the furnishings were outdated, everything was very clean.

Our first order of business was to call Hasham. Apparently the *Six Plus Two Conference*, also in Tashkent with Massoud present, had just started a few hours before our arrival. "Let the Big Game begin!" I commented. The United Nations was sponsoring this event. It was for the representatives of Afghanistan's six neighbors plus Russia and the US to encourage Iran to talk to Pakistan and to get the US involved. Hasham sent a car to pick us up immediately to go to the Embassy. In the pleasantly decorated waiting room, the secretary brought tea and hard candy, and when Hasham arrived to meet us, I was surprised to see his tall frame in Western clothes. At prior meetings, I had always seen him wearing a *shalwar-kamese* or combat fatigues. During our meeting he made arrangements for our Tajikistan visas and a car to drive us from Tashkent to the border of Tajikistan. We talked about the possibility of meeting with Ahmed Shah Massoud before leaving Tashkent. As Hasham had many other duties, his attention to our expedition gave me a sense of the Alliance's appreciation for my projects.

That evening we wandered past many works of local artists gracing the parks and exuberant fountains, belying the arid environment. Unlike the desert at its outskirts, the city is colorful. Art school students selling copies of old masters' works lined the streets with their oil paintings. We stopped to marvel at a family of gypsies performing acrobatics, with their young son showing how every joint could be turned inside out. At one of the umbrella-covered tables placed near carts selling shish kabob, bread, and fruit, we enjoyed our evening chicken dinner grilled by a street vendor.

On a walk the next morning Gail was preparing to take a photo of a bank building when a policeman blew his whistle to stop her. Uzbeks still prohibit photographing official buildings, which is probably a holdover from communist security.

When we returned to our hotel, Hasham's assistant took us to the Tajikistan Embassy to obtain our visas. This was necessary because there is no Tajikistan Embassy in the United States. Then they informed us that we had to have a letter from our government requesting a visa for Tajikistan. When the Ambassador entered the room, he was extremely angry that the attendant had let us in. Knowing that we could not obtain such a letter from our State Department staff, we returned to the Afghan Embassy.

Hasham said, "I will give you a letter."

And when Hasham's assistant took us again two days later, this time the secretary made us wait outside on the concrete Embassy steps while an armed guard watched us through a narrow opening in the concrete wall. Hasham's assistant finally negotiated our visas at a cost of US$100 each.

With visas in hand we were scheduled to leave at nine o'clock the next morning. We waited anxiously. When our escorts arrived at eleven, they seemed confused over their directions and the mission to get us to the border of Tajikistan. We finally decided to go directly to the taxi station to obtain a fast car to catch up with Massoud who had left 40 minutes before. We wanted to connect with Massoud to make the border crossing together which would expedite our passage; but although our young driver sped over the Soviet-constructed roads at 70-to-90 miles an hour, we still could not make up the time difference.

It was a dry, hot, cramped nine-hour ride. The only relief came from our stop at a mountain pass restaurant for lunch. As it turned out, a relative of our driver operated the restaurant. Situated under the trees on what looked like a rope bed with cushions piled high, we enjoyed a meal of fresh-cooked shish kabob and watermelon. Arriving at this out-of-the-way crossing at eight meant that the gates were down and the border was closed for the night. The guards spoke no English.

We finally convinced one of them that I was a diplomat sent to meet an Afghan on the Tajik side of the border. While Beverly, Gail, and Derrold waited with the driver and a gathering crowd of curious children on donkeys and bicycles and, incongruously, a well-dressed

Afghan, I accompanied the guard some two hundred yards down the dark road to find six uniformed Tajik border guards sitting under a tree. Saleh Registani, our contact in Dushanbe, was nowhere in sight.

The border was to reopen at eight the next morning, so using hand signals I got our driver to take us back to a hotel in the last village. Twenty minutes later, we had the bags unloaded into an antique deserted-looking three-story building. When I asked our driver the price of rooms, he wrote the equivalent of $100 on a piece of paper. He meant $100 for each room. "No way," I said in a loud voice for all to hear, and we all started to pick up our bags. Then the guard wrote another figure on my paper. This time it was the equivalent of $3. Our driver obviously wanted to rip us off and leave. Wanting to be sure our driver would come back for us in the morning, I refused to pay him until he got us to the border.

The rundown hotel was dark. Two women were in what seemed to be the kitchen. One of them escorted us up three flights of concrete steps to our rooms. When we inquired about the facilities, we were escorted back down the three flights of stairs to the back of the building. There in the field we could relieve ourselves. The only other guests were a lady of the night and her companion. For security the four of us took the thin mattresses off the beds and slept together on the floor in one room.

The next morning, Beverly and Gail wandered out back to discover a smelly outhouse, with a hole in the dirt floor, about fifty yards from the hotel. Beverly opted to use the field. Gail decided to use the facility but quickly fled after seeing a rat run below in the hole.

"I don't blame the rat for running away," I told Gail as she related the story to Derrold.

To our pleasant surprise and relief, the driver returned to take us back to the border. He demanded an extra $10.00 US in Uzbek cym for the ride. To avoid a hassle, we simply agreed and gave him the money.

At the border the kindly Afghan in suit and tie approached us. He clearly wanted to help us even though he could not speak English. Motioning us to follow him into the custom building, he assisted us through the formalities of both countries. The guard, an ardently dedicated young worker, insisted on seeing our *bank* papers for the Uzbek money we carried. As we had no such papers, our Afghan friend

The guard

interceded with the supervisor who circumvented the issue by asking us to fill out new forms showing no money. Then we got our stamp of approval. Beyond the hundred-yard border crossing, once again the Afghan helped us, this time by arranging for a cab driver to take us to the Hotel Tajikistan in Dushanbe. I'll never know for sure, but the appearance of our unknown Afghan benefactor was suspiciously well-timed both at night and again in the morning. I guessed he was in Massoud's secret service.

Although modern, Dushanbe is a dangerous city to foreigners. Heavily armed police lined the streets. Two-by-two, they work their beats by randomly inspecting vehicles. *For safety* the NGO strictly enforces a nightly curfew of eight o'clock.

The Dushanbe Hotel was *upscale.* The bathroom was completely tiled with a shower attached to the sink, so that we bathed standing in the middle of the room. Each day they notified us about which hour we would have hot water. The balcony overlooked the city and the mountains in the west. Our floor had a pleasant lobby complete with an omnipresent desk monitor, and our room was obviously bugged as we could see the monitor in each corner of the room.

After we had settled our bags, I called Saleh Registani, Massoud's Military Attaché assigned to the Afghanistan Embassy. He had visited

Amrullah

me in Athens, Alabama earlier in the year to discuss our program and trip. Seeming surprised that we had arrived before Ahmed Shah Massoud, who had overnighted in Samarkand, he said, "Amrullah and I will be over shortly. We will take all of you to lunch." Amrullah now served as Massoud's aide in Dushanbe. Previously he had been Massoud's public relations man in Kabul, where I had met him in 1992.

Over lunch, we learned that Ahmed Shah Massoud had arrived in Dushanbe. According to Saleh and Amrullah, from the Afghan perspective, Massoud harbored no illusions about destroying the Taliban. Its forces had grown too strong. As a minority Tajik in a country previously dominated by Pushtuns, he held out little hope of heading a future government. Rather, Massoud aimed to take enough territory to force the Taliban to hold elections. If Massoud was successful, Afghanistan could find itself at peace for the first time in more than a quarter of a century. Should he fail, there would be many more months of fighting and suffering.

As we left the restaurant, Saleh warned, "Be careful what you talk about at the hotel. They have only five rooms for foreigners – all bugged." Then he arranged to pick us up for dinner at seven.

Saleh Registani

The maid unlocked the room door and stepped inside before us. She put her finger to her lips and with the other hand pointed to what looked like a two-inch microphone near the ceiling. After the maid departed, Beverly and I found three more microphones.

Dinner with Saleh that evening was at a brightly-lit casino, which had been built for the Tajikistan Army officers. We feasted on savory borsch, chicken, and potato salad, followed by a surprisingly good Soviet wine. Making the evening even more festive, some Tajik men joined by the restaurant cook danced in front of a live band playing Turkish music.

After dinner we realized that police had filled the streets and were stopping cars. "Security has been increased," Saleh said. "It is much safer than three months ago."

"Good!" I said. "When he gave us our visas, the Tajik Ambassador in Tashkent instructed us not to leave the hotel."

"If you have any problems in Dushanbe, go to the nearest policeman," Saleh said. "They are very helpful."

During the next week, as we waited on approval and arrangements for our trip, Saleh called to say, "I know a Tajik man who needs money and wants to sell a 50-carat rough ruby. If you are interested, I will take you to see him."

"I'm always interested in good material," I said.

I rode with him to a private home near the Afghanistan Embassy. A well-dressed Tajik man opened the door to greet us. We were invited into the living quarters and served tea. When our host left us for five minutes to fetch the ruby, I unpacked my scales, jewelers loupe, and penlight.

Then the man handed me a dark red crystal. In the beam of the flashlight, one end of the crystal glowed like a stoplight. I weighed it on my small scales at 50.10 carats, the best portion being maybe 15 carats. Perhaps even a 30-carat very red heart-shape could be cut from the crystal.

"Saleh, this is a very good ruby. I would like to buy it!" I said.

"How much shall I offer the man?" Saleh questioned.

Knowing we were going into negotiations, I replied, "Five thousand US dollars."

Saleh talked to the man for several minutes and then turned to me. "He wants $15,000."

"Saleh, it is a very nice ruby, but I honestly feel that $7,000 is my top price."

Again Saleh turned to the man for a long discussion. After several minutes he turned back to me. "The man said that he will take no less than $10,000."

"Please tell the man that in my honest opinion, it is only worth $7,000; however, if it helps him and we can start doing business, I will consider paying his requested $10,000. Unfortunately, I did not bring anywhere near that amount of money with me to Tajikistan. What can we do?"

After another conversation with the man, Saleh said, "We agree you can take the ruby with you and wire the money to his personal account in Dubai when you return to the US."

"In that case, I agree," I said. I placed the ruby in my pocket where it would remain for the rest of the trip unknown to any of my traveling companions.

The next morning, I received a phone call telling me to meet Massoud at two o'clock. Beverly and I waited in our room until three when I received a call from Saleh.

"Gary, come down to the lobby by yourself," he instructed.

"Be right down," I replied.

Saleh was at the elevator as it stopped at lobby level. "Follow me!" he said.

I followed him into his car. He turned out of the driveway, drove across town, and pulled up to a wooden gate. When he honked, armed guards unlocked the gate from the inside. "Follow me," Saleh said. Another armed guard held the door as Saleh and I took off our shoes and entered the house.

Massoud came out of a side door of the living room to greet me. He appeared well-rested, dressed in a new khaki-colored safari suit. I noticed a streak of gray in his hair. He had aged since our last meeting, but his presence had grown steadily more commanding since our first meeting at Farkhar eleven years before. For more than 20 years, he had maintained the respect of his followers. I had yet to meet a man in his command who would not have given his own life for Ahmed Shah Massoud.

Presenting his hand, he smiled and shook hands with me. In that moment I knew my own commitment to help this man in any way I could to bring peace to Afghanistan. Then he motioned for me to sit beside him on the couch.

Commander Massoud and Gary

Saleh and Amrullah sat across from us. Although Massoud understood some English, he was more comfortable in Persian and French, so Amrullah translated. After addressing one another's welfare, we got down to the business of discussing my proposal for geological mapping of the emerald deposits. I described Derrold's work in the field and asked if he and Gail could join Beverly and me in Panjsher Valley. I told Massoud that Derrold had the satellite maps at the hotel, which he could bring for him to see. Massoud was interested in seeing the maps.

Saleh called Beverly and told her to get Derrold and Gail and go out the front door of the hotel. Saleh's accented English was difficult for Beverly to understand. Knowing the room was bugged she was nervous about asking any questions for clarification. Later she told me that she wasn't sure about the license number he had given her for the Embassy cars. Saleh told her to get into one by herself and that Derrold and Gail should ride in the other.

In the parking lot, a stranger motioned for them to get into their respective cars. Without a word he drove away to the rendezvous location. The streets were busy and the police were stopping vehicles. Beverly in her car went in one direction, Derrold and Gail in another, just as if they were in a "James Bond" movie.

Derrold with satellite map of Panjsher Valley

We talked with Massoud for more than an hour about our plans and the emerald business while Beverly filmed part of the conference. Massoud then asked one of his assistants to bring in a small collection of rough gem crystals for our discussion. Massoud was no dealer. He, like many Afghans, liked to pick up a gemstone here and there like people pick up shells at a seashore. We drank tea and ate candy while looking at his collection. The meeting ended with Massoud promising he would arrange for a driver, interpreter, and helicopter to take us to Takhar and on to Panjsher the next day.

The next morning Rashuddien, Massoud's brother-in-law whom I had met the year before in Peshawar, flew in from Takhar to accompany us to Panjsher. We were to be guests at his family home in Bazarak, 64 miles north of Kabul.

At noon we had moved down to the hotel lobby with our bags. At four o'clock the desk clerk called me to the phone. Saleh said, "I'll meet you in front of the hotel in five minutes." Tired of waiting, we gladly gathered our baggage to meet the three-vehicle escort in front of the hotel. With a Tajikistan Army uniformed soldier in the front passenger seat, we drove to the back gate of the airport. A few words

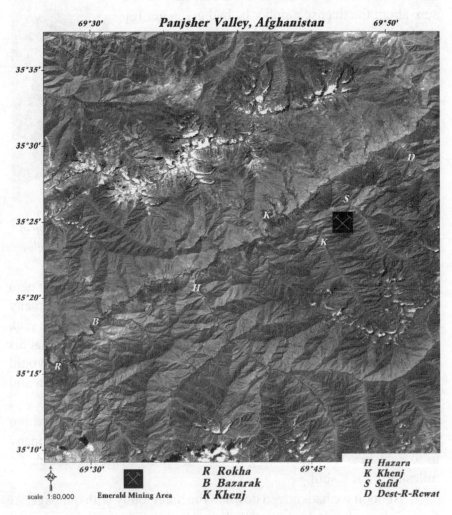

Satellite map of the Panjsher Valley

from the driver to the armed guard opened the gate. We drove down a runway and onto the grass next to a waiting helicopter.

Haji Timar, the ex-manager of the Kabul airport, was there to meet us. At his side was a Tajik immigration officer who stamped our passports. We boarded the helicopter and flew over the high mountains for one-and-a-half hours into Panjsher Valley. We videotaped a majestic view with our new DX Canon XL1 digital video camcorder held at the open windows. With no seat belts we were thankful for a smooth ride.

As we landed on the grass helipad on the outskirts of Bazarak Village in Panjsher, people lined the field. Armed Afghan soldiers stood by large Soviet-made trucks. We were escorted to a truck and taken for a rough, dusty ride directly to Rashuddien's family home, the largest in the village. With a Soviet glass front and chandeliers hanging in a spiral staircase, the home was still under construction, sanguinely awaiting the arrival of peace in the valley before getting the finishing touches.

When we arrived, Rashuddien's family told us that the Taliban, with the support of the Pakistan Army and bin Laden's Arab soldiers, had just launched a major offensive north of Kabul. At first the action had been limited to both sides firing rockets at each other's positions. The next morning Rashuddien informed us that one of Pakistan's top ISI leaders, with years of experience in Afghanistan, had been killed by rocket fire.

Early in the evening I spotted Jon Mohammad of the famed *Jon*

Team arrives in Panjsher aboard Hind helicopter

Mohammad Express. Several times in the past he had ensured my safe passage to and from Afghanistan. As he came into the courtyard, I ran out the door to greet him with a big bear hug. We discussed the Pakistani border crossings, trout fishing, and friends that had been killed. Jon Mohammad had not changed since I last visited him in Kabul five years before. He was still as hospitable as always, insisting that we come to his house for dinner soon. Then he shook my hand and left.

Jon Mohammad

Derrold and I began the first day climbing the mountains east of Rokha with Rashuddien. Our goal was to take GPS readings and refine ground-truth on the satellite map we had carried from the US. In addition, we hoped to verify reports of new emerald deposits that Rashuddien had previously surveyed. During our absence Beverly and Gail visited with the women and the rest of the family in the dining area, something that a man does not have the privilege of doing.

Prior to our trip Sher Dil had received satellite phone messages from Rashuddien stating that the village people had located emeralds in new areas south of the old mines. Although Derrold and I were excited to explore that area, getting there reminded me of the first day of high school football practice – difficult and tiring. When we reached 9,000 feet the first day out, I began to move slowly – very slowly. My legs were still strong, but my wind was short. And my accelerated heartbeat thumped in my chest. Acclimating to the altitude usually requires a day for each 2000 feet.

At the first mine site, we found a green opaque material, but it was not emerald. We gathered samples that I later showed Dr. George Rossman at California Technical College. Using his $80,000 Nicolet 860 Magna Series FTIR (Fourier Transform Infrared) spectrometer, he identified the material as green grossular garnet. The spectrometer measures the reflection of infrared (thermal) radiation. In a single mineral family the bands of different compositions register in unique positions, enabling fine distinctions much like a fingerprint.

Derrold and I walked back down to the 7,000-foot level to join the villagers for the night in a home that overlooked the village of Rokha. Early the next day we visited what was touted as a second mine, but we found only a hole with some quartz crystals. Hiking for four hours back down the mountain, we encountered a funeral procession for a Panjsher commander who had been shot the night before at the frontline. There were more than a hundred sad faces. Some said *"Salom-o-alaikum"* in soft voices. Others just walked by with bowed heads. Their grief reminded me of our close proximity to the war. Once again I wondered, "Is this trip a mistake?"

We returned to Rashuddien's home to find Beverly and Gail helping to prepare dinner, which included watching the chicken's throat being cut as the chicken faced Mecca. Beverly and Gail were sure their domestic prowess was being tested. They remained stoic during the slaughter, but Beverly didn't fare as well in subsequent challenges. Zia, Rashuddien's mother, who was younger than Beverly, had had 19 children. She exercised her Afghan sense of humor by inviting Beverly onto the roof to see how they dried mulberries. The last rung of the ladder required a stretch, and when Beverly needed a boost, all the olde

Gary and Rashuddien with local men

women laughed. Later, they laughed harder when she tried to follow Zia stepping rock after rock across a stream and fell in. Despite the friendly teasing, the women embraced the friendships that were being forged.

The following day Rashuddien and our team drove to several village bazaars south of Bazarak. The valley fields were fertile with golden wheat and green cornfields incongruous to the signs of war everywhere: defunct tanks, destroyed rusted artillery and newer equipment waiting for action. In the bazaars, we talked to many people about the gem materials they were finding, but we gathered no word of major finds – only talk of war throughout the villages. We saw many trucks with supplies and men headed south toward the frontlines. As they rode along, the soldiers sang Farsi songs about fighting and killing.

On the fifth day, Rashuddien's brother Amand escorted our party up the beautiful, remote Parandeh Valley, which is famous for its aquamarine-blue crystal-clear water. Beverly and Gail climbed up to visit an Afghan family while Derrold and I continued up the mountain to look for gem deposits.

The view from the house was breathtaking. The terraced fields

Soldiers on their way to the battle front

below were filled with grain blowing with the wind set against rugged mountains jutting endlessly into the clear sky. In the dimly lit room, a young girl with her son approached Gail and wanted a photo taken. Her husband had been killed in the war, and his brothers would now take care of her. Beverly filmed Gail interviewing Amand in a window with the mountains and setting sun as a backdrop.

Derrold and I returned shortly before dark with no finds other than several bombed-out homes. The next day we started at Bazarak and hiked with Rashuddien to two mine locations directly to the northeast. Our total climb was two hours with stops once for tea and fruit and later for lunch of goat cheese, yogurt, nan, apricots and tea. Most of the trail was ten inches wide with a steep incline up the mountains and a major drop of 50-to-100 yards on the opposite side. Although we had set out at eight, with a half-hour lunch break, at six o'clock we had yet to see gem crystals – only one-by-one foot holes. Derrold and I were beginning to think that this was Rashuddien's Afghan joke on us when he said, "There is a mine up over the next mountain." Derrold and I looked at one another and replied, "You bring us samples of the material to see." And to our surprise, Rashuddien departed, leaving one of the villagers behind with us.

We waited until six-thirty before starting back down the mountain to the village. As we reached the village, the man with us asked us to sit down. We rested for 15 minutes and decided to start back to Bazarak.

Green grossular garnet located by
Rashuddien and Gary in this hole

Darkness was setting in. When we stood up to leave, the villager very patiently asked us to sit down. We refused, and he looked upset. Again he motioned for us to sit down. When we refused again, the villager pulled out his pistol. When an Afghan takes responsibility for others, he sometimes employs strong measures to fulfill his duty.

I told Derrold, "I think Rashuddien made this man

responsible for us. His life is on the line if we get hurt or lost."

Derrold said, "Let's go! I don't think he will shoot us."

"No, let's give Rashuddien another 15 minutes before trying to leave," I cautioned.

After ten minutes, a young boy of about 14 came out to talk to the villager. He smiled at us and motioned for us to start down the mountain. We did. While there had been no problem hiking in the daylight, nightfall brought new challenges. With only a little moonlight to guide us, we were ever in danger of losing our footing. An hour later Derrold and I stopped outside a village unsure of which path to follow. We decided to wait for Rashuddien who appeared 30 minutes later wihout any gem samples.

Once again we returned long after dark, sweaty and exhausted, without emeralds. Beverly and Gail had also experienced disappointment that day. The Afghan women attempted to teach them how to wash clothes by hand, village fashion. The Afghans did not understand that the modern synthetic fabrics in Gail's expedition gear could not withstand the harsh soap and vigorous scrubbing. Consequently, the American women did not scrub hard enough or rinse and wring enough to satisfy Rashuddien's mother.

With no emeralds from the Bazarak area, we were ready to head north to visit some operating emerald mines. We moved our team to a home in Khenj village where Haji Dastagir and his village friends had prepared a banquet for us. Haji Dastagir had been the commander responsible for the emerald mines during my first trip with Atiquillah in 1989.

At that time there were about a thousand miners. Badly wanting for geological mapping, modern equipment, and technology, they were still working the mines as they had been doing for the previous 16 years. They were still using too much dynamite and too short wicks; both techniques were dangerous to the men and to the emeralds. And the miners desperately needed better blasting materials. When Derrold and I walked into some of the tunnels to witness the results, we saw many shards of crystals that had been destroyed before they could be taken from the mountain.

In the village of Mokoni we stopped to collect further GPS data.

Dinner at Haji Dastagir's

Emerald mine surveyed

A refugee approached Rashuddien to request transportation. "The fighting is bad!" He told us. "The Taliban have broken Massoud's line of defense by forcing Tajik children to walk across the minefields. Now they have entered Panjsher Valley."

This meant that the Taliban had come within 18 miles of Rashuddien's home. Rashuddien spent the next 2 minutes on his cell phone frantically trying to get news. Then he reported, "Things are not good."

"What do you mean?" I asked.

"It is true that the frontlines have broken. Thousands of refugees are coming north to avoid being killed. We must return to Bazarak." Bazarak was two hours away.

We started south passing more than a hundred struggling refugees. Stopping at Jon Mohammad's home, we found that he had left an hour earlier to assist refugees. More than one hundred thousand refugees were expected to be coming in the next day. The mark of our host – before leaving, Jon Mohammad had prepared a fresh trout for our lunch. We ate and immediately left for Bazarak. I missed seeing my long-time friend. Who knew if we should ever meet again?

As we continued towards Bazarak, the refugees came in larger waves up the valley. More than 75 had stopped at Rashuddien's home for food and shelter. Beverly and Gail had been invited into the family dining room, a room that was off limits to non-family men such as Derrold and me. The room had been filled with some 50 women and children. Rashuddien's mother had prepared food, drink, and shelter for all of them. There was now an armed guard stationed at the house gate to stop more people from coming into the house, which had reached its capacity.

After many cellular phone conversations, Rashuddien informed us Bazarak might be bombed by Taliban and Pakistan aircraft. Massoud's forces had been unable to hold back the attackers. The next morning, we were to be evacuated by helicopter.

All night long scores of refugees continued to flow past Rashuddien's home, heading north away from the fighting. At daybreak we, the lucky ones, were sitting with our bags packed and ready to go. By eleven o'clock we started pacing the floor.

Massoud's helicopters continued to fly over the house, shaking it with sound. We saw many soldiers on the dirt road overcrowded with women and children refugees. But we did not receive any orders to proceed to the helipad.

By two o'clock I was telling Derrold about the Anjuman Pass in the north that must be crossed to get to Pakistan. How would we get Beverly and Gail up and over the 14,900-foot pass? Then Rashuddien yelled from a back room, "Let's go! Massoud is sending a helicopter to take the four of you to Dushanbe. My brother will accompany you." We grabbed our luggage and rushed out the door.

Our bags were piled high in the Toyota four-by-four truck. Rashuddien pressed the gas pedal to the floor and leaned on the blaring horn. Hundreds of refugees parted as we passed. The helicopter pad was one mile away. His grip tight on the steering wheel, Rashuddien dodged potholes and refugees in a race against time. The four of us were crushed in the back seat of the truck, I clutched Beverly's hand to reassure her, but I truly did not know if we would make it to the helicopter in time. The situation was so perilous that I feared the chopper would leave without us.

We raced onto the grass field, and with a screech of brakes Rashuddien pulled up to the waiting Soviet helicopter, engine running, blades spinning, ready for take-off. Soldiers swiftly carried our bags from the truck to the helicopter. Fear goaded us into a mad dash. As we limbed in, each of us hurriedly shook Rashuddien's hand. He was risking his life to help us. The navigator slammed the door, and the pilot gunned the engines. We lifted into the air over the main road through Panjsher Valley. Stretching out below us, a solid line of refugees grimly marched northward. The chopper rose, higher and higher, and we escaped toward Dushanbe, Tajikistan.

Safe now, breathing a little easier, we looked for seat belts – none. Just then Amand, Rashuddien's brother, strolled in from the cockpit, a big grin on his face. "You might like to know," he told us, "that this helicopter was just captured from the Taliban!"

We looked at one another. Surely, there would be no maintenance records on it. But Massoud had come through for me once again! Beverly and I hugged one another, and Derrold and Gail looked overjoyed. We were flying to safety.

Two days later Ahmed Shah Massoud recaptured all the territory he had lost. The Taliban bombed Bazarak, and the Great Game continued. One week after our group escaped from Panjsher Valley, an airplane dropped a bomb 30 yards east of Rashuddien's house blowing out all the glass windows on the east side and killing 20 people. Body parts were found in fruit trees a quarter of a mile away.

Massoud's tanks ready to roll

Gary on the 14,600-foot Anjuman Pass

Chapter 18
The War Years

Wars do not determine
who is right or who is wrong,
just who is left.
– Author unknown

July – August 2000

As I prepared to return to Afghanistan, Mohammad Es'Haq, the Alliance of the North representative assigned to Washington, DC, emailed me the following message on June 19, 2000:

E-mail from Es'Haq

Dear friend:

Last night I talked to Commander Massoud and based on conversation with him I have prepared the following press release.
Yours,

Es'Haq

Engineer Mohammad Es'Haq

Press Release Draft

Washington, DC – June 19: Preparations for launching a major offensive by the Pakistanis and the Taliban against the Mujahideen in Shemali and Kunduz fronts of Afghanistan have been almost completed and fighting could start any moment.

This was revealed by Ahmed Shah Massoud whose forces are preparing themselves for the defense of the territory they control.

Massoud said 2500 fresh Pakistani fighters have reached Afghanistan, around 1500 of whom are stationed in Shemali Front and the remaining in Kunduz.

He said General Saeeduz Zafar of the Pakistan Army has been appointed to command the operation and Brigadier Ershad will serve as his deputy. Ershad has already reached Afghanistan and Zafar is expected to reach Kabul soon.

He said based on the evidence available the fighting this year would be as severe as the fighting of last summer.

On July 23, 2000 I enjoyed a 60th birthday dinner with Hasham at an outdoor restaurant in downtown Tashkent, Uzbekistan. Two days later, Engineer Mohammad Es'Haq joined us. I handed him a draft copy of this book to review over the next couple of weeks, when we were to meet again in Panjsher Valley. At the meeting Hasham informed Es'Haq and me that the Taliban had just captured Nahrin Village, west of Panjsher. That was bad news for my trip as it placed the Taliban where they could launch an attack on Panjsher.

The problems I experienced obtaining a Tajikistan visa detained me in Tashkent. There had been recent changes at the Tajikistan Foreign Ministry. The US was not granting visas to the Tajiks, so they were refusing to grant visas to Americans. Saleh Registani, the Afghanistan Minister of Defense in Tajikistan, was communicating with the Foreign

Minister in Dushanbe in an effort to obtain my visa. Without it I could not travel by helicopter to Panjsher with Engineer Es'Haq.

Over the years I have learned to practice patience. Life centered on Afghanistan has become a waitig game. As I might have anticipated, ten days later I was still in Tashkent. While reading a book in Ambassador Hasham's Consulate office, the Afghan Foreign Minister, Dr. Abdullah, walked in.

"Good to see you again, Gary. I have heard about your delay. Would you like to ride with me to Tajikistan tonight at midnight?" Then he added, "We can resolve your visa problems at the border."

"Thank you, yes! Sounds like a good plan to me."

Lunch was served at the Embassy. Afterward I returned to my room at the Diplomat Hotel to get ready for the trip to Tajikistan and to call my young Tajik friend Chad Katilov who had attended college in the US. Chad and I had met the year before, and since then we had stayed in contact via email. He was interested in the gem business. I had informed him in my last communication about my difficulties in obtaining a visa, and he had called a few days later offering to approach his Tajik government contacts if the Afghans were not successful in their efforts.

From the hotel, I walked five blocks to the Internet Café where I logged onto my AOL email account. For the next hour, I read and answered my e-mail messages. The cost for the computer time was US $2.

Exactly at midnight Hasham's office assistant knocked on my room door. He picked up my small suitcase while I carried my bag of cameras. We drove across Tashkent to where Dr. Abdullah was staying in an apartment, and 15 minutes later I was in the backseat of a dark blue Mercedes sedan with Hasham driving and Dr. Abdullah sitting in the front seat. Another car from the Afghanistan Embassy followed u. As we reached the outskirts of Tashkent, the cars stopped, and Hasham moved to the second car. Another man took his place as driver. I lay down on the back seat and went to sleep.

Four hours later, I woke up as we stopped at the turnoff to Samarkand so that Hasham could trade places with our driver. Then we continued to the border of Tajikistan. I woke up the second time at seven. Dr. Abdullah was serving cookies and tea from a thermos. At ten we arrived at the border and met Massoud's Ambassador to Tajikistan with my entrance visa. Then Hasham bade us farewell and returned to Tashkent.

An hour later I was in the Afghanistan Embassy sitting wih Saleh and Amrullah. Dr. Abdullah had departed for a meeting with the Tajikistan authorities. Saleh reminded me, "Before you can leave for Afghanistan, we still have to get you a multiple visa so you are allowed to re-enter Tajikistan. I have talked to the Foreign Minister, and it should be approved tomorrow. After lunch I will drop you at the hotel."

Mohammad Hasham Saad and General Mohammad Asef Delaware

During lunch we discussed how the fighting in Afghanistan was getting worse,with no end in sight. When I asked Saleh about Massoud's supplies and the helicopters, he said, "For you, the maintenance problems with the helicopter are probably more dangerous than the fighting." Then Saleh went on to explain that they were on a higher level of alert in Dushanbe. One of the ISI generals who worked with the Afghan Mujahideen in Afghanistan had now been appoited as the Pakistani Ambassador to Tajikistan. His office was on the same side of Dushanbe as the Afghanistan Embassy. That is pobably why Hasham had taken the extra precautions of escorting Dr. Abdullah and me to Tajikistan.

Dr. Abdullah

The following day after breakfast, I walked to the Afghanistan Embassy where Amrullah greeted me, "There is a helicopter coming, but we do not know when."

"Is Saleh here? I still have to get my multiple visa," I asked.

He had left for an emergency at the border, but we called him, and a few minutes later Saleh instructed his assistant to take me to the Tajikistan Foreign Minister's office for my visas. An hour later I was back at the Embassy with my Tajikistan visa. The helicopter arrived at five-thirty. When the pilot called the Embassy, however, he said that it was too late in the day to fly to Panjsher, so we would leave the next morning.

Shortly after I returned to the hotel, Saleh called to say, "The man you purchased the ruby from last year is in Dushanbe and wants to show you some new rubies."

"That's good news," I said, "I was very happy with last year's purchase, and I'm interested in more. I'll see you when I return."

At eleven the next morning, I put my things into one of the Embassy cars for a trip to the helipad. In a repeat of the year before, we drove through the back gate of the airport and down the runway to the patched-up Soviet-built helicopter. Saleh had been right. It looked worn out. I took a photo of the threadbare tires.

Bullet-riddled helicopter

Two cars pulled up to the helicopter. The first contained the pilot, co-pilot, and engineer. The second held a Kyrgistan reporter and his cameraman along with a Tajikistan reporter. After the Tajikistan airport authorities reviewed our passports and luggage, they motioned for us to board.

Three hours later with a fuel stop at a border post, we landed at Bazarak in Panjsher Valley. Two drivers in pickup trucks were waiting. The three reporters and I rode through the bazaar heading for Tajuddin's guesthouse, where I had stayed the year before. I was pleasantly surprised when I spotted Tajuddin, Jon Mohammad, and Dr. Abdullah standing in the road. I jumped out of the Toyota and greeted them. Dr. Abdullah quickly reported, "Commander Massoud has approved your plans for further

emerald ex-
ploration and
mapping. And
he has ap-
proved your
request to make
a documentary
film of the
emerald and
lapis mines. He
also approved
your offer to
create a

L-R: Jon Mohammad, Dr. Abdullah, Jan Tajdaamin

website for him on the Internet." I was excited to hear the good news.
Dr. Abdullah continued, "Engineer Es'Haq is expecting you. Get some
rest tonight, and Jon Mohammad will come tomorrow morning with
transportation to take you to Rokha, near the front lines. Es'Haq has
set up an office there. I am going north to Takhar to be with Commander
Massoud. When you finish your work here in Panjsher, we will send a
helicopter to bring you to Takhar. From there you can return to
Dushanbe." Following this exchange of information, Dr. Abdullah and
Jon Mohammad took turns bidding me farewell, then climbed into an
idling jeep and sped away. The rest of us followed Tajuddin to our
assigned rooms. Remembering me, the houseboy motioned for me to
move into the same room Beverly and I had shared the year before. I
lay down on the bed: resting, reflecting and waiting to be called for
dinner.

Prior to dinner, the houseboy delivered tea. I was taking in the
second sip of tea when Dr. Ilhom Narzier, the reporter from Tajikistan,
motioned for me to bring my tea to the roof lanai. On the lanai, I found
Dr. Narzier sitting with the two men from the helicopter. They introduced
themselves in broken English as Alexander Al Knizev, a special
correspondent for Central Asia, and Victor S. Tkachenko, engineer and
cameraman from Russia. We struggled with language for the next hour
as we discussed Central Asia and their mission to interview Massoud
and visit the people of the Wahkhan Valley for a report on their lifestyle.
Each of us had stories of how the fanatical Moslems were creating

problems, from open warfare in Chechnya to kidnapping and killing citizens in Tajikistan, Kyrgistan, and Kashmir.

During our storytelling we discovered that we had mutual friends, specifically Tony Davis, an Australian news reporter, and Jon Mohammad.

"We are planning to travel and explore the Wahkhan and Shighnan areas," the engineer, Victor, told me.

I answered that the area was reported to be very dangerous because of druglords controlling much of the area. "Transportation is very difficult to obtain, and I was held under house arrest in Shighnan."

The houseboy asked if he could bring food.

Before answering him, I asked, "Where are the people who were living in this house last year?"

"They moved to Tajikistan after the bombing." I walked to the side of the roof and stared at the trees. They appeared to have been trimmed by a hurricane.

Remembering the news of the bomb dropping just after our departure from Panjsher, I saw in my mind's eye the faces of the neighbors as they waved to me just one year ago at this spot on the roof. My image of their disaster was sickening. I went to my room and slept.

At four o'clock I heard "*Allah Akbar*," the morning call to prayer reverberating from the village loudspeaker. Shortly, thereafter, the rooster crowed.

I joined the others on the roof for breakfast. I had just finished when Jon Mohammad appeared. We all motioned him to join us.

But Jon Mohammad said, "We do not have time. I have come to take Gary to Massoud's Army Headquarters in Rokha." We had lunch in Rokha. Afterwards, a jeep arrived to take me south to meet with Engineer Es'Haq. The driver and I left the jeep on the road and climbed half-a-mile up the mountain to Engineer Es'Haq's home. We were greeted by his teenage daughter who told us that her father had left for Jabul-Saraj. After tea and grapes, the driver and I walked back to the jeep and drove to Jabul-Saraj. We stopped several times to ask for Eng. Es'Haq. As we approached the frontlines of the war, the driver began to get nervous, so I motioned that we should return to Bazarak.

The next morning Dr. Abdullah and Jon Mohammad appeared at my open room door, "We have located Eng. Es'Haq. He is expecting you in Jabul-Saraj. Tomorrow the helicopter will take you to Takhar to meet with Commander Massoud. From Takhar you will leave for Dushanbe."

I picked up my books, placed my brown Chitrali cap on my head, and walked to the dirt road with my friends. The shops were open and men were going about their regular business. I climbed into one jeep as they boarded another, and we went our separate ways.

On the outskirts of Bazarak the driver pulled into the petroleum storage dump for gas. Large tanks of gasoline were buried, whereas new supplies were still stored in 55-gallon

L-R: Commander Ahmed Shah Massoud, Commander Bismillah Khan, and Eng. Mohammad Es'Haq

drums stacked in the open air. To obtain gas, the driver dropped a gallon can attached to a rope down a two-foot diameter tube made of corrugated tin, as if to get water from a well. As he emptied the first can into the gas tank, he glanced up at me with a concerned look on his face. He was listening to something. His look turned to fear, "Jet!"

At first I could only hear the roar; then I spotted it high in the sky. I heard others yell, "Jet" as they ran behind a pile of 55-gallon drums of gas. I shook my head. I would rather take my chances in the open than hide behind gasoline drums. A second later BOOM! I heard the sound of a bomb hitting on the mountain one mile east of where we were standing. I moved a few steps next to the jeep. BOOM! BOOM! Two bombs exploded on the other side of the mountain near the Salang tunnel, where Massoud's forces were actively fighting the Taliban. Then, *Whiz Pop*, a midair explosion. The jet gave off a trail of black smoke as it fell from the sky.

The driver quickly finished filling the jeep and motioned for me to climb in. We had driven 15 minutes in a southerly direction when he received a call on his handheld radio. He reported to me, "They captured the pilot."

"Pakistani?" I asked. He shrugged to indicate that he did not know.

We located Eng. Es'Haq in a new office building. He was lying on long padded cushions reading the draft of my book, which I had given him in Tashkent. Es'Haq had been a writer and editor of a Kabul newspaper, so I expected some good advice.

He shook my hand and said, "Let us have tea while we review your book."

"Did you find some errors?" I asked.

"Only a few and they are on the spelling of Afghanistan names."

We started page by page to change the spelling. His only substantive objection was the report on Massoud's having trouble controlling his troops in Kabul.

"I was there. This report of rampage did not start with Jamiat commanders as someone reported to the U.S. State Department. There were problems between soldiers and girls on the outskirts of Kabul. Reporters said a thousand girls were involved. This was not true," he said.

I made a note, and we then got into a discussion over my chapter on bin Laden and how the US claimed to be neutral between Massoud and the Taliban. American aid in the form of loans, direct funds, schoolbooks, and supplies were only being given to Pakistan, who were, in turn, supplying the Taliban. America was not sending aid or financing to Massoud. In addition, American press and the government did not condemn the Pakistani military for fighting with the Taliban. Before coming to Panjsher, I had met with Nancy Dupree in her office. Seeing a map on the wall of schoolbook distribution, I asked Nancy, "Why aren't schoolbooks being sent into Massoud's areas?"

She replied, "They are too difficult to deliver."

"I can solve that problem," I said.

"It would not be easy to get permission to send books into that area," Nancy said.

I dropped the subject not wanting to cause Nancy any problems. I knew the US would not help Massoud against Pakistani wishes.

"May this change in the future to at least a position of true neutrality." I said.

"*In She Allah* (God willing)," Es'Haq replied. "I'll be back in the US next month. We can keep in touch by email. Let me find you a jeep and driver," he said, as he walked out of the door.

It was five o'clock as I entered Tajuddin's home. I was dusty from head to toe from my ride on the dirt roads. The house was void of people. I showered and stretched out on the bed to review my meeting with Eng. Es'Haq. After 15 minutes I started to doze off – *KaBoom!* My bed shook like an earthquake high on the Richter scale. Then I heard a second *KaBoom*. This time there was only a slight movement of my bed. More blasts came a few seconds later. I counted ten bombs exploding across the mountain to the east of Panjsher towards Nahrin, where Massoud's forces were still fighting the Taliban and bin Laden's forces.

I continued to stay on the bed listening for more bombs and writing in my diary. Again I started to fall asleep as the houseboy appeared with a tray of food for dinner. By the time I had finished dinner, it was dark. I only had an oil lamp for light, so I crawled into bed for a good night's sleep.

I was up at six a.m. packing for my departure. It was a pleasant, sunny day with the temperature in the '70s. A slight breeze was blowing, just like in Hawaii, but that's where the resemblance ended. Unlike Hawaii's villages, here the homes lay in shambles from the recent bombing, and rusted-out Soviet tanks still dotted the landscape from the earlier war. Massoud had asked most of the women and children to abandon the village, so only the old men remained.

Dr. Abdullah had not given me a departure time, but it did not matter. I was ready to go. To my disappointment no one came for me. At dusk I moved to the rooftop lanai to enjoy the stars and listen for the war.

Tajuddin stopped by to say there was no news. Before he left, a tall, thin, dark-haired, young man appeared. He introduced himself as Jon Mohammad's nephew Lafullah Latif. His English was good from studies in Pakistan. He had heard that Massoud was being attacked at Takhar. So that was why Massoud and Dr. Abdullah had left for that area. Massoud had always amazed me with his ability to think one step ahead of the enemy.

I wondered how I would reach Takhar and go on to Dushanbe? I would have to fly in that very slow helicopter over the Taliban-Pakistani Army. I had lost interest in taking such a risk after seeing the jet shot down. A helicopter was much slower than that jet.

The flights were not the only problem. The Taliban-Pakistan and bin Laden forces were now fighting Massoud's forces on three sides of my position in Panjsher. Only the mountains to the west remained a safe zone, but they were too high for the helicopter. I knew the way from previous trips. It would be a long hard drive with two passes over 14,800 feet (Anjuman and Dorah). The trail was still under Massoud's control but for how long no one knew. The year before, the Taliban had tried to come to Afghanistan through Chitral to surround Massoud's troops. They had been quickly defeated in a heavy battle. They just might try it again.

Haider and his friend from the Afghan-Pakistan border had told me in Peshawar that the area was clear of Taliban just the month before. Haider's friend had a *chai-khana* in Shasidim, right on the border. If the border guards gave me a hard time, he would be my clearing agent into Pakistan.

I waited two nervous days to see if the situation improved. At two in the afternoon on August 9, I asked Tajuddin if I might call Dr. Abdullah on a satellite phone. I wanted to discuss my plans to leave and to obtain permission for gasoline that was controlled by the military. This would allow me to go to the end of the road at Eskazer by jeep. Tajuddin took me to a hidden phone, and I called Dr. Abdullah. It took us 15 minutes to contact him, and the line was bad because of the static on the other end.

"Hello, Hello," Dr. Abdullah's voice was barely audible as he explained the situation, "Massoud and his troops are pinned down on a mountaintop with intense enemy rocket fire. Use of a helicopter is out of the question."

More interference. "Commander Massoud's forces have captured a tank and approximately 300 enemy soldiers. They were engaged with a large enemy force, and Massoud was forced to give up many miles of territory.

"At this moment we do not know what will happen. We will arrange to have someone with a jeep pick you up," Dr. Abdullah promised.

"If you can just clear me for gasoline use, I can work things out here," I said.

"OK," he replied.

"Please be careful, and I wish you the very best. May God be with you, and I will see you in New York," I said.

"*Khuda Hafez* (Goodbye)," we both said.

Because I did not want to be a burden to Tajuddin nor depend on the military, I located the Frenchman Johan Freckhaus, who had been using Tajuddin's home as a stopping place. Johan spoke Farsi. I asked if he would assist me in negotiating for an interpreter and a jeep from Panjsher to Eskazer. He agreed to help me. Still, Johan was a foreigner, so we decided to send Latif, the houseboy, to the bazaar to locate transportation and get a price.

Latif returned an hour later to say, "The road is bad. They will only go for $500 to Eskazer." I knew Eskazer was 39 miles from the Pakistan border. I asked about an interpreter in case I had language problems. Latif said, "My friend and I will go with you."

"Let me get Johan," I said.

I found Johan and asked him to use his language skills to help me negotiate. When we all gathered in my room, I asked Latif how much he would charge to go with me to the Pakistan border.

He immediately replied, "We want US$600 a day each and US$1,000 for the return trip.

Johan and I stared at each other knowing the maximum wage in Panjsher is $100 a month. This price was not only outrageous, it was more than I had with me. Either they did not want to go or they thought they could make their fortune. With such attitudes, I was no longer interested in traveling with them.

"I will take a chance without an interpreter," I told Johan and Latif.

Johan said, "Let me go to the market alone and see what I can find for a jeep."

It was now four o'clock, too late in the day to think of starting a journey. Johan returned two hours later and joined me for dinner; he shared the bad news that he was unable to find transportation.

"I will go out again early in the morning," he said.

When I woke up the next morning and knocked on Johan's door, no one answered. I assumed he was out looking for a jeep, so I decided to wait with my bags packed.

At ten Johan knocked on my door. "It was not easy, but I found a driver with a decent jeep. He is preparing for the trip and will arrive here in two hours. Would you like me to go with you to Eskazer?"

"Yes," I replied.

Four hours went by before the jeep arrived. Johan and I moved rapidly to place my baggage into the jeep. To protect them, I had placed my computer and digital camera in my hard-shelled suitcase. We were driving out the gate of Tajuddin's home when Jon Mohammad blocked our way. I stepped out of the jeep and briefed him about my plan to go to Pakistan. His face turned serious as he looked at me with sad eyes, "Too dangerous, Taliban," he said.

"Where are they?"

"Chitral. And you will have border problems too," cautioned Jon Mohammad.

"No problem. I will call Haider at the Mountain Inn," I said.

"Maybe big problem," came the reply.

Just then Tajuddin walked up to us. He took Jon Mohammad by the arm and stepped back a few feet from Johan and me. I could only hear part of the conversation as Tajuddin told Jon Mohammad that Dr. Abdullah had concurred with my plan. They then started to whisper, and the discussion became heated. Jon Mohammad's face turned red, but Tajuddin seemed to be holding his ground.

Then Jon Mohammad turned to me, "OK! We go see Panjsheri."

He got into the jeep with us, and we headed north out of Bazarak. On the outskirts of the village Jon Mohammad motioned for the driver to stop. He climbed out of the jeep and said, "Wait here." He walked into a stone building. Three minutes later, he waved for me to join him. In the office Jon Mohammad introduced me to a good-looking, well-dressed man in his '60s.

"This is Panjsheri," said Jon Mohammad.

"Please have a seat and tell me your plans," said Panjsheri in excellent English.

I told him of the plan to take a jeep to Eskazer and then to locate a horse to ride and walk over the mountains to Shasidim, Pakistan. Once in Shasidim, I meant to call my friends to clear me through the border.

Panjsheri thought for a minute and then said, "I will give you a letter for Commander Malik at Eskazer. You stay with him. He will make sure you get a good horseman and horse to take you to Shasidim. Once you leave Eskazer, there is no security."

"*Tashakoor*! Thank you very much," I said in Dari and English.

Panjsheri said, "Will you join us for lunch?"

"Thank you for the invitation, but we are very late getting started. Maybe on my next trip to Panjsher," I replied.

Jon Mohammad followed me to the jeep. As we approached, he looked me in the eyes and said, "Please wait." Then he disappeared for four or five minutes. When he returned around the building, a soldier armed with an AK-47 accompanied him. "This man's name is Gulam Rahsool. I'm sending him with you to Eskazer," he said.

"Thank you, my friend," Jon looked at me long, concerned that this might be our last meeting.

We were finally on our way to Parian where we had planned to spend the night. However, as we reached Khenj two hours later, the carburetor was acting strangely and the engine was misfiring. The driver asked us to wait at a *chai-khana* while he located a repair shop.

Johan, Gulam, and I climbed the stairs to a second-story wooden *chai-khana*. As we entered, I recognized an emerald miner. He was pleased to have a visitor. After he greeted me, I asked him to find Mohebullah and Haji Abdul Rahim, both of whom had houses just across the river. Fifteen minutes later Mohebullah came in with a grin. Two other miners followed him into the small room. When they heard of our problem, they dispatched a fourth person to assist our driver.

For an hour, we sat drinking tea and eating cake imported from Iran. Mohebullah and I reminisced about our previous trips to the emerald mines. Then he explained that they were now digging around a spring near the top of the mountain. He showed my companions and me some top quality emeralds from the new deposit.

I jokingly told Mohebullah to keep the emeralds as I planned to return the following year to film the emerald mines for a TV documentary.

Mohebullah said, "My house and generator are yours."

When the jeep was repaired, the miners stocked us with grapes and cookies for our trip. Mohebullah said that he hoped to see me in Pakistan in a couple of weeks.

We had traveled only another hour when the fan belt broke. The driver had a spare, but it was larger than the broken one. By moving the alternator, they made it work even though it continued to slip. Thus, the driver had to keep stopping for water to prevent overheating the engine. It was eight o'clock and dark when we reached the house of Gulam Rahsool at Parian. We had a chicken dinner with fruit and tea before retiring for the night.

The next morning the driver told Johan that he was going to leave us and return to Bazarak. An argument ensued which involved everyone but me. I had learned from past experience to stay away from these heated discussions whenever possible.

After readjusting the fan belt, the driver, who was not given a choice by Johan, continued to drive towards the 14,600-foot Anjuman Pass. Luck was with us as we met Commander Baz Mohammad on the road. He invited us for breakfast and told the driver that he had some fan belts. He was able to install a new fan belt with few tools and a lot of Afghan ingenuity. Then he joined us for a breakfast of nan, melon, and tea. After breakfast, we continued up the

Commander Baz Mohammad and Gary

pass, but halfway up the jeep stopped again. This time it was the distributor. With a small piece of metal and some emery cloth, the driver fixed it in 30 minutes with the help of four mechanics who had been passing in fuel trucks.

Because of the loss of Taloqan territory, the fuel trucks had to come from Tajikistan via Ishkashim, Barak, and Eskazer to Panjsher. Because of breakdowns each truck had to have a mechanic on board, and one-to-three extra people were needed to help repair broken-down bridges.

Near the end of the pass were large mountain lakes filled with colorfully spotted King Zahir Shah brown trout, which I was told the British military had stocked in the early '70s for their officers' fishing enjoyment. I asked two men at the *chai-khana* how large the trout were in one lake. Both replied they did not know as they kept breaking their poles. We stopped at the lakeside *chai-khana* for a trout lunch. I consumed ten of the fish myself. With a full stomach and a vehicle to travel in, I hadhigh spirits indeed. The countryside was shiny green with grass, golden with wheat, and red with clay foothills.

By late in the afternoon, we were approximately four hours from Eskazer. Unfortunately, when we discovered two gas trucks stuck in the mud, blocking the single-lane dirt road, we could not simply drive around because the fields on both sides acted like quicksand when they were wet. After two hours, the trucks were towed out. Then it was our turn to be pulled through the muddy path by the jeep ahead of us. Again we were on our way. All was well until we reached a steep road about ten miles from Eskazer. After six attempts of our vehicle to climb the hill, the driver refused to try again. None of our party disagreed. Even though we had pushed and pulled, our assistance on the last three attempts had failed to obtain results. This left us standing on the road with unloaded baggage in the black night as a truck full of grapes arrived. The driver was in good spirits and agreed to squeeze Gulam, Johan, and me in for a ride to Eskazer.

At Eskazer the road was barricaded by Commander Malik's armed troops. I handed the first guard my letter from Panjsheri. He read the note and asked us to follow him up the steep hill to the command post. While we waited for Commander Malik to appear, we were served

Coke and tea. Within 20 minutes Commander Malik had added his note to my letter, asking the commander at Tope-Khana to provide safe passage. However, he added that I would not find any security from Eskazer to Tope-Khana. He sent one of his soldiers to locate a strong horse and horseman who could be trusted to travel with me for the next three days to Shasidim. Just as we were finishing our chicken dinner, the soldier returned.

"Your horse will be ready at four in the morning. I will wake you then to take you to the horseman."

As I had slept in my clothes the past three days, I couldn't see any reason to change. There was no way to bathe, so I just took off my shoes and fell into a deep, exhausted sleep. I woke up and was getting my bearings when the soldier came to my side. Johan woke up as I was pulling on my tennis shoes. We wished each other good luck as I walked past him to the door.

In the small bazaar with less than ten small shops, I met my horseman Mohammad Sayyef. The soldier informed me that the price was to be 40,000 Afghanis (US $64) which I approved. We added my small suitcase and my sports bag with cameras to the grain bags on the black

Mohammad Sayyef

stallion. This placed me high on the horse with only reins to hang onto. I was a bit apprehensive about my balance as we started down the trail. This feeling soon intensified. Directly in front of me was a rapidly moving wide stream that I had to ride across. I would have liked an hour to renew my riding abilities before attacking the stream.

Fortunately, my stallion was strong. He slowly picked out his footing across the rocky-bottomed stream, only twice slipping slightly as the surging water hit him in the side. My shoes, socks and legs were soaked by the cold water, but I reached the other side safely. "Pakistan here I come!" I thought.

For the next three days, we traveled from high mountain pass to high mountain pass. Mohammad and I shared the horse by taking turns hiking. On some of the steep, sandy passes neither one of us could ride. We traveled from five a.m., when it was still dark, until dark returned each day. Near dusk we would start looking for a chai-khana in which we could find food and a place to sleep. During the next few days men with their donkeys loaded with lapis would stop and share their lunch of stale bread and tea heated in a pot over a sage fire.

The high mountain passes become very cold at night, and with only my patu for warmth, sleep was difficult for me. One of the men who had shared his lunch with me placed his only blanket over me for warmth. Thanking him, I covered myself. As soon as I did, hundreds of fleas from the infested blanket began furiously biting me. Thankfully, the night's darkness kept the man from knowing that I had immediately flung the blanket away from where I was sleeping.

Still itching from the fleabites, late in the afternoon of the third day, I arrived at the Tope-Khana command post. The guards told us that the commander was not present and that we would have to wait for his return to pass through the territory. This was fine with me. I was tired and wanted assurance from the commander that it was safe before continuing over Dorah Pass. During dinner I met a Chitrali who was on his way home. I asked him to carry a letter to Haider asking for transportation from Shasidim to Chitral.

Gary's traveling companions met on the trail

By eight p.m., a messenger arrived at the *chai-khana* with a handwritten permission note in Dari from the commander for us to proceed. At ten o'clock Mohammad and I reached the lake at the base of the Dorah Pass. I looked up. Geologists claim that these mountains are growing at the rate of human fingernails. I'm not so sure. The Dorah Pass seemed to have risen another half mile since my last trip. In actuality, it was much steeper due to the condition of the road. Wanting to prevent a second Taliban attack, Massoud's forces had all but destroyed it.

Mohammad and I climbed for three hours to reach the top. We found snow on the last two hundred yards. Too tired to appreciate the sun's beauty as it glistened radiantly on the freshly fallen snow, I counted my steps. One, two, three, slowly to a set of 25, resting after each set to catch my breath. Nearing the top exhausted and weak, I sat down for the final time before heading down the opposite side of the pass toward Pakistan. Not far from the top of the pass, we stopped at a *chai-khana*. There a man in his late '30s was suffering from altitude sickness. As two men held him, a third man was throwing cold glacier water on his face. The man with the water bucket looked at us, "He is dizzy from the mountain. His heart is going boom, boom, boom. Do you have any medicine?"

"Sorry, no," I replied, noting that the man was sweating profusely.

"I'm not a doctor, but it appears your friend has altitude sickness. I recommend you use a horse to take him down the mountain immediately."

They took my advice and started down the mountain.

Mohammad and I entered the *chai-khana* and asked the men for a phone and information about conditions ahead at the border post.

The owner replied, "No phone and no problem for Pakistani and Afghans, but I do not know about foreigners."

"Do you know Haider Ali Shah from Chitral?" I asked.

"Yes, he is a friend of my brother," the owner replied.

"Do you have a phone," I asked.

"No!" was the reply.

"I'm a friend of Haider's. Do you know anyone who can help me at the border or at Shasidim?" I asked.

"You should see Gulam Es'Haq. He is from Chitral. He has a shop at Shasidim," he replied.

Two hours later my horse apparently realized the lower altitude and the upcoming end to the trip. He started prancing down the mountain trail leaving Mohammad a few hundred yards behind. My light-headedness ebbed, and my strength returned. I knew that the arduous journey would soon be over.

Approximately one hundred yards from the first building in Shasidim, my horse came to an abrupt halt before a wire strung across the road. At the end of the wire on the right side of the road sat three Chitrali Scouts on rocks. The first I approached appeared friendly; however, after smiling, he motioned for me to turn around and go back up the mountain. I motioned to him that I wanted to go into Shasidim. He shook his head no!

I looked back to see Mohammad coming. I pointed at Mohammad and motioned that I was waiting for him. Unfortunately when Mohammad arrived, he immediately got into a disagreement with the guards who obviously desired us to return from whence we had come. They refused entry to both of us.

The guard who had shaken my hand earlier stepped back to get away from the discussion. I walked over to him. Pointing to the shops ahead I said, "Gulam Es'Haq." It worked as well as *Open Sesame*. Immediately he smiled, walked over to the other guards, tapped them on the back and said something to them. Then he turned to me, smiled and motioned for us to continue into Shasidim. I shook his hand again and continued to lead the horse down the mountain into the bazaar.

It was a small bazaar with 20-to-30 new wooden shops facing each other on both sides of a narrow dirt road. Behind the shops, I could see three or four small stone-and-mud homes and a large corral full of horses. In addition to the shopkeepers, there appeared to be approximately a hundred Afghan horsemen purchasing supplies for a return trip to their villages. Beside the last shop, I could see five very large Pakistani brightly-decorated trucks that had apparently just delivered goods to the shopkeepers.

At the first shop I looked at the shopkeeper and asked, "Gulam

Es'Haq?"

The shopkeeper pointed two doors down and across the road. As I walked to the shop, I saw a dark-haired thin man wearing a Nike baseball cap.

I said, "Are you Es'Haq?"

"Yes," he replied in English.

"I'm a friend of Haider Ali Shah. I just arrived from Panjsher Valley."

"Come into my shop," he replied.

I followed Es'Haq to a 12-foot by 12-foot back section. Within three minutes, he had served me tea and cookies. I told him about sending a note to Haider. He informed me that if Haider did not arrive, he would arrange other transportation to Chitral in the morning.

"There may be some problem with the Pakistani Army guards for you on the way. I will talk to some friends to solve the problem." Es'Haq reassured me.

"Thank you! Is there a place I can stay the night?" I asked.

"You are welcome to stay here in the shop with us," he said. "Just relax, and we will have dinner prepared in two hours."

Mohammad excused himself to take care of the horse. I gave him $20 in Afghani, the balance of the money for the horse rent plus a $10 tip. He was very happy. I knew he would want to shop before returning to Afghanistan.

That night as we started to eat dinner, a uniformed policeman entered the shop. He avoided looking at me and only talked to Es'Haq. Thirty minutes later he got up to leave and smiled at me for the first time. As soon as he departed Es'Haq said, "I asked him to go all the way to Garam Chasma tomorrow morning to see that you are not bothered by any guards."

Feeling safe, I slept very well on the wood floor that night. The roosters woke me up as the sun was rising. Es'Haq and his helper were still sound asleep. I crept out of the shop and went to a stream just outside the village to wash as much of my body as I could without taking off my shalwar-kamese. Then I sat for some 15 minutes watching the sun over the high mountains.

Mohammad had disappeared after we arrived, but then I spotted him coming up the road with the stallion. I caught up with him as he stopped at the shop where I had been. He was looking for me to say goodbye. Es'Haq convinced him to have breakfast before heading home. Mohammad had admired my tennis shoes, and he had traveled the whole trip in sandals. I asked Es'Haq to translate that I had a mountain trip planned with Haider. We were going to search the base of Mt. Tirichmir for fossils. Once the trip was completed, I would find a way to send my shoes to Es'Haq so Mohammad could pick them up on his next trip to Shasidim. At first Mohammad refused to accept the gift.

"Tell him I insist."

Then Mohammad smiled deeply and shook my hand.

By noon there was no sign of Haider. Es'Haq said, "You can rent a jeep for US$100, and the policeman will go with you."

"How much shall I pay the policeman?" I asked.

"Nothing. He is doing this as a favor for me. He could get into trouble if he accepts money." Es'Haq said.

That sense of ethics was a pleasant surprise to me in this land of *bakshish*. Thirty minutes later I was in a jeep on the way to Garam Chasma and on to Chitral. For the first time I would be able to see the pass to Garam Chasma in the daylight. The green valleys with ripe crops and fruit trees looked especially enchanting from the seat of a vehicle. At one spot steaming hot sulfur water was flushing out of the ground like a fire hydrant. It reminded me of how pleasant it would be to take a bath.

When we reached Garam Chasma, the driver stopped to let the policeman out. He had just turned the key to start the engine when a red jeep pulled up and blocked our path. Haider had sent the driver to fetch me. I felt as if I were home with family. It felt good, but I would soon be ready for more adventures.

Massoud's forces are in Panjsher Valley (Kapisa Provence) while heavy concentration (est. 15,000) of Taliban and al-Qaeda (est. 5,000) are moving north, east and south from Kabul, Salang, Pul-i-Khumri, Baghlan, Nahrin, Eshkamesh and Taloqan. (August 2002)

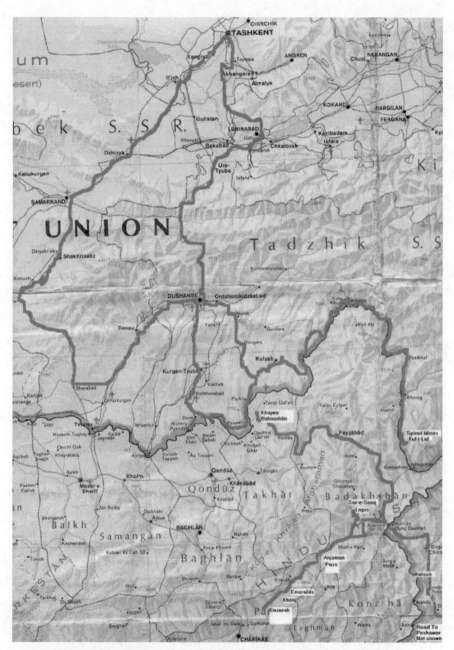

Gary's 2001 ground travels in Afghanistan,Tajikistan and Uzbekistan

Epilogue

2001 – 2003

If this tale were a movie, the good guys would arrive to save the settlers, just in the nick of time. In the old movies, the good guys wore white hats, and the bad guys wore black hats making them easy to identify. There would be a happy ending. Unfortunately, real life seldom happens this way, and it has never happened like this in Afghanistan. Reality there has always been much more complex.

During the summer of 2001, I explored for gems in Tajikistan and traveled along the Tajikistan side of Afghanistan's northern border. My discoveries from that trip are for another book, later in life.

When I left Tajikistan at the end of July, I continued on to Peshawar, Pakistan for my prearranged meeting with a European film crew. Once there, I met up with Paul Reddish, Wolfgang Knopfler, Ian McCarthy, Joe Knauer and my traveling companion Khudai. Together we managed to sneak across the border into Afghanistan. Our goal was to shoot film footage for a one-hour documentary film to be titled either *The Gem Hunter in Afghanistan* or *The Lost Mines of the Pharaohs*. The script called for us to visit the lapis and emerald mines of Afghanistan that I described in this book – which was in draft form at

Film crew on the trail in Badakhshan

2001 Documentary film
"The Gem Hunter in Afghanistan"
aka "The Lost Mines of the Pharaohs"

Paul Reddish, film director,
reviews film script

Paul Reddish and Ian McCarthy
shoot Alexander the Great scene

Kalash dance

Gary and Khudai Nazar discover vein of lapis in the Sar-e-Sang lapis mines

Riazudin, Haider Ali Shah, and Pahlawan Bahader portray Marco Polo, his father and uncle

Film crew dinner at Jon Mohammad's Guest House in Panjsher Valley L-R: Ian McCarthy, Paul Reddish, Gary, Wolfgang Knopfler, and Joe Knauer

that time. This we did.

Before leaving Pakistan, we learned that it had become Pakistan's plan to destroy Commander Massoud and his forces, thus controlling Afghanistan by controlling the Taliban. We were glad to leave Peshawar as it was becoming a very dangerous place for Westerners.

We had a fairly peaceful trip filming in Afghanistan, meeting with friendly local tribesmen, and even trout fishing near Anjuman Pass. However, when it came time to meet with Massoud, we discovered that he was in heated battle against Taliban and al-Qaeda forces. We were taken to the frontlines at Khawja Bahaouddin where we experienced the war first-hand as we interviewed Massoud.

At that time, the battles were not going well for Massoud. Pakistani irregulars were flooding into Afghanistan, loaded with heavy arms and equipment, to join the Taliban. We wondered if Massoud could hold out. His only tactic was to delay the Taliban and al-Qaeda forces, praying for justice for his people and hoping for Western intervention on his behalf.

Sitting at a table with Commander Massoud after our film interview, I asked if he would be willing to come to Washington, DC to meet with U.S Secretary of State Colin Powell at the State Department. Colin Powell and I had been U.S. Army Captains in Viet Nam at the same time even though we never met. Massoud agreed to attend a meeting if it could be arranged. It was a long shot, but worth a try.

When it came time to leave, Massoud graciously offered to airlift the film crew and their canisters of exposed film to Tajikistan's safer grounds. The grateful crew was airlifted out while Khudai and I crossed northern Badakhshan by vehicle to Tope-Khana near the border of northwest Pakistan. Once through the minefields at Tope-Khana, we split up. Khudai was off to Panjsher, and I headed for the Dorah Pass and Pakistan.

While in Peshawar, I witnessed arms and collections of money for Afghanistan to support the Taliban and al-Qaeda. This was as distressing as it was maddening! What about the United Nations' ban on weapons to Afghanistan? One Pakistani told me smilingly "No problem, we are topping off the arms shipment with wheat – food items can be sent legally!"

Osama bin Laden
t-shirts on sale in Peshawar

When I returned to the U.S. on August 31st, I immediately called the U.S. State Department in Washington, DC. A number of the officers that I had known in the past had been transferred, but Geeta Pasi, Afghanistan Desk Officer, agreed to meet with me on September 6th in her office.

I drove to Washington and arrived at the State Department on time and was cleared through security. Geeta had arranged for her supervisor, Pushpinder Dhillon with the Pakistan and Afghanistan Affairs Office, to join us. I told them of my meeting with Commander Massoud, the weapon shipments from Pakistan into Afghanistan, the Taliban and al-Qaeda cash collection boxes, and the large number of Pakistani fighters crossing into Afghanistan to join the war against Massoud.

They listened and seemed concerned until I asked them to assist in arranging a meeting between Commander Massoud and Colin Powell. Their reply still rings in my ears to this day.

"There is no interest in such a meeting."

Upon hearing this, I asked them to simply pass the request along to Colin Powell. Our meeting ended shortly thereafter. We shook hands, and I left the State Department with a lump in my throat and a large pit in my stomach.

On September 9th, 2001, just three days after my fruitless trip to the State Department, the world received news that Ahmed Shah Massoud had been fatally injured by two Arab suicide-bombers who had gained access to him by posing as TV journalists. Massoud died from his wounds soon after.

Two days later, the world was shaken by the horrifying events of September 11th. Al-Qaeda had brought its hatred of the United States to American soil and had killed innocent Americans within our own borders.

This unspeakable horror pushed death on a mass scale right in our faces. The spectacle of planes crashing into the twin towers causing explosions, smoke, flames, and victims leaping to certain death were right there on television, over and over again, for all to see. It was unreal! I watched and watched: shocked, horrified, numbed, and finally worried for a world in which such things were allowed to happen.

Then the anger set in. I began to think "Great job, State Department! If you are doing your job, why do so many millions of people – from Burma to Bangladesh to India to Pakistan to Afghanistan to Iran to Iraq to Syria to Saudi Arabia to Palestine to Lebanon – hate the American Government? Who are you people? What are your credentials? Where is the wisdom and insight that we as Americans have every right to expect from those who are supposed to be serving our needs? Who is really in charge at the State Department, and to whom do they truly answer? Why do we fund and support countries that support the likes of the Taliban and al-Qaeda?

Why? Why?

If we are such a great democratic country and such decent people with so much wealth and technology to share, why do so many people hate our government?

I tried to comprehend the magnitude of the suffering in New York and in Washington and in Pennsylvania ... and in Afghanistan: the dead, the dying, the eight million hungry Afghans, the injured children, the soldiers killed by friendly fire, the limbs of so many, many villagers shattered by land mines. Then I tried to stop. To stop staring out the window, to stop waiting for another jet to demolish a building, to stop fearing what was to come next.

Within a few days of the aftermath of *9-11,* the aftershock caught up with me. My jeweler friends abruptly canceled all but two of the *Afghan Connection* fall jewelry store events. They feared the possibility of some sort of Afghan backlash. Without these shows at which to sell my gems, I was out of business! Few people wanted to hear – or cared – that by purchasing gems mined in the Northern Alliance areas they were giving financial support to the only people in the world who were actively fighting al-Qaeda and the Taliban in open battle. Both Western journalists, as well as our own State Department, apparently lost this fact. No one seemed to hear that Afghans were *not* flying those planes on 9-11! All I heard was "Blow Afghanistan off the map!"

Being without work was a major financial setback, but it offered me time on my hands and that was OK. I was starting to receive calls from various U.S. intelligence organizations. I soon returned to Washington, DC, armed with my photos, my maps, my knowledge of minefields and caves in Afghanistan, and perhaps most mportantly, my knowledge of *Who Was Who* in Afghanistan.

Our Gems-Afghan.com website received over one million hits in two weeks because we were reporting news about Afghanistan. I appeared on the TV show *Good Morning America* and on CNN News. At least I had an opportunity to speak favorably of the Afghan people and point out the Afghan good guys to our Defense Department. And if nothing else, I had an opportunity to make a small contribution to the memory of Ahmed Shah Massoud and his noble cause by stating his case in various intelligence meetings I was invited to attend.

Furthermore, as for Ahmed Shah Massoud, he had been an emerging player on the world stage, perhaps a champion of justice, maybe even a hero. He certainly had the potential to be one of the cornerstones in a more enlightened Central Asian foreign policy. But his death went mostly unnoticed here in the U.S., lost in the shadow of the monumental events here at home. Most Americans disregarded the death of one more Afghani fighter compared to the *mother-of-all-senseless-acts.* But to Afghans the world over, the loss compared to losing a father, a hero, and all hope for a free country. To this day, pilgrims visit his green-domed mausoleum above his beloved Panjsher River and think about what might have been if he had survived to lead his nation. Some want to nominate him for the Nobel Peace Prize.

Massoud's colleagues and followers have taken many of the important positions in the new Afghan government. Dr. Abdullah is the Minister of Foreign Affairs. Anwar Khan, a Pashtun, is the Mayor of Kabul. Mohammad Es'Haq is in charge of Afghanistan's Television and Radio Organization. Former Northern Alliance leaders hold most of the important positions in Hamid Karzai's cabinet. And despite the multitude of Tajiks and Uzbeks among them, they have the support of the majority of Pashtun citizens in Afghanistan but not of the treacherous and ever-so-wily Gulbuddin Hekmatyar who now says that the US is the main enemy of Islam. Hekmatyar is the same guy our CIA supported for many years with money and guns and is accused of recent attempts on the life of President Karzai.

Finally, it seems that some of our policymakers now recognize that Massoud's Northern Alliance, the ones who finally chased the Soviets out of Afghanistan, the ones who were the only viable resistance to the Taliban and al-Qaeda, were the ones that our government should have been supporting all along. And if we had supported Massoud all along, would 9-11 have even happened?

If he were still here, I genuinely believe he would have been able to unite his country, based on his presence, his calm attention, and his faith. But he is dead. God bless him.

I returned to Afghanistan in August 2002 and then again in April 2003 with copies of the documentary film *The Gem Hunter* and my proposal to form an Afghan non-governmental organization to provide gem exploration and training for gem miners. As of this date, my proposal appears to be lost in the bureaucracy.

Afghanistan/Pakistan border taken from the Pakistan side

Gary entering tribal area on way to Khyber Pass

Gary signing in at Afghanistan border post

I will continue to go to Afghanistan but not to run mines or build empires. I will go to teach, to share what I know, to help where I can, to see old friends, to experience the raw beauty of this magnificent country, and to help create opportunities for a better tomorrow. I now find pleasure in what I can see and in what I can feel: in the pleasure of a hot shower and a fresh *shalwar-kamese* after a week in the mountains, in a simple cup of tea, and in the light glimmering off the mountain peaks in the morning sunrise.

Come with me to Afghanistan. Sit with my friends. Talk. Listen. We'll have a cup of tea. And in doing so, we will find a way to build a new tomorrow.

G.W.B

Gary presents Dr. Abdullah, Foreign Minister, with copy of "The Gem Hunter in Afghanistan" film

Afghan News as Reported by Mr. Gary
1/24/97-7/6/02

July 06, 2002

KABUL, Afghanistan – Gunmen firing assault rifles assassinated Afghan Vice President Abdul Qadir, a veteran Pashtun, as he was leaving the Ministry of Public works. Roadblocks were set up throughout Kabul but all the gunmen escaped.

Abdul Qadir was a leading rebel commander during the war against the Soviets in the 1980s. He was one of the prominent Pashtuns to join the alliance of the North. His brother, Abdul-Haq, a legendary anti-Soviet commander was hanged by the Taliban last October.

Residents of Nangarhar's capital, Jalalabad, suggested the killing could have stemmed from manifold personal, political and economic rivalries in the province.

This slaying will create further unrest through out Afghanistan.

—MrGary

June 22, 2002

Kabul, Afghanistan – Additional Ministers appointed and approved by the Loya Jirga:

Justice Minister – Abbas Jarimi

Information and Culture Minister – Saeed Makdoom Rahim

Reconstruction Minister – Mohammed Amin Naziryar

Urban Affairs Minister – Yusuf Pashtun

Public Works Minister – Abdul Qadir

Social Affairs Minister – Noor Mohammed Karkin

Water and Power Minister – Ahmed Shakar Karkar

Irrigation and Environment – Ahmed Yusuf Nuristani

Martyrs and Disabled Minister – Abdullah Wardak

Higher Education Minister – Sharif Faez

Civil Aviation and Tourism Minister – Mir Wais Saddiq

Transportation Minister – Mohammad Ali Jawad

Rural Development Minister – Hanif Asmar

In addition to being Minister of Education Yunus Qanooni has been appointed as Special Advisor to the President on Security Issues.

The Minister of Women's Affair's remains vacant as of this press release.

—MrGary

June 20, 2002
Kabul, Afghanistan – One giant step forward for Afghanistan this week. The Loya Jirga by a show of hands approved President Hamid Karzai's multiethnic nominations for cabinet post and ministerial appointments as follows:

Defense Minister – Mohammad Qasim Fahim

Foreign Minister – Dr. Abdullah

Interior Minister – Taj Mohammad Khan Wardak

Finance Minister – Ashraf Ghani

Education Minister – Mohammad Yunus Qanooni

Commerce Minister – Sayed Mustafa Kazemi

Planning Minister – Haji Muhammad Mohaqqeq

Public Health Minister – Suhaila Seddiq

Agriculture Minister – Sayed Hussein Anwari

Refugee Minister – Enayatullah Nazeri

Mines and Industries Minister – Engineer Juma Mohammad Mohammadi

Small Industries Minister – Mohammad Alem Razm

Border Minister – Arif Khan Norzai

Telecommunication Minister – Masum Stanekzai

Vice President – Marshal Fahim

Vice President – Abdul Karim Khalili

Chief Justice Supreme Court – Fazl Hadi Shenwari

This is truly a historic day for Afghanistan!

—MrGary

June 13, 2002
Kabul, Afghanistan – Mr. Hamid Karzai has been officially confirmed as the head of state today at the loya jirga in Kabul.

—MrGary

June 11, 2002
Kabul, Afghanistan – Today former king Mohammed Zaher Shah formally convened the loya jirga or grand council in a 230' by 130' white air-conditioned tent on the Polytechnic University Campus on the outskirts of Kabul. For days, over 2,000 people from all over Afghanistan have been arriving via horseback and helicopter.

The former king and President Burhanuddin Rabani, president of the post communist government had announced prior to the opening that they had withdrawn their candidacies for head of state in support of Mr. Hamid Karzai.

All but 500 of the 1501 official members of the loya jirga were previously selected in regional elections. A twenty-one member loya jirga commission selected the remaining members which includes 160 women.

—MrGary

April 18, 2002

(BBC News) Florence, AL – BBC broadcast that "Former Afghan king Zahir Shah has returned to Kabul from Italy amid tight security after 29 years in exile. Delegations from all over Afghanistan – holding flowers and pictures of the former king – greeted him at the airport, overjoyed at his return. In his first message to the nation, broadcast on the BBC Pashtu service, he described it as the happiest day of his life, and pledged to do all he could to serve his country."

—MrGary

April 11, 2002

Kalamazoo, MI – Turkish and Greek troops have now joined the American and British peace keeping forces – International Security Assistance Forces (ISAF). However, there is a call from inside and outside of Afghanistan to increase their numbers. These forces need to be present in additional cities at least during the Loya Jirga.

The Interim President, Hamid Karzai and Dr. Abdullah, the Foreign Minister are holding onto power amongst continual conspiracies and infighting of old rivals often leading to bloodshed. The country continues to move towards the June deadline for a Loya Jirga. (Click here for the full Procedures, downloadable zip file)

More than 100,000 Afghans have returned home from Pakistan refugee camps. Many aid organizations have worked out programs to assist in relocation and reconstruction. GeoVision, Inc (www.gems-afghan.com) has held it's 8th Symposium on The Gems and Minerals of Afghanistan and is attempting to locate financial support to jump start a program of exploration and training, which will create much, needed employment and provide taxes and foreign currency.

Hundreds of women have applied to Kabul University for entrance. This is a right denied them during the fives years of Taliban law.

Mother Nature with snow, fierce blizzards near Salang and an earthquake centered near Narin killed many people during February and March. In addition, reconstruction projects were delayed. ACBAR Resource and Information Center (www.afghanresources.org) has resumed services in Kabul.

DVD tapes of "The Gem Hunter in Afghanistan" scheduled to be released after many delays. This film of the Afghanistan lapis and emerald trade takes you from the Namak Mandi, Peshawar gem market to inside the gem mines in Afghanistan.

—MrGary

January 30, 2002

Honolulu, Hi – The Interim President, Hamid Karzai and Dr. Abdullah, the Foreign Minister visit the USA for a series of meetings and to reopen the Embassy of Afghanistan in Washington, DC. Haron Amin is appointed the Charge D'affaire. GeoVision, Inc. announces the 8th Symposium of the Gems and Minerals of Afghanistan.

—MrGary

January 21, 2002

Honolulu, HI – The Afghanistan situation continues to improve as well as can be expected. I have been fairly silent of late. Do you remember my November 23, 2001? I reported that secret flights were ferrying Pakistan Officers out of Afghanistan. Now this story has been revived by Seymour Hersh in the current issue of The New Yorker, where he has been publishing a series of sensational investigative articles. Here is a key excerpt: "In interviews, however, American intelligence officials and high-ranking military officers said that Pakistanis were indeed flown to safety, in a series of nighttime airlifts that were approved by the Bush Administration. The Americans also said that what was supposed to be a limited evacuation apparently slipped out of control, and, as an unintended consequence, an unknown number of Taliban and al-Qaeda fighters managed to join in the exodus. "Dirt got through the screen," a senior intelligence official told me. Last week, Secretary of Defense Rumsfeld did not respond to a request for comment."

Great move guys! Did Osama bin Laden get a free ride?

—MrGary

December 24, 2001

Kalamazoo, MI – Did the US authorities depend on Pakistan authorities to capture Osama bin Laden and his al-Qaeda leaders? Apparently American authorities still do not understand the real life situation in Pakistan/ Afghanistan. They have paid little attention to the warnings of this or other Afghanistan news columns. Now we, the American citizens, have a real problem! When will Osama bin Laden and al-Qaeda strike again? From where? Now our legal ability to capture or destroy members of al-Qaeda is in jeopardy. The following articles printed outside the USA support my feelings and opinion:

"(PTI) Beijing, December 23 – Aided by Pakistan's secret services, Osama bin Laden has fled to Kashmir, according to an informer who appeared on Italian television network RaiTre. The unidentified informer who appeared on the public television in Rome on Friday, his back to the camera, said bin Laden had left his secret base in the Tora Bora Mountain area in eastern Afghanistan on December 12.

The informer, carrying documents said to be belonging to the Pakistani secret services, also said that 2,000 al-Qaeda men had succeeded in fleeing Afghanistan to various places including Kashmir and the breakaway Soviet republic of Chechnya."

"Hindustan Times (India) December 24—Most Taliban leaders have escaped the American dragnet and remain free because the Afghan and Pakistani authorities lack the political will to arrest them, it was claimed yesterday. Suspects wanted by the US are living openly after returning to their villages or slipping across the border into Pakistan, where they could be picked up within hours, according to an intelligence source who named the alleged location of several senior officials." Rory Carroll in Kabul, December 24, 2001 The Guardian (UK)

When will we as American learn not to lean and depend on Pakistan for help in this crises?

—MrGary

December 22, 2001

Kalamazoo, MI – FINALLY! PEACE looms over Afghanistan! More than 2,000 people crowded into the Interior Ministry Hall in Kabul as Hamid Karzai is sworn in as prime minister, with the blessing of outgoing President Burhanuddin Rabani. Just to have a past ruler present for a change in governments sets a new record for Afghanistan.

The new government established in Bonn, Germany will rule for six months. At the end of that period a tribal council called a "loya jirga" will convene to plan a two-year administration that will take Afghanistan toward a permanent constitution.

During the three-hour ceremony attended by many foreign representatives, a large portrait of Ahmed Shah Massoud was draped behind the podium as speaker after speaker referred to him reverently. Massoud was probably smiling to hear of the Pakistani, Taliban, and Osama bin Laden's troops on the run out of Afghanistan.

—MrGary

December 6, 2001

London, England – We can all sleep tonight with thoughts of peace as the Bonn agreement is signed. A copy of the complete text with the official appointments listed is available for your review.

—MrGary

November 23, 2001

Honolulu, HI – After years of Pakistan governmental denial of Pakistan troops assisting and even controlling the Taliban war, two Pakistan Air Force helicopters pulled out two of their top military commanders trapped in the besieged Kunduz town. Two officers, both of Brigadier rank, were said to be part of 1000-strong regular Pakistani army men trapped in Kunduz. The rescue operations were mounted by Pakistan's elite Special Services Group. This is the second time in recent weeks that reports have surfaced of Pakistani helicopters or aircraft landing in Afghanistan on "mysterious missions." Earlier, CNN had reported a Pakistani Air Force plane landing in Taliban's southern Afghanistan stronghold of Kandahar.

In Islamabad yesterday, the Pakistani leader, General Pervez Musharraf, called on the International Red Cross to try to save his fellow countrymen and other foreign fighters who were captured by the Alliance. But Jakob Kellenburger, the Red Cross' president, said the organization could not "get involved in political negotiations on conditions of surrender."

Some al-Qaeda fighters are also believed to have escaped. Donald Rumsfeld, the US Defense Secretary, said bluntly that "al-Qa'ida's foreign fighters must be apprehended and disarmed" but he neglected to mention the Pakistani army personnel.

Truth prevails with American security forces closing their eyes in defense of Pakistan!

—MrGary

November 13, 2001

Kalamazoo, MI – THE NORTHERN ALLLIANCE (UNITED FRONT) TAKES AND CONTROLS KABUL!

—MrGary

November 12, 2001

Kalamazoo, MI – A bad news day! An American Airlines Airbus with 246 passengers and nine crew members crashed in a New York City residential area. The Pakistan Dawn paper reported the arrest of two retired nuclear scientists who were instrumental in the development of Pakistan's atom bomb. They have been in Afghanistan and are supporters of Osama bin Laden and

the Taliban. The only good news is that the Northern Alliance (United Front) forces, with American support, have broken the Taliban front lines near Kabul.
—MrGary

November 11, 2001

New York City, NY – The Taliban defeats reported on all fronts

North and North East, Afghanistan: The Northern Alliance (United Front) has captured Mazar-e-Sharif and Taloqan, the provincial capital of Takhar province. Pul-e-Khumri is now under Northern Alliance control which blocks the escape route of the Taliban forces in the Northeastern region.

Western, Afghanistan: Commander Ismail Khan's forces have captured Qala-u-Naw, the provincial capital of Badghis which opens the road to Herat.

South and Southeastern Afghanistan: The Pashtun tribesmen are starting to organize for a movement against the Taliban.

This war may end sooner than most experts predict!
—MrGary

November 3, 2001

Washington, DC – The Northern Alliance (United Front) and the US Department of Defense are formulating joint operation plans for Afghanistan and Osama bin Laden. FINALLY!
—MrGary

October 31, 2001

Washington, DC – Terrorists suffer heavy casualties. Sections of the front lines manned by Taliban, Arab and Pakistan fighters have been hit hard. Most of the fixed-wing planes of the Taliban and some of their helicopters have been destroyed. Besmullah Khan, a senior Mujahideen commander fighting against the Taliban north of Kabul, described the US attacks as "precise," but said they were not intensive enough to change the military balance quickly. The air campaign has resulted in the destruction of air defense and radar systems of the Taliban and their ammunition and fuel dumps. He said US air raids have succeeded in destroying six Taliban tanks and a large number of their heavy guns close to Bagram Air Base, 30 miles north of the capital Kabul.
—MrGary

October 30, 2001

Washington, DC – The following article was e-mailed to me today: "Veiled but deadly – female fighters who defy Taliban By Philip Sherwell in Qalai Khoja – news.telegraph.co.uk – Sunday 28 October 2001

ARMED with Kalashnikov assault rifles and machine guns, the women of Bagram are ready for the Taliban. In the male-dominated Islamic territory of northern Afghanistan, the opposition fighters have a secret weapon – their wives.

Sharifa rarely leaves the mud-walled compound of her home on the front line, 25 miles north of Kabul. She is forbidden to socialize with men who are not immediate relatives, and she sees the world through the mesh of a head-to-foot burqa.

Three years ago, however, after the Taliban militia briefly stormed her village of Qalai Khoja, her husband taught her to use an AK47. Her prowess with a gun saved her life last year when the Taliban staged another raid on the village while the men were away in the trenches.

From their roofs, the women of Qalai Khoja saw the intruders coming. Nine of them, including Sharifa, grabbed the weapons their husbands had left for them and saw off the attackers in a firefight in a cornfield. She recounted proudly: "I fired 500 bullets and we killed 25 Taliban." Asked what she would do if the Taliban attacked again, she said without hesitation: "I would shoot them. I wouldn't ask questions."

—MrGary

October 27, 2001

Washington, DC – The Frontier Post Reported that "Taliban militia Friday mowed down former Mujahideen commander Abdul-Haq after capturing him in Loghar province. Haq, who had attracted widespread media attention after returning to Peshawar recently and making known his intention to embark on a peace mission, had slipped into Afghanistan to prepare ground for a broad-based government led by former monarch Zahir Shah. Taliban's official Bakhtar news agency said he was executed for treason. Haq was captured early Friday, apparently after one of his sponsors in Afghanistan betrayed him."

—MrGary

October 19, 2001

Washington, DC – American and British troops are entering Afghanistan on two fronts near the Pakistan borders on the south and east. The southern group is reported to be 100 US Army Rangers with a mission to raid the USA constructed Kandahar airport. Kandahar is the base of the Taliban leadership. The Northern Alliance reports that they have yet received any of the arms nor ammunitions promised. This will hinder their ability to control the areas recently captured around Mazar-e-Sharif.

—MrGary

October 17, 2001

Kansas City, MO — The undersigned has unconfirmed news that the Northern Alliance (United Front) has entered Mazar-e-Sharif, the northern gateway city of Afghanistan from the south and south-east. Mazar-e-Sharif could provide US troops with an airport and operational base location inside Afghanistan.

—MrGary

October 14, 2001

Washington, DC – Per AP, "American troops can operate from an Uzbekistan air base and the United States pledged to protect the security of the former Soviet republic on Afghanistan's northern border, an agreement between the countries says."

—MrGary

October 10, 2001

Washington, DC – Central Asia is starting to cooperate with the USA. The undersigned received information that Tajikistan, with its more than 800-mile border and bridges into Afghanistan, will allow U.S. open airspace and bases.

—MrGary

October 9, 2001

US Continues to Hit Afghan Targets

Washington, DC – The United States launched a third night of raids on targets in Afghanistan. Members of the Northern alliance claim to have cut off the main north-south supply route for troops of the ruling Taliban, putting the Taliban forces there in jeopardy.

A Northern Alliance representative informed the undersigned that the alliance troops took control of the route through the western Baghlan province Monday night when 40 commanders and 1,200 fighters allied with the Taliban defected.

Northern Alliance Foreign Minister Abdullah Abdullah told reporters that "U.S. and British airstrikes have cut off the Taliban air supply routes to the north, leaving the Taliban only a long circular route through western Afghanistan to supply the north, Abdullah said. This has put the Taliban in a very difficult situation."

Defense Secretary Donald Rumsfeld told a Pentagon briefing on Tuesday that attacks against targets in Afghanistan had damaged air defenses to the point that raids could now be flown at will and around the clock. "We've struck several terrorist training camps. We've damaged most of the airfields — I believe all but one, as well as their anti-aircraft radars and launchers."

—MrGary

October 8, 2001
US Hits Afghan Targets

BBC News Monday, 8 October, 2001, 02:25 GMT 03:25 UK – The United States and Britain have launched a series of strikes by warplanes and cruise missiles against targets in Afghanistan. Fifteen bombers, 25 strike aircraft and 50 Tomahawk cruise missiles fired from navy vessels in the Arabian Sea were used against targets including the Taliban regime's air defenses and aircraft.

—MrGary

October 4, 2001
Washington, DC – An outbreak of ebola-style killer virus which causes patients to bleed to death has been reported on Afghanistan's southern border with Pakistan by Tim Butsher of The Telegraph-UK. "At least 75 people have caught the disease so far and eight have died."

—MrGary

September 30, 2001
Washington, DC – President Bush says "We will strike the Taliban," and "We need a program to make it happen." However, it is a fact that American officials have not contacted officers of the Northern Alliance who are in Washington, DC and on the Afghanistan battlefield with the forces fighting the Taliban and Osama bin Laden. Our US newspapers report aid to Pakistan and Afghan refugees. Yet, they have not discussed even medical aid to the Northern Alliance.

The undersigned met personally with Engineer Es'Haq, the Washington, DC representative of the Northern Alliance to confirm the above. On September 29, 2001 David Rohde, NY Times News, quoted General Baba Khan, saying "American military officials have not contacted them in search of that information." Both Engineer Es'Haq and General Baba Khan stressed that they and others in the Northern Alliance would like to assist our officials with information. Why do we not ask for information? If the American officials are afraid of direct contact with the Northern Alliance, they can contact me. I will get the information for them.

—MrGary

September 25, 2001
Washington, DC – Engineer Mohammad Es'Haq, representative of the Northern Alliance-Massoud's followers, informed the undersigned in a long meeting last night that no one from the US Government has discussed working with their forces or providing aid. Es'Haq's statement was confirmed today by the undersigned talking with several US Government personnel about working with the Northern Alliance.

Some of our supporters are copying our Afghan News from January 24, 1997 to date and mailing it to their Senators, Representatives and local news papers. Maybe they will better understand the problem with the situation summarized in front of their eyes.

Please feel free to copy this news from the beginning and pass it on!

—MrGary

September 23, 2001 – Editorial

WARNING! AMERICA

IS OSAMA BIN LADEN THE BAIT IN THE TRAP?

Pittsburgh, PA – Warning! Osama bin Laden may be the bait in the trap to severely damage the American Military. History may repeat itself! Americans, remember how General George Custer rushed into battle against the American Indians with a superior trained force. Remember how the British were going to control the Afghans with a controlling force. Both armies were totally annihilated to the last man.

During 1979 and 1980, the Soviet Union was determined to take over control of Afghanistan with 100,000 troops. Ten years later, they returned home after a loss of between 50,000 to 100,000 soldiers. They never came close to controlling the country.

Now comes America! We are threatening to charge into Afghanistan after Osama bin Laden and the Taliban. The American troops will find that Osama bin Laden and the Taliban forces are ready and on their own turf. On the west and south of Afghanistan is Pakistan, whose citizens are hanging President Bush in effigy. In the northwest we have poor relations with Tajikistan. On the northwest, Turkmenistan has been having friendly relations with the Taliban. On the east is Iran and Iraq. No help for America! Now let's take a look at the superpowers! We had a heavy hand in destroying The Soviet Union forces in their attempt to control Afghanistan. Recently America criticized Russia for attacking Osama bin Laden's followers and other Moslems in Chechyna. China is on the move politically to attract Pakistan into their sphere of influence. A weaker USA is to their advantage. Saudi Arabia recently announced that they do not want us to launch any war from their territory.

American foreign policy and aid has for year's ignored the Northern Alliance. The Northern Alliance is recognized by the United Nations and more than sixty other countries as the legal government of Afghanistan. They have an army in the field fighting Osama bin Laden's Arab followers, the Taliban, and its Pakistani supporters. The American forces need to enter Afghanistan with the support of the Northern Alliance and with the objective to protect and free the Afghan people from foreign oppression.

—MrGary

September 22, 2001

Peshawar – BBC reports:

(1) "On Thursday, hundreds took to the streets of the northwestern city of Peshawar chanting anti-US slogans and torching an effigy of President George W. Bush."

(2) "Protesters in Peshawar, a trading city near the Afghan border, shouted 'Death to America,' 'Long Live Osama bin Laden,' and wrote 'Dog Bush' on an effigy of the US president."

On the wire – Jeff Franks and Arthur Spiegelman (Reuters) report:

"The United States launched what it originally called 'Operation Infinite Justice' to move military equipment and personnel into place should military action be needed. The government said it would put up to 500 U.S. warplanes within striking distance of Afghanistan and ordered U.S. Army units to deploy for possible operations. Defense Secretary Donald Rumsfeld said the campaign's name likely would be changed to something less offensive to Moslems, who believe that only God or Allah can mete out infinite justice."

Van Wert, OH – We at GeoVision, Inc. (The Afghan Connection) have survived the web attacks-so far. We received this message:

"I have found that most Afghanistan websites – pro or anti Taliban – are off air due to hacking attacks – except the Afghan New Network, the Revolutionary Association of the Women of Afghanistan, and the Afghanistan Voice The Afghan Online Press states 'We apologize to all of our loyal visitors for the recent outage in our service. This was due to a series unfortunate of attacks, and threats by ignorant and potentially violent individuals. Again, we in no way condone terrorism in any form, and our sympathies go out to all those affected by the recent terrorist attacks.'"

GeoVision, Inc. has, however, had events canceled and a few e-mails stating they will never buy anything from Afghanistan. These people do not understand we are supporting the only force fighting Osama bin Laden and the Taliban.

My friend, Fred Ward received such e-mails. We liked his response!

"re: two messages on Afghanistan.

"'I am totally in favor of boycotting any material that comes from the area of the aggressors of the World Trade Towers & Pentagon. The only problem is that I do not know what material I should be avoiding! I would not consider purchasing any Afghan lapis or tourmaline but what else should I avoid?

Doug'

"Hi Doug, it occurs to me that this would be a great opportunity to test everyone's 'gem geography!' Let's see if we can't get a list of materials coming from Afghanistan, shall we? I will start -As much as I am opposed to the 'conflict diamond' issue because I feel it is impossible to administer and would affect all the wrong people, I am even more opposed to an Afghani gem boycott. The folks who either are terrorists or are harboring terrorists in Afghanistan are NOT the gem folks. In fact, quite the opposite is true.

The gems (lapis, emeralds, aqua, spinel, tourmaline, and others) are located in the small region where the anti-Taliban rebels are in control. The very people who are fighting bin Laden and the crazed fundamentalist Taliban leaders would be the ones you would hurt by avoiding Afghan gems. My friend Gary Bowersox just returned from his usual summer gem buying trip inside Afghanistan and was here two weekends ago and will be back this weekend. He met with Commander Massoud again while there just a few days before the rebel leader was assassinated (an event that now seems certainly to have been a precursor to the USA attacks). Gary is now in Tenn. starting his fall gem tour of the USA and he has already had his next two week's events canceled in US jewelry stores..... because business is down and because jewelers and customers are already saying they don't want to support anything from Afghanistan.

"So, who will be impacted by this decision. Certainly not bin Laden or the Taliban. But Gary already is affected. So will the gem miners who live and work in the area opposed to the Afghani Taliban government. And regular folks in the ravaged impoverished areas will starve as the noose tightens. Gems (and unfortunately drugs) are their only cash crops. Let's not cut off the only legitimate source of income the people who are fighting the terrorists inside Afghanistan now have.

Fred Ward

Gem Book Publishers"

Osama bin Laden's goal is to "divide and conquer." We must continue to educated ourselves, keep up with events as they happen, communicate, and not allow the terrorist attacks to divide us.

—MrGary

September 21, 2001

Van Wert, OH – My E-mail box is beginning to fill with distressing e-mails such as this one from my good, long time friend in Peshawar, Pakistan. Sadly to say, this is only the beginning.

"Dear Mr Gary.

I hope my this e message will finds you in best of your health. We all are OK here. At the moment the situation in Peshawar is very bad. Today everything was closed and there was a strong agitation against USA attack on the region. Because 15000 US army is close to the region with 100 F-16 devastating aeroplanes.

As we are very close to Afghanistan so all the pressure is on Peshawar. There has been a lot of movement of Pakistan Army and in against Afghan Taliban. All the native people of Peshawar they are stuck. We are in the middle of both sides, with the guns and cannons. All over is police and army. Taliban have threatened Pakistani people. In favor of them Russia will also favor them and Iran also, in against Americans.

I strongly condemn the incident happened in World trade center, but I am against the fighting's and attacks from US. Anyway you please pray for us, that God may end this bad situation. We the people from Peshawar have been suffering since long as the Soviet regime came in to Afghanistan and the refuges in Peshawar. You know Peshawar people are all good people and always be helpful and serving to foreigners in all respects. You have a very good experience since 20 years. Can someone tell to the US govt, that Peshawar people are innocent why should they suffer for all.???

Anyway God will help us to over come this situation. Anyway I always pray for your good life and good running business.

One thing I tell to the world that all the people from this region are not bad people. You know my father served you for years, although he was not that educated. He always respected you. It really doesn't matter that if someone is not a Moslem and we should not give him respect and have brotherhood. So this is narrow minded thinking to create such distance of telling Christianity or Moslems. The media is putting so many things in wrong directions. So I tell you that we will come more close to show a fantastic example to the world that we could easily become good brothers irrespective of nation, tribe, cast and religion. So I tell you that you are my very good elder brother whom I will respect as long as I am alive.

Shortly I pray that the situation will end in a good manner. At the moment I say good wishes and I pray God may end this very bad situation soon.

Best regards from my elder brother Dr Ishaq.

Yours loving brother,

Sabir"

Note: Sabir is a Pakistani living in Peshawar It is impossible to avoid the personal emotions that hurt so deep!

—MrGary

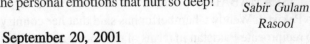

Sabir Gulam Rasool

September 20, 2001

Van Wert, OH – The President, in his address to the nation, said "We condemn the Taliban regime." The US government has directed the Taliban to turn over Osama bin Laden and all members of al-Qaida or share their fate. Our military is on full alert, and the hour is coming when we will act. All countries must determine whose side they are on.

The Taliban announced that Osama bin Laden would be allowed to leave Afghanistan, if he wants too.

President General Pervez Musharraf at 0800, September 20, 2001 addressed the nation of Pakistan, saying "The Government is trying to find a way to save Afghanistan and Taliban."

For a chilling mapping of Osama bin Laden's al-Qaida organization, click here or go to http://www.newsday.com/news/local/newyork/sns-worldtrade-graphics1.gallery.

This organization was established by Osama bin Laden in the late 1980s to bring together Arabs who fought in Afghanistan against the Soviet invasion. Their goal is to establish a pan-Islamic Caliphate throughout the world by working with allied Islamic extremist groups to overthrow regimes it deems "non-Islamic" and expelling Westerners and non-Moslems from Moslem countries. He is said to have issued a statement under the banner of "the World Islamic Front for Jihad Against the Jews and Crusaders" in February 1998, saying it was the duty of all Moslems to kill US citizens—civilian or military—and their allies everywhere.

Al-Qaida believes Islamic governments less extreme than the Taliban— in countries like Egypt, Algeria and Turkey—must be replaced with fundamentalists.

Internet research reveals that Muhammed Atef (AKA: Abu Hafs; Abu Hafs el-Masry el-Khabir; Taysir; Sheikh Taysir Abdullah), Co-founder of al-Qaida and Egyptian, who was indicted for alleged connection to the African bombings, is believed to be Osama bin Laden's successor in case bin Laden is killed or captured.

THE WAR HAS STARTED! THIS COULD BE A VERY DIRTY WAR! SADLY WAR ITSELF DOES NOT DETERMINE WHO IS RIGHT-ONLY WHO IS LEFT! MAY GOD BLESS AMERICA and ALL OUR FOREIGN FRIENDS!!

—MrGary

September 20, 2001

ISLAMABAD, September 20 (Pakistan News Service): "US ambassador to Pakistan Wendy Chamberlin has said that her country is weighing options to reciprocate Pakistan in terms of economic and political assistance in return of its co-operation during the ongoing crisis." How many billions of dollars is this going to cost the USA? In whose pockets will this money go? How effective can a dictator or president be without the support of a counties population?

In another article on the Pakistan News Service "A survey conducted by PNS here Friday in the backdrop of terrorist attacks on US and repercussions of possible US attack on Afghanistan under plea of Osama disclosed that people were unanimous in their opinion that any bid by US to launch attack on Afghanistan will not only endanger the security of the whole region but will also slide the country into unending civil war."

I continue to preach "Let's work with the Alliance of the North who have been fighting Osama bin Laden since 1996." They have the will, the desire, and troops already in the field fighting with Osama bin Laden's forces. I can not understand why we are not supporting them.

—MrGary

September 19, 2001

Washington, DC – I'm including a portion of a speech in the text of this news update as it supports much of what I have been reporting since 1996. It even adds some very disturbing details.

—MrGary

September 17, 2001

The Honorable Dana Rohrabacher (R-CA)

U.S. House of Representatives Floor Speech

Mr. Speaker, it is in deep sadness that I rise today to speak to my colleagues and to set down a record that I believe necessary to understand the horrible loss that we have suffered.

(Some paragraphs deleted)

... in 1996, a new force appeared seemingly out of nowhere—the Taliban.

These were fresh, well-equipped forces who had, by and large, sat out the war. They had been in Pakistan in what were called schools (Taliban means student, even though many, if not most, of the Taliban are illiterate.) All of the money America provided the Mujahidin during the war had to go through the Pakistani ISI (their CIA) and, apparently, enough had been siphoned off to create a third force—the Taliban. When the war was over, with the other factions bled white, they could dominate Afghanistan.

Also behind the Taliban is and has been Saudi Arabia. During the war against the Soviets, the Saudis provided the Afghan resistance with hundreds of millions of dollars. Unfortunately, they were financing anti-Western as well as anti-Communist Moslems, one of whom was bin Laden. I met the head of Saudi intelligence, Gen. Turki, and suggested to him that the exiled King of Afghanistan be brought back. It was King Zahir Shah's overthrow in 1972 that started the bloody cycle of events that eventually led to the Soviet invasion in 1979 and the subsequent war against the occupation. The Saudis wanted nothing to do with bringing back the moderate, good-hearted exiled

King. They and their Pakistani allies were in the process of creating a secret third force – the Taliban – to take over and to do their bidding.

When the Taliban first arrived on the scene, people believed they would be a force for stability, so, by and large, they were welcomed-except in the northern provinces of Afghanistan where the Taliban were blocked by local commanders unwilling to permit these unfamiliar troops to take over their territory.

All too soon, the people of Afghanistan and the rest of the world were to discover that the Pakistanis and the Saudis had created a monster. The Taliban were and are Medieval in their world and religious view: violent and intolerant, fanatics, totally out of sync with Moslems throughout the world, especially Moslems living in the Western democracies. The Taliban are best known for their horrific treatment of women, but they are violators of human rights across the board. They have jailed and threatened to execute Christian aid workers, allegedly for daring to espouse a belief in Jesus Christ. They have ended all personal freedoms; freedom of speech and press are not even a consideration. They rule by fear.

The Talibans believe they have a private line to God. The rest of us, with our religious convictions, according to the Taliban, are not only wrong but evil. That is why they have been willing to give safe haven to the likes of bin Laden, the Saudi terrorist who has been in Afghanistan for years training terrorists and planning out his attacks. Oh yes, bin Laden has an army of several thousand gunmen who have been maurading around Afghanistan like a pack of mad dogs, fighting the to keep the Taliban in power. These foreign religious fanatics have killed thousands of Afghans. So the Taliban and bin Laden are despised in most of Afghanistan.

For these last few years, the Taliban, with support from Saudi Arabia and Pakistan, have captured control of all but a small portion of the country. Only the northeastern Panjshir Valley territory in northern Afghanistan and the Shamali Plains north of Kabul, under the control of a legendary and dashing leader, Commander Massoud, remained free of Taliban domination.

The day before the attack on the United States, there was an attempt to kill Commander Massoud. Although he was reported dead, he struggled for life another five days.

The attack on Massoud told me something was about to happen, because Massoud was someone bin Laden's enemies would obviously turn to in an attack on the Taliban. I was so concerned I made an appointment to see top NSC officials at the White House. My appointment was for 2:30. At 8:45 that morning the first plane slammed into the World Trade Center.

But the Taliban domination of Afghanistan need not have happened. As a member of Congress, for years I pleaded with the Clinton Administration to provide some kind of help for the Northern Alliance. President Clinton would have none of it and, in fact his administration was, in many ways, responsible for keeping the Taliban in power.

Every time I suggest this, some people go ballistic because they believe I'm being partisan at this moment when national unity is obviously the order of the day. Unfortunately, I am not being partisan. As a senior member of International Relations committee, I officially requested State Department documents that would prove or disprove my suspicion that the Clinton Administration was secretly supporting the Taliban. I was stonewalled for several years. My request for those documents pertaining to the development of our government's policy toward the Taliban was ignored. I was given meaningless documents and the State Department made a joke out of Congress's right to oversee America's foreign policy.

By the way, in Afghanistan, it is commonly believed that the United States put the Taliban in power and supports the regime. There are reasons they believe this.

In 1996, for example, the Taliban overextended their forces and thousands of their best fighters were captured in northern Afghanistan. The Taliban regime was vulnerable as never before or since. It was a tremendous opportunity. The Alliance could have easily dealt a knockout punch to the Taliban. At that time I personally was in contact with the leaders of the Northern Alliance and recommended a quick attack and bringing back the old King, Zahir Shah, until some form of a democratic process could be established. This was a turning point.

Who saved the Taliban? President Bill Clinton. And please, I beg of you not to dismiss what I say. I am not being partisan. That would be sinful at a time like this. What happened was that, at this moment, when the Taliban could have been eliminated, President Clinton dispatched Assistant Secretary of State Rick Inderfurth and Bill Richardson, our United Nations Ambassador, to convince the leaders of the Northern Alliance not to go on an offensive against the then-vulnerable Taliban.

These two high-level American officials, sent by President Clinton, convinced the Northern Alliance to accept a ceasefire and a supposed arms embargo against all sides. Of course, the minute the ceasefire went into effect, the Saudis and Pakistanis began a massive rearming and resupply effort that rebuilt the Taliban forces. Our intelligence knew of the massive resupply effort, but we conveniently left the Northern Alliance in the dark. The Taliban offensive then started again and they drove most of the Northern Alliance out of the country.

For years I begged the Clinton Administration, our government, to support those resisting the Taliban regime, to support the former King, Zahir Shah, to let him head an interim government until a more democratic process could be put in place. Instead, the only response was a stonewalling of my request to find out what was our government's real policy toward Afghanistan.

All the while, bin Laden, who had killed American military personnel and had declared war on the United States was running around Afghanistan, using it as a base of operations, a safe haven for terrorist attacks on the Philippines (he tried to kill the Pope) and other places. We did nothing. We were, in fact, supporting the Taliban. This as part of an understanding with Saudi Arabia and Pakistan, to let them dominate Afghanistan. This understanding was obviously turning into a nightmare; yet our leaders lacked the will to change the situation. Over and over again, I warned that our policy toward the Taliban would come back to hurt our country. I was ignored and at times belittled.

But why weren't we warned by others of the horrific attack about to be launched against us? There was a headline in the Washington Post on September 14th suggesting that America's intelligence services have been conducting a secret war against bin Laden for a several years. If that is true, then we need to fire the incompetent leaders of that covert war because they were responsible for protecting us from this heinous and cowardly gang. Instead, there was no warning, yet we were told the heads of our intelligence organizations were focused on bin Laden. We spend tens of billions of dollars annually for good intelligence and have tens of thousands of people committed to this endeavor. And they totally miss a terrorist operation of this magnitude run by their number one targeted terrorist leader. This was clearly the worst failure of intelligence in American history.

I can't help but remember a few years ago I was called by a friend who worked in Afghanistan during the war against the Soviets. He indicated that he could pinpoint bin Laden's location. I passed on his phone number to the CIA. After a week, when he had yet to be contacted, I called again. After another week of no response, I contacted the Intelligence Committee here. Porter Goss, chairman of the committee, set up a meeting with the bin Laden task force (CIA, NSA, FBI). They, too, left my friend waiting by the phone. After weeks and weeks, my friend was at long last contacted. He described the agents who talked to him as somewhat disinterested. That may have been because by that time over a month had passed and the tip off was a little stale.

My friends, the slaughter of these thousands of Americans must be avenged and we must see to it that such a monstrous crime can never happen again. To accomplish this we must be strong and smart. We do not need to use our troops to invade Afghanistan. We should already be dispatching special forces teams and Rangers to those countries on Afghanistan's northern border. Those teams and other military units should establish a system to supply and equip those Afghans friendly to the United States, so that they can free themselves, with our help, from the Taliban rule. We can then join them in hunting down and killing every member of Ben Ladin terrorist gang and hanging their bodies at the gate.

Revenge is not an end in itself; otherwise we would be inconsistent with our own convictions. But by killing bin Laden and his gang of fanatics and by joining in an effort to stamp out the scourge of terrorism, we are setting a moral standard.

First, our American dead will be avenged, which will hopefully deter at least some of those swine who contemplate such attacks in the future. Second, we are affirming that targeting unarmed noncombatants, anywhere in the world for whatever reason, will no longer be tolerated. If this is to be a better world, if we are to build upon the ashes of this tragedy, we will do it by seeing to it that the bin Ladens of this planet are never given a safe haven again. And that those countries which harbor such criminals will themselves pay a price for this criminal disregard for the victims of such terrorism.

There must be an accounting. At home, those top government executives whose policies protected the Taliban, those intelligence officers who were so incompetent that this attack came without warning, must be cleared out. Those countries, Afghanistan, Pakistan, Saudi Arabia have a price to pay, and finally the murdering terrorists themselves.

We will have victory over those ghouls who murdered our defenseless fellow Americans. We will win because we are unified as never before and because this generation of Americans has the courage, tenacity, and ideals that have always been America's greatest source of strength. It's up to us and we will do our duty. And nothing will deter us.

September 19, 2001
Washington, DC – More on Pakistan's loyalty to America, copied from the Pakistan news service on the web (http://www.paknews.com/).
"China, Pakistan agree to keep close contacts
"Updated on 2001-09-19 14:12:04
"ISLAMABAD, September 19 (PNS): Pakistan is keeping close contacts and consultation with China in the backdrop of changing situation in the

region in the aftermath of US tragedy. Sources told that Chinese deputy foreign minister has delivered a special message from his government to President General Pervez Musharraf during his meeting with him held here Tuesday. Chinese deputy foreign minister also held talks with high-ranking officials at Foreign Office. He held a meeting at length with General Pervez Musharraf and discussed matters relating to prevailing situation in the region in the context of terrorist attacks on US, US demands and prospects of US likely attack on Afghanistan. Official sources said that China has elaborated its stance while Pakistan has also made its position clear in the present situation. Sources told that General Musharraf has made it clear that Pakistan will take into confidence China and other friendly countries before making any decision in response to US demands to stave off any deterioration in the prevailing situation. Chinese deputy foreign minister has also apprised the President of his government policy on the possible US attack and arrival of US forces in the region. President also told him about talks held between Pakistan delegation and Taliban leadership. Pakistan and China in a meeting held at foreign office have decided to continue the consultative process on the strategy to be evolved in the current situation."

I continue to say that "We Americans should be working with the Alliance of the North, already fighting Osama bin Laden in Afghanistan." The people of Pakistan are not going to shoot their neighbors, friends, and children of the Taliban for America. We are creating a real problem attempting to force them into such a position. This summer, during a visit to Pakistan, the undersigned heard many stores of a rapid increase in the numbers of Chinese businessman visiting Pakistan.

—MrGary

September 16, 2001 – Editorial

For 23 years, Commander Ahmed Shah Massoud, "The Lion of Panjsher," fought for the freedom and justice of the Afghan people. His moral and physical courage against unbelievable odds, combined with his brilliant military strategy, made him a legend in his time. He was a true hero to so many people, including me, from the first time I met him in 1988 (see story, Chapter 7, *The Gem Hunter*), through our last meeting this August. Massoud and his followers were one of the first groups to challenge and repel the Soviet troops during their invasion of Afghanistan (1979).

In 1994, the USA, Pakistan, and Saudi Arabia backed the Taliban in their effort to control Afghanistan. Massoud withdrew his troops safely without a fight to some 20 miles north of Kabul, where they still control that line of defense just outside Panjsher Valley.

Osama bin Laden and his followers, desiring a base of operations for their terrorist activities, associated themselves with the Taliban against Massoud's forces in an attempt to control all of Afghanistan. The USA continued to support Pakistan, who maintained the Taliban and who, in turn, supported and received support from Osama bin Laden and his followers.

Now the USA finally recognizes Osama bin Laden and his partners, the Taliban, as true enemies. Why then does the US turn to Pakistan, with its highly questionable loyalty? Instead, by honoring Ahmed Shah Massoud's vision and assisting his strong forces and the other tribal commanders already at the battlefront, we could accomplish all our aims: We could enlist the resources of native Afghans in our pursuit of bin Laden; we could defeat the radical forces of the Taliban; and we could foster and support moderate tribes in their bid for a FREE Afghanistan.

—MrGary

September 14, 2001

Oak Ridge, TN – Commander Ahmad Shah Massoud "The Lion of Panjsher" has died in Dushanbe, Tajikistan. He never recovered from wounds received when a camera bomb was exploded by two Moroccans or Algerians during an "interview" assassination plot in Khawja Bahaouddin. May God Be With Him and Guide Those Who Take His Place To Continue The Fight for Justice and Freedom in AFGHANISTAN.

—MrGary

September 11, 2001

Oak Ridge, TN – Today, a well planned, well financed group of terrorists flew two large planes owned by American and United Airlines, with passengers aboard, into the World Trade Center towers located in New York City. A third plane was hijacked and flown into the Pentagon building in Washington, DC. A fourth commercial plane was hijacked and crashed Southwest of Pittsburgh. Is this the beginning of a long World War?

—MrGary

September 9, 2001

Khawja Bahaouddin, Afghanistan – Two men, Moroccan or Algerian, posing as journalists with Belgium passports, set off a camera bomb while interviewing Commander Ahmad Shah Massoud in his office. Engineer Assim and one of the assassins died immediately. Commander Massoud and Massoud Khalili, the Afghan Ambassador to India, were wounded. The second assassin was shot dead as he grabbed a rifle to escape. Commander Massoud was reported to be in a coma with shrapnel lodged in his head, plus leg wounds and burns. What's next?

—MrGary

September 6, 2001

Washington, DC – The undersigned has heard Afghanistan and Pakistan reports of radical Moslems placing collection boxes to gather funds in mosques around the world and smuggle weapons into Afghanistan under wheat shipments. This disturbed the undersigned who personally reported this to the Afghanistan Desk Officer in her office at the US State Department in a personal meeting today. Obviously these radical people have decided to make Afghanistan their territorial base of operations. This appears to be a resurgence of the Mujahideen resistance (Wahabi) movement started in 1831 to destroy the British in Bengal and the Sikhs in the Punjab. The British were effectively harassed until 1902. The Wahabis, named after Abdul Wahab of Nejd, born in 1703, condemn any social or religious practice which has no justification in the sacred text of Islam. Beware!

—MrGary

August 20, 2001

Khawja Bahaouddin, Afghanistan – Early this morning, ten miles west of Khawja Bahaouddin, a battle started on the Afghanistan/Tajikistan border between the forces of Commander Massoud and the combined forces of the Taliban, Pakistan and Osama bin Laden. A helicopter was sent to evacuate the film crew to Dushanbe, Tajikistan. After their departure, the battle subsided and the undersigned departed by vehicle for Pakistan. See map and photos.

—MrGary

August 19, 2001

Khawja Bahaouddin, Afghanistan – Commander Ahmad Shah Massoud, Engineer Assim, Wolfgang Knoepfler, and the undersigned were watched by an international film crew as they sat peacefully at a table located under a shade tree outside of Massoud's office to exchange greetings and information. Massoud had just completed a filmed interview about the beautiful scenery and gemstones of Afghanistan for a TV documentary to be released during January 2002. The undersigned asked Massoud if he had any plans to meet with top US State Department officials in America to discuss their mutual problem – Osama bin Laden. Massoud replied that he had no current plans for such a meeting. The State Department Officials and Massoud need to talk.

—MrGary

April 1, 2001

New York – Mullah Muhammad Omar's decision to destroy the Great Buddha of Bamiyan sculptures along with continued protection of Osama bin Laden, poor treatment of women, and increased opium production is being critically reviewed by the international community and the new American administration.

Russia and the USA worked in tandem to gather United Nations Security Council (UNSC) support for sanctions against the Taliban and indirectly Pakistan. The sanctions are a necessary step towards curbing the exploitation of Afghan territory by the international Moslem extremist network.

If the USA and Russia provide support for the multi-tribal alliance being organized by Commander Ahmed Shah Massoud, the Taliban movement could possibly be neutralized within six months. Commander Massoud is now planning to increase pressure on the Taliban by building a 20,000 man force for summer 2001. These multi-tribal forces will be lead by Ismail Khan, Herat, Haji Qadeer, Kunar, Karim Khalili, Bamiyan. If these Pushtuns, Tajik, and Hazara (Shiite) leaders can neutralize the Taliban and convince Pakistan that peace is best handled via UN negotiations and elections, there is hope for the future of Afghanistan.

—MrGary

January 28, 2001

Honolulu, HI – The battles between Afghanistan's Northern Alliance and the Taliban/Pakistan forces continue on several fronts through this unusually mild winter. Early spring battles are expected. Any Taliban success will depend on its ability to draw on Pakistani "volunteers" to increase its forces and to cut off the Northern Alliances supply lines via Tajikistan. Any Northern Alliance's success may depend on the USA/Soviet actions taken against bin Laden.

—MrGary

August 10, 2000

Panjsher Valley, Afghanistan – Another "hot" summer of fighting with more people killed and little real estate exchanging hands. In June the Taliban attempted to take Panjsher Valley from the South and failed. In July they tried again via Nahrin, west of Panjsher Valley. In August the Taliban tried to gain control of Taloqan and failed with many people being killed. Massoud then gained some ground in the South east while the Taliban soldiers were busy in the North. Isn't it time for everyone to stop fighting?

There is good fishing in Anjuman pass, crops to raise and children that would like to play games with their parents.

—MrGary

June 19, 2000

Kalamazoo, MI – Mohammad Es'Haq e-mailed out the following press release after talking to Ahmad Shah Massoud last night...

"Washington, DC – June 19: Preparations for launching a major offensive by the Pakistanis and the Taliban against the Mujahideen in Shemali and Kunduz fronts of Afghanistan have been almost completed and fighting could start any moment. This was revealed by Ahmad Shah Massoud whose forces are preparing themselves for the defense of the territory they control.

Massoud said 2500 fresh Pakistani fighters have reached Afghanistan, around 1500 of whom are stationed in Shemali Front and the remaining in Kunduz. He said, General Saeeduz Zafar of the Pakistan Army has been appointed to command the operation and Brigadier Ershad will serve as his deputy. Ershad has already reached Afghanistan and Zafar is expected to reach Kabul soon. He said based on the evidence available the fighting this year will be as severe as the fighting of last summer.

Massoud said his forces were ready to put up a tough resistance against the Pakistanis and their Taliban surrogates and asked all Afghans to pray for the success of the defenders of independence and territorial integrity of the country. The Mujahideen have learned that the Pakistan air force has assigned a number of warplanes based in Kamra Air Base to take part in support missions inside Afghanistan. In the fall of 1988 and summer of 1999 Pakistani fighters from the same base took part in the operations against the Mujahideen. The Mujahideen repulsed the Taliban's attacks on Salang some weeks ago inflicting heavy casualties on them.

Forces loyal to the Islamic State of Afghanistan control 25 percent of the territory of Afghanistan and enjoy sympathy and support of a large section of the Afghan population."
—MrGary

July 2, 1999

Kalamazoo, MI – As Summer battles heat up around Kabul, the Afghanistan capital, President Clinton orders ban on U.S. trade with and investment in the 85 percent of Afghan territory under Taliban control. Official figures show the United States exported $7 million in goods to these areas last year and brought in imports worth $17 million.

About 15 percent of Afghanistan is controlled by a rival group lead by Ahmed Shah Massoud.

Clinton's trade ban includes the provinces of Kandahar, Farah, Helmand, Nimruz, Herat, Badghis, Ghowr, Oruzghan, Zabol, Paktia, Ghazni, Nangarhar, Lowgar, Vardan, Faryiab, Jowlan, Balkh, and Paktia.

For more detailed information, see http://www.treas.gov/ofac.
—MrGary

January 7, 1999

Pittsburgh, PA – Winter sets in and fighting slows as Afghanistan enters its 20th year of war. All parties of the Great Game appear to have turned their attention from winning battles to internal problems. The Taliban strategy remains to win militarily but they have not succeeded in moving Massoud. They, however, refuse to negotiate a settlement. Massoud and the Alliance of the North only have to prevent Taliban victory during the next few months to receive a moral victory. They have accomplished this effectively so far. This, however, is not a strategy for long term success. Russia, Uzbekistan, Tajikistan and Kyrgistan continue to deal with their own differences and distrust rather than deal with the Afghanistan situation. The US has pulled back its political staff and concentrated on Osama bin Laden. Narwaz Sharif has to be concerned with Pakistan's internal problems and two serious attempts at his assassination.

—MrGary

October 26, 1998

Kansas City, MO – Heavy fighting on three fronts continues between The Alliance and the Taliban. International sources are placing pressure on Russia, Uzbekistan, Tajikistan and Kyrgistan to stop assisting the Northern Alliance with military supplies. The US has yet to condemn Pakistan for its support of the Taliban with equipment and manpower. However, military experts in Pakistan are reported to believe that there is now a coordination between Iran and India to place pressure on Pakistan. There is a genuine fear that the Iranian and Indian exercises might be linked to the situation in Afghanistan.

According to the Dr. Jassim Taqui in the Oct 14th issue of the Frontier Post, "There could be two scenarios: First, Iran would attack Afghanistan through some stage of its ongoing military exercise. The target could be Kabul, Mazar-E-Sharif and Bamiyan. By conducting military exercises closer to the Pakistani border in Sindh and Punjab, the Indian objective might be to prevent Pakistan to come to the rescue of Afghanistan and to completely neutralize Pakistan. Second, the Iranian and Indian military exercises might aim at pressurizing Pakistan to "tame" Taliban in Afghanistan and to force them to accept the formation of broad-based government in Afghanistan."

—MrGary

October 13, 1998

Washington, DC – The arms companies must be smiling as the US, Russia, and Iran consider shooting expensive missiles into Afghanistan. The US is upset over Osama bin Laden's involvement in international terrorism which killed Americans. Iran is upset over the killing of their diplomats by Taliban soldiers at Mazar-E-Sharif and the Sunni Moslem Taliban killing Shiite Moslem Afghans in Bamiyan. Russia is worried about the spread of the Taliban form of Islam and the loss of oil reserves. The UN envoy for Afghanistan, Lakhdar Brahimi, has been flown to the region to search for solutions as world powers reach a boiling point.

On the ground, the Taliban forces and the soldiers of Ahmad Shah Massoud started what they consider to be the decisive battle before Winter. The major battle ground will be only 15 miles (25 kilometers) from Kabul. Fighting also has started between the two last powers in Kapisa and Baghlan provinces.

Could this be the beginning of World War Three?

—MrGary

August 15, 1998

Kabul, Afghanistan – All is jubilant and secure in Kabul as the Taliban, with the assistance of Pakistan, take over Mazar-E-Sharif. Rumor in Peshawar, Pakistan and in Kabul is that another 2,000 students primarily from the Jamiat Ulema-i-Islam in Pakistan will be joining the Taliban within a few days. Now the Taliban will concentrate on the Hesb-i-Wahdat, commanded by Karim Khalili in Bamiyan. If successful, the Taliban will then take on Ahmed Shah Massoud.

As the Taliban moves against the Hesb-i-Wahdat, tension from Iran will increase. Iran is already concerned over a Pakistani controlled Afghanistan. The US support for Pakistan's backing of the Taliban is continuing to weaken because of the Taliban support of Osama bin Laden, increase in poppy production, and its policy towards women.

—MrGary

July 14, 1998

Peshawar, Pakistan – So much for peace talks! US envoy Bill Richardson's peace drums are silent as another American white knight rides off into the sunset after a very short tour of Afghanistan and Pakistan.

The catastrophic earthquake in Takhar Province left more than 4,500 dead.

Battles are now being fought in the field and political conference rooms. Active fighting is taking place in the provinces of Kunduz, Faryiab, Wardak, Kapisa, Konar, and Kabul. The Taliban appear to be gaining some ground in Kunduz, due to infighting amongst General Aburrasheed Dostum's commanders. There is little change in the front line north of Kabul. Last week, the Taliban dropped some bombs in the Charikar area and Commander Ahmad Shah Massoud shot some missiles into the Kabul airport area. In

Konar, the battles between the Kom and the Kshto tribes over water and lumber continue. Three Kshto villages were destroyed and burned by the Kom tribesmen. Over 75 people were reported dead.

The US Government, which was previously but unofficially undeclared behind the Taliban last year, appears to be moving into a more neutral position. Secretary of State, Madeleine K. Albright, publicly warned Pakistan that Washington would no longer condone the Taliban's barbaric policies, particularly toward women and children.

Other countries active in the Afghanistan Great Game line up as follows:
Taliban: Pakistan and Saudi Arabia
Alliance of the North: Uzbekistan, Tajikistan, Russia, India and Iran,

The Alliance of the North continues to hold the official positions with the United Nations and maintains consulate offices in over 100 countries. There are reports of large arms shipments. In April, the Afghan News stated that "In March 6th Washington Times, national-security reporter Bill Gertz quoted US Intelligence officials as saying that Ukraine had 'recently' shipped 55 cargo plane loads of arms and ammunition to the Taliban by air via Peshawar, Pakistan."

In that a decisive battle between the troops of Ahmed shah Massoud and the Taliban appears currently to be out of the picture, the only long range solution available is a reuniting of the Pashtuns, which is the largest tribal group in Afghanistan. Their political influence and manpower behind either Ahmed Shah Massoud or the Taliban would create an imbalance of power within Afghanistan and break the stalemate.

—MrGary

April 20, 1998

Atlanta, GA – The Afghanistan picture brightens as tribal leaders and foreign governments search for peace. The Afghan warring parties have agreed to meet on April 27th to discuss a peace plan under UN and OIC auspices in Islamabad, Pakistan. A cease-fire is now in affect.

One of the key members in this action is Bill Richardson, who holds cabinet status in the US government as Washington's ambassador to the United Nations. Mr. Richardson is the most senior Western official to visit Afghanistan since the Soviet invasion of 1979. His efforts are supported by Japan, Germany, Britain and are in conformity with the UN and US State Department plan.

The Afghan factions have agreed on the following issues: 1) stopping new military offensives, 2) exchanging prisoners, 3) cooperating on humanitarian aid, 4) preventing Afghan soil from being used for terrorist activities, 5) stopping the cultivation of poppy growing, 6) lifting the blockade of Hazarajat, and 7) concessions on women's rights, etc.

With this peace announcement, GeoVision, Inc.'s President, Gary Bowersox, released a bulletin that he has received permission from both the Alliance of the North and the Taliban to proceed with the planned Summer Expedition to the gem and mineral area of Afghanistan. Information on this Expedition can be reviewed on the internet at http://www.gems-afghan.com/news.htm

—MrGary

January 24, 1998

Honolulu, Hi-The Afghanistan battlegrounds are now covered with snow. Bad weather conditions have curtailed the fighting in many areas. There has been some talk of peace. However, the U.N. reports arms, money and supplies are still being sent to preferred factions by outsiders. All parties to the war are currently discussing a selection of religious scholars to represent them in peace talks. This may be disrupted by differences between the U.N. and the Pakistan government over how to administer the situation.

—MrGary

November 11, 1997

Seattle, WA-During the last two months both sides continued to battle over the Mazar-E-Shrif territory. Many people were killed but little ground was gained or lost by either side. With the start of Winter the year appears to be ending with only some faint talks of a peace conference and shortage of food.

Problems between General Malik and General Dostum appear to be solved with General Dostum returning from Turkey and sharing command in the North with General Malik.

The last formal list of leaders of the Northern Alliance reads as follows:

Prime Minister, Mr. Abdul Ghafoor Rawan Farhadi;

President, Professor BurhannuddinRabani;

Minister of Foreign Affairs, Mr. Abdul Malik;

Minister of Defense, Mr. Ahmad Shah Massoud;

Minister of the Interior, Mr. Haji Mohaqiq;

Vice President, Mr. Ahmad Shah Massoud;

Vice President, General Abdul Ghaffar, Party: Jumbish Milli;

Vice President, Mr. Sadiq Parwani, Party: Hesb-i-Wahdat;

Vice President, (To be submitted after further consultations).

The President of Turkmenistan announced on November 10, 1997 his support for Unocal (USA) to head an international consortium to build a pipeline from his country via Afghanistan to Pakistan.

Yar Mohabbat, charge d'affairs in Washington D.C., announced on October 14, 1997 the new Afghanistan Embassy (USA)

GeoVision, Inc. announced the 7th Symposium of Gems and Minerals of Afghanistan to be held in Tucson, AZ (USA) on February 4th and 5th, 1998. Information is on line at: http://www.gems-afghan.com/7-symposium.

—MrGary

September 6, 1997

Chicago, IL-Decisive battles have been delayed. Ahmed Shah Massoud continues bombarding front lines of the Taliban troops around Kabul while attempting to take control of Kunar and the Jalalabad area. If accomplished, this would cut the Taliban supply route from Pakistan. Both sides have offered peace talks with no results.

The newly named Prime Minister for the Northern Alliance, Abdul Rahim Gaffurzai, was killed when his plane crashed at Bamiyan airport. This was a major loss as he was one of the few career diplomats from Afghanistan with service at the United Nations.

The US State Department ordered the Afghan Embassy in Washington D.C. to close on August 21st. The closing statement commented that the US wanted to remain neutral.

—MrGary

August 3, 1997

Austin, TX-Decisive battles for Kabul and Herat could start any minute. Ahmed Shah Massoud's troops are gathering and repairing bridges to deliver heavy equipment to the front lines at Kabul. General Abdul Malik is amassing troops to attack Herat. Residents of Kabul are fleeing once again. The Taliban are arresting Kabul Tajiks, Ismailis and Shiites in an attempt to stop an uprising within Kabul. For two weeks the Taliban and the Northern Alliance have been battling within rocket and artillery range of one another with some villages changing hands many times.

The Taliban are actively recruiting troops in Pakistan to replace he large number of soldiers lost in and around Mazar-I-Sharif and Pul-I-Khumri.

The UN attempts to bring peace have been stalled pending the outcome of the forthcoming battle over Kabul.

Stay tuned to this page for word of any changes in Kabul.

—MrGary

June 26, 1997

Rochester, MN – Damage control and attack were the key elements to Commander Ahmed Shah Massoud's campaign during the last 30 days. Throughout the month major battles with rockets, artillery, and aircraft continued in Northeastern Afghanistan. The Taliban and their associates

(Pakistan) were caught in an over-committed position in Mazar-i-Sharif and Pul-I-Khumri. When the Salang tunnel was blown up Taliban soldiers were trapped and surrounded in Pul-I-Khumri. By June 15th, the Taliban had lost all the territory conquered since January.

Currently, General Abdul Malik is neutral and regarded as undependable by both sides. Generl Dostum has dropped out of the situation by moving to Turkey. Ismail Khan was captured and turned over to the Taliban. The Taliban Foreign Minister, Abdul Mohammad Gous, and Northern Military Commander Razzaq were captured by the northern opposition.

Russia and the USA appear to have backed down on active support for either side. The US State Department has been reported to have announced the establishment of a commission to seek political, military, trade, investment, and energy cooperation with Uzbekistan. The US Department of State allowed Yar Mohammed Mohabbatt, Charge de Affairs, Afghanistan Embassy, Wash D.C. (appointed by Pres. Rabani's government) to retain his position after a claim by Seraj Jumal, secretary, that he represented the Taliban.

When the Taliban attempted to disarm the civilian population of Marzar-i-Sharif and convert them to their form of Islam, the people revolted and routed thousands of Taliban from the area, killing hundreds. There have been reports from Kabul, Kunar, and Herat of civil resistance and disturbances in response to the Taliban. This resistance may have been responsible for the exploding of an ammunition dump near the Bala Hisar Fort in Kabul.

Stay tuned for more reports as fighting continues.

—MrGary

May 24, 1997

Wash. DC – During the last month, military action heated up on all fronts as predicted. Unpredicted, however, was the mutiny of General Abdul Malik Pahlawan (Uzbek) and some of his troops in Faryiab province. Some people believe this break with General Roshid Dostum was a result of General Malik's brother's (Rasul Pahlivan) assassination last year. During this mutiny, renowned Commander Ismail Khan was captured and handed over to the Taliban. For years Commander Ismail Khan controlled the Herat area, part of the planned oil pipeline route. Ahmed Shah Massoud sent additional troops to General Dostum who replaced General Malik wit Alen Razem, a former air force commander.

Pakistan expelled anti-Taliban Afghan provincial governor, Haji Abdul Qadeer, of Nangarhar. Haji's son Zahir had been killed by the Taliban and paraded on a vehicle through Jalalabad.

Ex-Saudi citizen Osama bin Laden has moved to Kandahar, headquarters of the Taliban. He is regarded as one of the world's most wanted terrorists who has declared Jihad against the US. He is believed to be involved with two bombings in Saudi Arabia including the one killing 24 American soldiers and funding the plot against President Mubarak of Egypt.

Joining the move to Kandahar was the International oil and gas consortium. They are now renting offices in Kandahar with the desire to build a USD$2.7 Billion oil pipeline from Turkmenistan through Afghanistan.

Christopher Kremmer, Herald Correspondent in Kandahar wrote "When Soviet troops occupied Afghanistan from 1979 to 1989, gas was exported to the former Soviet Union. The country also has untapped oil potential."

The first known report was from Alexander the Great in 328 B.C. "Nothing says more for men's moods than how they interpret an omen, and as Alexander left Balkh in the spring of 328 for another year's fighting, he chanced on a very revealing one. When camp was pitched by the river Oxus two springs welled out of the ground near the royal tent, the one of water, the other of a liquid which gushed forth no different in smell or taste or brightness from olive oil, though the earth was unsuited to olive trees." (Fox, Robin Lane. 1974. Alexander the Great, Great Britain, The Dial Press.)

The undersigned and his party of three also witnessed oil in Badakhshan while exploring Badakhshan for the historic ruby/spinel mines described first by Marco Polo.

This now has become a war over oil!!

—MrGary

April 26, 1997

During the last month military action continued with fierce battles between the Taliban forces and the Supreme Council for the defense of Afghanistan. The battle areas were primarily in Bagdhis, Bamiyan, Shebar Pass, Ghorband Valley, and Herat Areas.

An ammunition dump in Jalalabad exploded, killing a reported 50 people and wounding over 100.

World aid continued with reports of Germany ($2.0 mil), Great Britain and Netherlands ($10mil), Canada ($7-12mil), and Japan ($10mil) in US Dollars.

Pakistan authorities banned the export of wheat to Afghanistan.

UNDCP reported plans to work with the Taliban who control 95% of the county's drug-producing areas.

It has been reported that the Taliban leader Mullah Omar declared himself leader of Moslems worldwide. Central Asian leaders have taken this as a threat.

Who's backing who in this fight for leadership of Afghanistan:

Supreme Council   Taliban

Inside Afghanistan:

    Commander Ahmed Shah Massoud   Mullah Mohammed Omar

    General Rashid Dostum

    Shi'ite Karm Khalili

    Governor Ismael Khan

Outside Afghanistan:

Tajikistan	Pakistan
Uzbekistan	Saudi Arabia
Kazakstan	United States(undeclared)
Kyrgistan	Unocal
Iran	Turkmenistan
India	
Russia	

Massoud, with medium range scud missile launchers in Panjsher, has established supply air support in Southern Tajikistan and Iran. Dostum recently received 500 tanks from Uzbekistan and Russia. Russia has deployed four mechanized units 50 miles north of the Afghanistan border at Termez. In addition, they have over 25,000 troops in Tajikistan on the Afghanistan border. The Taliban have been receiving arms shipments via Turkmenistan.

As the long winter ends, the passes of the Hindu Kush will be open for spring military operations. The questions are: (1) Will Pakistan continue to support the Taliban? (2) Will Turkmenistan, Unocal and Saudi Oil Co. accept Iran's offer to build the oil pipeline thru Iran rather than war torn Afghanistan? (3) Will the US Government commit to a policy position on Afghanistan? Secondly, will it support its position? (4) Now that the Taliban have been forcing farmers to leave their lands and Pakistan has banned wheat export, who is going to feed the Taliban army?

Dark Clouds in the near future.

—MrGary

March 10, 1997

Since our last update, the Taliban forces have advanced into the Ghorband Valley where the Shiite Moslems have stalled their advance 100 miles north of Kabul.

The Iranian government still recognizes Burhanuddin Rabani, now in the north with Commander Ahmad Shah Massoud, as President of Afghanistan. The Iranians hosted the Afghan warring factions at a conference, except for the Taliban.

General Rashid Dostum blew up the strategic Salang Highway north of Kabul to stop Taliban advances. His forces are reported to have killed 350

Taliban soldiers in Qala-I-Nau, 330 miles west of Kabul. Diplomats claim Dostum is getting money fro Iran and Russia. He also received support from Russia, Uzbekistan, Tajikistan, and Kyrgistan by announcing a joint plan of action in case the Taliban bring the war to the border of Afghanistan.

The Taliban continues to ban television, music, women working and going to school, and the use of paper products (paper could be the product of recycled pages of the Moslem holy book, the Koran). They arrested two French aid workers and four Afghans at a luncheon sponsored by a French organization with Afghan women present. The arrested French are not allowed to shave and are to stand trial for fraternizing with Afghan women. Journalists are not to photograph or film people, as it violates tenets of Islam unless they are from a warring faction.

The United Nations attempted to broker peace talks in Islamabad, Pakistan, but the participants did not appear at the meeting.

Reports are that the Unocal pipeline has been postponed indefinitely due to security problems in Afghanistan.

Even GeoVision did not escape the Taliban banning. All books and magazines published outside Afghanistan are now banned. We have not received any special permission for our book *Gemstones of Afghanistan*
  —MrGary

January 24, 1997

As the New Year begins, the Afghans continue their battles for control of Afghanistan. The Taliban, backed by Pakistan, possibly the U.S., and Saudi Arabia, control Kabul, the capital. However, the recent alliances between commander Ahmed Shah Massoud, General Dostum, and the Shiites provides the opposition with a major experienced force not to be counted out. Once again outside influence via oil money will have to be considered in the equation.

Sources close to the situation have informed us that Taliban soldiers overran two opposition strongholds north of Kabul today (Gulbahar and Jabel-o-Siraj). They are now moving towars the Salang tunnel.

Earlier this week Rashid Dostum dropped at least four bombs on Kabul.

The Taliban troops are forcing over 50,000 people to leave their homes North of Kabul and walk through the snow to the city. This is due to the fact that many of these people will remain loyal to Commander Ahmed Shah Massoud and could instigate problems for the Taliban.

Talks continue on how to build the two billion US dollar plus pipeline from Turkmenistan to Pakistan via Afghanistan. This is an American/Saudi project (Unocal/Delta).
  —MrGary

Glossary

Many Central Asian words are not standardized and conflicts exist among scholars and experts. Therefore, for quick reference, I have attempted here to provide some definitions and some of the more common variations in spelling. Included below are many of the persons, places, expressions and acronyms found in the book.

Achaemenian   The dynasty that ruled Iran and parts of today's Afghanistan from the time of Cyrus the Great (559BC) to the invasion of Alexander the Great (330BC).

Afghani   A unit of Afghan currency.

Afghanistan   A 270,000 square mile, landlocked country of Central Asia bordered by Iran, Turkmenistan, Uzbekistan, Tajikistan, China, and Pakistan.

Ahmadjan, Al-Haj Mawlawi Ahmad

The Taliban Minister of Mines and Industry.

Akbari, Khudai Nazar

Author's Afghan guide and friend.

Akhtar, General Akhtar Abdul Rahman Shaheed

The Director General of Pakistan's ISI (1979-1985). Chairman of Joint Chiefs of Staff, 1985-88. Died with President Zia in airplane explosion, August 17, 1988.

Akiyama, Tetsuo   A former Japanese diamond wholesaler, who fled Tokyo after absconding with gems and monies belonging to his suppliers.

Allah (Allahu) Akbar God is Great. The initial sentence of the azam, the call to prayer.

Al-Qaeda (al-Qaeda) The Base. Originally Osama bin Laden's base of operations in southern Afghanistan. Now used as a general term to refer to bin Laden's terrorist members and to the organization as a whole.

Amin, Assadullah   Afghan Commerce employee who attended Hawaiian Symposium.

Amin, Hafizullah   President of DRA and secretary general of PDPA after Taraki assassination in September 1979. Killed by KGB special forces, December 27, 1979. He was a Pashtun born in Paghman (1929), and had attended Columbia University.

Amu Darya   The third largest Afghan river rises in Pamir at Lake
                   Zarkul and flows approximately 280 miles. It starts as
                   the Wakhan River, then joins the Pamir at Qala-e-Panja
                   and assumes the name Panj River. It separates Afghani-
                   stan from Tajikistan and Uzbekistan. The Greeks re-
                   ferred to the river as the "Oxus;" the Arabs as the
                   "Sehun."

Andar Shahr   The ancient jewelry bazaar located in Peshawar.

Anjuman   The name of both the village and the pass located at
                   the northern end of the Panjsher Valley.

Ariana Airways   Afghanistan National Airline.

ARIC   AKBAR Resource and Information Centre provides the
                   most comprehensive collection of materials related to
                   Afghanistan in the region. ARIC collects documents
                   generated by all members of the NGO community and
                   from the UN agencies working for Afghanistan. It then
                   disseminates information about these materials through-
                   out the aid community and to interested parties in Pa-
                   kistan and abroad, including donors and academic in-
                   stitutions.

Aryan   A race of peoples from the Central Asian steppes who
                   came down from beyond the Oxus River in about 2000
                   BC. Afghans, Persians and Kued are among the Aryan
                   tribes.

Assalam Alaikum   Peace be upon you. Peace be with you.

Ay Khanoun "Moon Woman"
                   The site of a Greek city located on the east bank of the
                   Kohcha River at the point where it flows into the Amu
                   Darya (Oxus River).

Babar (Babur), Zhir-ud-Din (1482-1530)
                   The Emperor of Hindustan who invaded Afghanistan.

Bacha, Sayed Roohullah
                   An Afghan/Russian code breaker, friend and sometime
                   traveling companion of the author. Deceased.

Badakhshan   A province in Northeastern Afghanistan with its capi-
                   tal in Faisabad.

Bagram (Begram)   A town and airport north of Kabul and five miles west
                   of Charikar where an air base was built by the Soviets
                   in 1950. It is believed by some to be the site of Alexan-

	dria by the Caucasus, built by Alexander the Great in 330-329 BC and destroyed by Gengis Khan in the 13th century.
Bakshish	Bribe or payment or gift.
Balass ruby	A spinel.
Balkh	A Northern Afghanistan province, or its provincial capital.
Bamyan (Bamiyan)	Located in central Afghanistan and controlled by Hesb-i-Wahdat; the political organization of mainly Shiite Hazaras.
Bazaar	A traditional market place.
BBC	British Broadcasting Company.
Bhappu, Roshin, Dr.	President of Mountain States R & D Co. Tucson, AZ, and a mining engineer who lectured at three GeoVision, Inc. symposiums.
Bhutto, Benazir	Daughter of Zulfikar Ali Bhutto. From 1985 and for many years after, served as Leader of Pakistan People's Party. Prime Minister of Pakistan, 1988-90, 1993-1996.
Bin Laden, Osama	A Saudi-born international terrorist. He organized and is the acknowledged leader of the international terrorist group al-Qaeda.
Borsch or Borscht	A soup made primarily of beets and served hot or cold often with sour cream.
Buddhism	A religion that emerged in Afghanistan and India during the 6th Century BC.
Burka (chaderi)	A head-to-foot billowing, tent-like garment with window netting for the eyes worn by Afghan women.
Buzkashi	The Afghan national game of "goat pulling." It is played on horseback by two opposing teams who use the carcass of a goat or calf as their object of competition. The purpose is to lift up the carcass from the center of a circle, carry it around a point some distance away, and put it again in its original place.
Carat	A unit of weight for gemstones. Five carats equal one gram.
Casey, William	Director of Central Intelligence for the U.S. Government, 1981-1986.
Central Asia	Generally referred to as the following group of countries: Afghanistan, Kazakhstan, Kyrgistan, Tajikistan, Turkmenistan, and Uzbekistan.

Central Intelligence Agency
> The U. S. intelligence gathering service, more commonly known as the CIA.

Chaderi (Chador, Chadari)
> Head-to-foot billowing, tent-like garment in a variety of colors worn by women. See burka.

Chai   Tea.

Chaikhana (Chai-Khana)
> A tea-serving place which often serves food and provides a place to sleep for travelers.

Chardin, Sir John   (1643-1713) Son of a wealthy French jeweler who wrote several volumes on his travels in Persia during the latter half of the 17th century.

Charikar   Provincial Capital of Parwan Province, Afghanistan.

Charsadda   Was captured by Alexander the Great in 324 BC. Thereafter it was the pre-Kashan capital called Pushkalavati, the Lotus City. It is located northeast of Peshawar in Pakistan's Northwest Frontier Province.

Chaudhary, Arif   Manager of Green's Hotel and Lala's restaurant in Peshawar, Pakistan.

Chinggis (Gengis) Khan
> Means world conqueror. The Mongol leader named Temujin changed his name to this in early 13th century.

Chitral Mountain Inn   A hotel owned and operated by Haider Ali Shah, located in Chitral in the Northwest Frontier Province of Pakistan.

Chitral Valley   A 200-mile-long finger-shaped valley with an elevation of 4,980 feet located in the Northwest Frontier of Pakistan and bordered by Nuristan and Badakhshan. Its main village is also named Chitral. Chitral's recorded history begins in the 5th century with Yue-Chi tribes, who were Hephthalite or White Huns, until later conquered by Uzbeks. It was a stopping point on the ancient Silk Trade Route and a slave-trading center. Buddhism existed until the 9th century under Jaipal King of Kabul and Chitral. It was then part of the Mongol Empire until the 18th century. The British were unsuccessful in their attempts to annex Chitral but subsequently the Durand Line placed Chitral in the NWFP

	where it was regarded as politically autonomous until 1966. It became part of the Malakhand Division of the NWFP in 1972.
CIA	The United States' Central Intelligence Agency.
Clutterbuck, Guy	A British gem merchant and friend of the author.
Daoud (Sardar Mohammad Daoud Khan) (Daud)	
	Founded the Republic of Afghanistan after leading a coup d'etat against his cousin Zahir Shahin in July 1973. President of Afghanistan from 1973 until when he was killed in a coup d'etat on April 27, 1978.
Dari	A Middle Persian language (Parsi) resembling Farsi which is spoken in Afghanistan. Dari is derived from dar or darbari, meaning court language.
Dean's Hotel	An old hotel in Peshawar, Pakistan that was torn down in 2001.
Dehzad, Engineer S. Hashem	
	At one time, served as General Director of Lapis-Lazuli, Mineral Exploitation, Ministry of Mines and Industry, Afghanistan.
Dilawar, General Mohammad Asef	
	The Afghanistan Army Chief of Staff who assisted Ahmed Shah Massoud in taking over Kabul.
Dorah Pass	A pass over the eastern Hindu Kush range on the Afghan-Pakistan border. Lying at an elevation of 14,800 feet, it is crossed by a route from Zebak, Afghanistan to Chitral, Pakistan.
Dostum, General Abdul Rashid	
	Ex-communist Uzbek general and leader of the Afghan Uzbek militia 53rd Division. He mutinied against Najibullah in 1992 with Ahmed Shah Massoud's assistance and became warlord of the north based in Mazar-i-Sharif. Allied with Massoud and then changed loyalties to Hekmatyar in 1994.
DRA	Democratic Republic of Afghanistan
Dubs, Adolph	The U.S. Ambassador to Afghanistan who was kidnapped, then shot dead in a botched rescue at a Kabul hotel in February 1971. The most popular story was that he was kidnapped by Maoists and killed when Afghan police along with Soviet advisors attacked the hotel room where he was held.

Dupatta   A flimsy scarf draped around the shoulders.
Dupree, Louis   An American educator, anthropologist and advisor to
                     the U.S. Government on Afghanistan. Director of
                     Middle Eastern Studies Program and professor of An-
                     thropology at Indiana University in Bloomington. Mar-
                     ried to Nancy Dupree. Deceased.
Dupree, Nancy Hatch Often referred to as the 'Mother of Afghanistan.' Mrs.
                     Dupree lived in Kabul for many years. She worked with
                     her husband Louis on many archaeological sites in
                     Afghanistan and assisted with the Kabul museum. She
                     is the author of The Afghanistan Travel Guide and many
                     other periodicals and books. For many years she has
                     been the Director of ARIC (AKBAR Research Infor-
                     mation Centre) located in Peshawar, Pakistan.
Durand Line   The dividing line by which Britain in 1893 defined the
                     border separating Afghanistan from what was then
                     British India. Named after Britain's Sir Henry Mortimer
                     Durand, who persuaded the Amir of Afghanistan to
                     accept it. It had the effect of splitting between the two
                     countries the tribal areas long occupied by the Pashtuns.
                     To this day, the Durand Line and its exact location is
                     still a point of contention for many Afghans.
Ensha 'Allah (Inshallah)
                     God willing.
Es'Haq, Mohammad, Engineer
                     Engineer Es'Haq is a Tajik from Panjsher who repre-
                     sented Ahmed Shah Massoud in Washington, DC. He
                     attended Engineering Faculty at Kabul University and
                     participated in the 1975 Panjsher uprising under Ahmed
                     Shah Massoud. In 1983 he negotiated with the Soviet
                     military after which he became the political officer of
                     the Jamiat-i-Islami and editor of AFGHANews. Owned
                     and edited the Payme Mujahid (Mujahid Message)
                     newspaper. Served as Director of the Afghan Mission
                     to Washington, DC, and is now Director of Afghani-
                     stan TV and Radio. A close friend of the author's.
Eskazer (Ascarza)   A crossroads outpost in Badakhshan where the north-
                     ern road leads to Sar-e-Sang and the lapis mines, the
                     western road to Panjsher, Farkhar and Nuristan, and
                     the eastern trail to Zebak and Pakistan.

Faisabad (Faizsabad) The capital city of Badakhshan province in northern
                     Afghanistan.

Farsi   An ancient Persian language.

Fatwa   A religious ruling.

Ferangi (farangi)(faranji)
                     Foreigners. Various other spellings including: ferengi
                     and feringhee

Foord, Eugene, Dr.   A geologist with the U.S. Geological Survey Team,
                     lecturer at the author's symposiums, close friend and
                     co-author of gem articles. Deceased.

Gadhafi, Mu'ammar (al-Qaddhafy)
                     Leader of Libya.

Gandhara Culture   A highly sophisticated culture located in the Indus Val-
                     ley that suddenly disappeared in 177BC.

Garam Chasma (Hot Springs)
                     A Pakistan border village located in the Northwest Fron-
                     tier Province at an elevation of 6,100 feet. It is twenty-
                     eight miles from Chitral, which is two hours in sum-
                     mer by jeep.

Gem Hunter, The   The author, Gary W. Bowersox.

Gemological Institute of America (GIA)
                     The world's foremost training and research center for
                     colored gems and diamonds.

GeoVision, Inc.   A US-based gem company owned and managed by the
                     author.

Ghazni   An ancient Afghan city located south of Kabul, known
                     for its jewelry making.

GIA   See Gemological Institute of America.

Golbahar (Gulbahar) A village on the west bank of the Panjsher river at the
                     opening of the southern- most end of the Panjsher Val-
                     ley.

Gorbachev, Mikhail S.
                     First Secretary, Communist Party of the Soviet Union,
                     1985-1991 and President of the USSR 1986-1991.

Green's Hotel   A hotel in Saddar Bazaar, Peshawar, Pakistan.

GRU   Glavnoye Razvedyvatelnoye Upravlenie, or Soviet
                     Military Intelligence.

Gunston, John   British Journalist famed for being smuggled by
                     Mujahideen Commander Abdul-Haq into Kabul to in-
                     terview Khad officers and an Afghan General.

Habibullah, Mulla   Taliban, President of Plan in Eastern Zone.

Hajj (Haj)   Pilgrimage to Mecca. A legal obligation of every able adult Moslem.

Hajji (Haji)   A title of honor for a person who has completed the pilgrimage to Mecca.

Hakim, Abdul   Author's guide on his first trip to the ruby mines at Jegdalek in 1992.

Halal   Lawful; permitted according to religious law.

Haq, Abdul   Moderate Hesb-i-Islami Commander and politician born to a prominent Pashtun family in Nangarhar province.

Harakat Inqilab Islami
   A political group led by Maulvi Mohammad Nabi Mohammadi.

Hazara   A Mongolian-Persian mixture of people who practice the Shiite sect of Islam, a Moslem religion. Iran supports them.

Hekmatyar, Gulbuddin   (Born 1947)
   A Pashtun, Mujahideen leader of the Hesb-i-Islami Party and Commander of one of the seven groups headquartered in Peshawar. Was heavily supported by the Pakistan Government but fell into disfavor with the Pakistanis in the early 1990's for his inability to gain control of Kabul. A bitter rival of Ahmed Shah Massoud.

Hepatitis   A disease of the liver spread from person to person by contaminated food and water. Symptoms of fever, nausea, lack of energy and pains around the liver appear from 15-to-50 days after infection. The skin and eyes turn yellow.

Hesb-i-Islami (Hesbi-e-Islami, Hisb-i-Islami, Hizb-i-Islami)
   An Afghan Pashtun party founded and led by Gulbuddin Hekmatyar in 1975. A second group of Hesbi is led by Maulvi Mohammad Younis Khalis.

Hesb-i-Wahdat   A political organization composed of mainly Shiite parties of Hazaras led by Karim Khalili and Ustad Mohaqiq and backed by Iran.

Hindu Kush   A mountain range of Northeastern Afghanistan, Northern Pakistan and Tajikistan reported by the Arab Moslem and traveler Ibn Battuta in 1334 AD on his journey to India. Hindu Kush means Hindu Killer, as many thousands of captives from India's lowlands perished trying to make it through severe conditions on the mountains. The highest elevation is at Tirich Mir 25,229 ft (7,690 m).

Homer, Richard A well-known American gem cutter and faceting teacher.

Imam A word used in several senses. In general use and in lower case, it means the leader of congregational prayers. As such, it implies no ordination or special spiritual powers beyond sufficient education to carry out this function. It is also used figuratively by many Sunni Moslems to mean the leader of the Islamic community. Among Shias the word takes on many complex meanings. In general, it indicates the particular descendant of the House of Ali Ibn Abu Talib, who is believed to have been God's designed repositor of the spiritual authority inherent in that line. The identity of this individual and the means of ascertaining his identity have been major issues causing divisions among Shias.

Inshallah (In sha'allah) (Ensha'Allah)
God willing; if God wills; may it please God.

Inter Service Intelligence
Pakistan's Intelligence gathering service. Commonly known as the ISI.

Ishkashim An old village located in Badakhshan, Afghanistan on the Amu Darya River.

ISI The Pakistani Intelligence Service.

Islam Islam is an Arabic word the root of which is Silm and Salam. It means among others: peace, greeting, salutation, obedience, loyalty, allegiance, and submission to the will of God. Islam is considered to be the fastest growing religion in the world.

Ismailiis Sometimes called Maulais, a Moslem religion. The original Ismailii people are believed to have come from Persia and were identified with the White Huns. Of the three Moslem sects, they appear to be the best organized having federal councils on regional, national and international levels.

Ittehad-i-Islami   A Saudi-backed Sunni Moslem party.

Jabul-Saraj (Jabal us Siraj) (Jabal-os-Saraj) (Jabal Al-Siraj)

                         A village north of Kabul where Massoud maintained a command post until 1996. Previously the center of a textile industry built by Habibullah in1906.

Jalalabad   Afghanistan's fourth largest city, which is located near the Khyber Pass and the border of Pakistan.

Jamiat-i-Islami   A political party founded and led by Burhanuddin Rabbani with the support of Ahmed Shah Massoud's forces after its first uprising in Panjsher Valley (1975).

Jegdalek   A village in Kabul Province, Afghanistan where the ruby mines are found.

Jehad (Jihad)   A holy war or great effort. To strive, struggle, resist, fight against, as an article of Faith. One of the main tenets of Islam. Jehad is derived from the Arabic word Juhud which means endeavor and to observe patience in the face of persecution.

Jirga   Assembly of Tribal Elders.

K2   Pakistan's highest mountain and the world's second highest.

Kabul   The capital city of Afghanistan and the name of the province that it lies in. Its population in 2000 was estimated at 1.5 million.

Kafir   Arabic for unbeliever or infidel; a name often given to non-Moslems and unbelievers or atheists.

Kafiristan   The land of infidels was an area in eastern Afghanistan now named Nuristan, the Land of Light, meaning the light of the Islamic religion, which was brought into the area by conquest in 1896.

Kaakaa   Uncle.

Kalash   Children of Nature regarded as a primitive pagan tribe known as Kafir Kalash living in three valleys (Birer, Bumburet and Rambur) in the NWFP of Pakistan. Their way of life has experienced little change over the last 2,000 years. One theory of their origin is that they are descendants of the Greek troops of Alexander the Great, who settled these valleys. They celebrate their religious festivals with group dancing, feasting and drinking. Some of their gods are similar to those of the Romans and Greeks; although, they strongly believe in ances-

	tor worship and use wooden effigies for this purpose. The Kalash women are striking with their coarse, black cotton, ankle-length clothes and headwear decorated with cowry shells, beads, buttons and bells.
Kalash Valleys	The valleys of Birer, Bumburet and Rambur in the NWFP of Pakistan located 34 km from Chitral, which takes approximately two hours by jeep.
Kamdeh	People of Kamdesh.
Kamdesh	A village in Northern Nuristan, Afghanistan.
Kamus	A village in Nuristan, Afghanistan.
Kandahar (Qandahar)	A Province name and also the name of the capital city of Kandahar located in south-central Afghanistan. The city was part of the Achaemenid Empire of Darius I (521-485 BC). It was rebuilt by Alexander the Great in 329 BC. It served as headquarters for the Taliban after they captured it in 1994.
Karat	A unit of weight for measuring gold, not to be confused with carat, a unit of weight for measuring gems.
Karmal, Babrak	The Afghan founder of PDPA. Deputy prime minister of DRA. Exiled to Russia in July 1978 but returned with Soviet troops in 1979. He became President of the Revolutionary Council from January 1980 to May 1986, when Dr. Najibullah took over control. He was an activist and known communist at Kabul University and jailed twice for his activities.
KGB	Komitat Gosudarstvennoi Bezopasnosti - the Soviet Committee for State Security. The Soviet equivalent of the CIA.
KHAD	The Afghanistan State Intelligence Service. It is reputed to control a thousand operatives and informers, as well as the National Guard and other fighting units. Afghanistan's secret police.
Khalis, Maulvi Mohammad Younis	
	Early leader of a Hesb-i-Islami group. Born in Nangarhar (1919) and educated in Islamic law and theology. He is a fervent anti-Communist who fled to Pakistan in 1974.
Khan	Title of tribal chiefs, land proprietors and heads of communities.
Khan, Akbar	(1948-1998) A gem dealer, business associate and close

friend of the author's. His office was located in the Namak Mandi bazaar, Peshawar, Pakistan.

Khan, Anwar   Commander of Jamiat-i-Islami forces in Jegdalek area who assisted author with his first trip to Jegdalek.

Khan, Gen. Bismillah One of Ahmed Shah Massoud's top commanders.

Khan, Gengis (Jenghiz)

Born Temujin (1167 -1227) Ruler of the Mongols who invaded Afghanistan in 1220 AD. Gengis Khan means World Conqueror.

Khan, Hulagu   (1217-1265) Son of Gengis Khan, known for building a pyramid of the skulls of scholars, religious leaders and poets skulls in Baghdad.

Khan, Ismail   Staff officer of Herat Garrision who lead March 1979 Herat Mutiny against Soviet advisors with Captain A'la'uddin Khan. Commander of Amir Hamza division and Amir of Herat Shura after April 1992. In 1998 he was captured and imprisoned by the Taliban and later escaped.

Khan, Sameen   An American-educated Pakistani law professor and writer. Author of A Strategic Doctrine for Pakistan (Defense Journal, Vol. XVI, Nos. 1-2)

Khan, Sardar Mohammad Daoud

President of Afghanistan (1972-1978). See Daoud.

Khost (Khowst)   An Afghan town and district near the Pakistan border in Paktia province where severe fighting took place during the Soviet occupation of Afghanistan.

A major Mujahideen camp was built there with funds provided by the CIA and built by Osama bin Ladin. Later, became an al-Qaeda base.

Khuda Hafez   Goodbye

Khyber Pass (Khibar) A famous historic pass leading through a gorge in the barren Sulaiman Hills in Pakistan, near the border of Afghanistan. It was used by the Achaemenians (6th century BC), later by Alexander the Great's legions, and much later by British-Indian expedition forces. The British annexed this Afghan outpost and placed it within the Pakistan territory.

Kim, Tae-Ik   Author's friend and hunting companion during author's Army tour in Korea.

Kirghiz   A tribal group living in the Wakhan Corridor of Af-

	ghanistan who were previously driven out of Central Asia (Kyrgistan) by the Soviets. Most are nomadic people who herd yaks.
Kishm	A valley district between Faisabad and Taloqan in Badakhshan, Afghanistan.
Kokcha	River in Northern Afghanistan that passes by the lapis mines and continues north into the Amu Darya at the site of the ancient city of Ay Khanoun.
Koran (Qu'ran)	The Moslem holy book that was compiled after the death of Mohammad. It is considered to be the very word of Allah (God) as revealed to his Prophet, Mohammad.
Kuh-i-Lal (Kukhilyal)	A mountain containing the Red Stone. Referred to by Marco Polo as the place where rubies were mined. The Kuh-i-Lal mines are located 1,000 feet above the Amu Darya, south of Khorogh, Tajikistan.
Kunduz (Qonduz)	A province in Northeastern Afghanistan. Also, the capital city of the province.
Kushtus	A village above Kamdesh in Nuristan, Afghanistan.
Lake Shiva (Siva)	A large glacier lake located at 12,500 feet elevation in Badakhshan between Shighnan and Barak.
Lala's	A famous restaurant located in Green's Hotel in Peshawar, Pakistan.
Lali, Yaqob, Dr.	A former Afghanistan Minister of Mines and Industry, a post he held for many years.
LaLonde, Dan	An American wholesale-retail gem merchant and long-time friend of the author's.
Landi Kotal	A Pakistani trading village located near the Khyber Pass.
Loi Jirga(Loya Jirga)	A great council or National Assembly of Tribal Elders.
Lorry	A large truck which is often brightly painted with carved, wooden doors.
Lowari Pass	A 10,400-foot pass in Pakistan located on the road between Dir and Chitral.
Lungi	A turban.
Madrasa (Madrassa)	A religious schools for Islamic students where the curriculum is often grounded in fundamental Islamic law. In NWFP, the madrasas, supported by Saudi funds, educated a generation of Afghan refugee students in religious extremism, which gave rise to the Taliban.

Massoud (Mas'ud), Ahmed Shah

Lion of Panjsher and commander of Jamiat-i-Islami forces. Raised in Kabul where he attended Polytechnic Institute. He joined the Moslem Youth and led the Panjsher Valley uprising in 1975 after which he joined the JIA in Pakistan. After 1979 he led the Panjsher resistance and negotiated a truce directly with the Soviets in 1983. Established Islamic Army in 1988. Cooperated with Dostum in capture of Kabul, April 1992 and became the first defense minister of ISA. Later became one of the few leaders to stand against the Taliban. He was assassinated in 2001. Supported the author's efforts to map and develop Afghanistan's gem deposits.

Mastuj

A valley and village where the Mastuj and the Yarkhund rivers meet in Pakistan's NWFP between Gilget and Chitral. The British had a fort palace there which is now occupied by Col. Shazada Khushwaqt ul-Mulk, a friend of the author's.

Matsunaga, Sparky M.

U.S. Senator from Hawaii. Decorated war veteran and peacemaker. Established the U.S. Institute of Peace. Deceased.

Mecca (Meccah)

The holiest city in the world of Islam. The birthplace of the Prophet Muhammad and location of the Ka'aba. All able Moslems are required to make a one-time pilgrimage to Mecca.

Mohammad (Muhammad)(Mohammed) and various other spellings

Leader and Prophet of the Moslem religion who began teaching in 612 AD. Born in Mecca 571 AD - died 632 AD.

Mohammad, Jon

Massoud's supply officer who developed the 'Jon Mohammad Express' to get journalists and author across the Pakistan/Afghan border.

Mohammad, Sher

Anwar Khan's Jegdelak commander and relative who guided author to the ruby mines at Jegdalek.

Mohebullah

A gem trader from Panjsher Valley who has sold gems to author in Peshawar since 1982.

Mokoni

Emerald mining area in Panjsher Valley.

Moleskin

A soft, self-sticking cotton flannel padding that protects feet from painful shoe friction.

Monteiro, Joao BascoA Brazilian gem merchant and friend who accompanied the author on a trip to Kabul to purchase rough
gem material.

Moslem (Muslim)   Followers of Islam, Mohammad's faith. Various other
spellings are often used.

Mujaddedi (Mujaddidi), Professor Sebqatullah (Sebghatullah) (Prof. Al
Mojaddedi)
Descendant of a centuries-old family of kingmakers in
Afghanistan. Leader of the Jabhi-i-Nejat-i-Melli party
and founder of the National Liberation Front. Also,
leader of Leadership Council after the fall of Kabul.

Mujahed (Mujahideen)
One who strives in the way of God. A champion of
liberty; a Moslem holy warrior. Those who take part in
Jehad against oppressions and aggression, as an act of
faith.

Mullah (Mulla)   A commonly used term for traditional Islamic leaders.

Nahrin   A village west of Panjsher Valley from which a road
leads to Taloqan. The village was known for its pista-
chio nuts before the war.

Najibullah, Dr.   The last President of the Soviet-backed regime, killed
by the Taliban when they entered Kabul. He was a
Pushtun born in Kabul, a student leader of PDPA-
Parcham at Kabul University. Taraki exiled him in July
of 1978. He served as Director General of KHAD (Afghan Intelligence) from1980 to November 1985. He
became General Secretary of PDPA and President of
Watan Party. He became President of Afghanistan in
November 1987 and held the position until overthrown
on April 15, 1992. He took refuge in the United Nations office in Kabul where he was located by the
Taliban upon entering Kabul and then killed.

Namak Mandi   A section of Peshawar which was historically the salt
market. It is now known for its gem market.

Nameemi, Mohammad Wali
First Secretary & Vice Consul General of the Islamic
Emirate of Afghanistan.

Nan   A flat, platter-shaped, unleavened bread of rough-milled
wheat flour that serves as an Afghan diet mainstay. It

	is usually baked on hot stones.
Nassaeri, Dr.	Professor of Geology, University of Kabul, who provided the author with detailed knowledge of the Afghan gem and mineral industry. Deceased.
Nemaz	Prayers.
Northern Alliance	The political and military alliance of all anti-Taliban groups, led by Commander Ahmed Shah Massoud before his death.

Northwest Frontier Province (NWFP)

A province of northern Pakistan in which Peshawar, Chitral, Garam Chasma, the Khyber Pass and the Dorah Pass are located.

Nuristan	A northeastern province of Afghanistan lying along the Pakistan border. Nuristan was a part of ancient Kafiristan.
Nuristani	An ethnic person from the province of Nuristan in Afghanistan.
NWFP	See Northwest Frontier Province.
Olafsen, Lt. Ollie	Danish explorer and soldier who participated in two expeditions to the Pamirs in the late 1800's. He is known to have visited Kuh-I-Lal and wrote Through the Unknown Pamirs in 1904.

Omar, Mullah Mohammad

Founder of the Taliban Islamic movement and Commander of the Faithful. After the Taliban were overthrown, he went into hiding and is believed to have found refuge in the mountains of southern Afghanistan.

Oxus	The ancient Greek name for the Amu Darya, a river flowing on Afghanistan's Northern border. See Amu Darya.
Pakistan	Land of the Pure, was formed on August 15, 1947 when it gained independence from Great Britain. Originally composed of East Pakistan and West Pakistan with India in the middle, but in 1970 East Pakistan became the independent nation of Bangladesh.
Palau Quabli	A special casserole dish of rice with boiled meat, raisins, slivered carrots, chopped almonds and/or pistachio nuts.

Pamirs — A mountain range called the roof of the world with some 3,000 glaciers extending over 8,400km of mountains including Communist Peak at 24,590 ft (7,495m) and Kongur peak rising to 25,325 ft (7,579m).

Panja — The Wakhan branch of the Amu Darya river in northeast Afghanistan.

Panjsher — An historic valley seventy miles north of Kabul where the emerald mines are located. The valley served as the base of operations for Ahmed Shah Massoud and the Northern Alliance.

Panjshiri, Dastagir — A founding member of the PDPA of the Khalqi faction who became minister of education and minister of public works. He was born in the Panjsher district in 1933 and educated in Kabul.

Papruk — An area in northeastern Nuristan.

Parandeh — Side valley in Panjsher where copper minerals were discovered.

Paroun — The name of the upper part of Pach Valley in Nuristan, Afghanistan.

Paryan — A village at the northern end of Afghanistan's Panjsher Valley.

Pashto (Pashtu or Pakhto) — The Indo-Iranian language spoken by Pashtuns. Two main dialects are spoken the hard or Peshawari called Pakto, and the soft, or Kandahari, called Pashto.

Pashtun — Also known as Pathan, Pakhtuns, Pushtoon, Pashtoon, Paktoon, and Pathan. The largest tribal group in Afghanistan and Northwestern Pakistan founded in 1747 by Ahmed Shah Durrani. Afghanistan has traditionally been dominated politically by the Pashtuns.

Patu (Petou) — A blanket often used as a coat, knapsack, tent, stretcher, and ground covering for kneeling on during prayers. Carried by Afghan travelers, it is usually dull brown in color.

PDPA — See People's Democratic Party of Afghanistan. A Marxist party.

Pearl Continental — A five-star hotel located in Peshawar, Pakistan.

People's Democratic Party of Afghanistan (PDPA) — The principal Soviet-oriented Communist organization

	founded in 1965. In 1967 the party split into two factions; Khalq, led by Nur Muhammad Taraki and Hafizullah Amin; and Parcham, led by Babrak Karmal. In 1977 the Soviets pressured them into a reuniting.
People's House	The former royal palace in Kabul, renamed by Hafizullah Amin.
Persian	Used to mean race, language, culture or nationality. The Persian language originated in Persia (the Persis of the Greeks and the Fars of the Arabs).
Peshawar	A large historic city and now the capital of the Northwest Frontier Province of Pakistan. It has a population of approximately 750,000 plus an undeterminable number of Afghan refugees, believed to be in excess of 3 million.
Pir	A religious leader; old man; title given to heads of safi orders.
Plausible deniability	A government cover-up.
Prokofiev, V.	A Soviet citizen working for the UN in Kabul who assisted the Afghan government with their development and promotion of exports. He assisted the author in the export of lapis to the US.
Qissa Khani	The ancient storytellers' bazaar in Peshawar, Pakistan.
Rabbani, Burhanuddin	
	A Tajik born in 1940 in Faisabad, Badakhshan. He was educated in Islamic studies at Kabul University and Al-Azhar University in Cairo, Egypt where he received an M.A. degree in 1968. He became the leader of the Shura of Islamic movement in 1974 resulting in his exile to Pakistan where he became the leader of Jamiat-i-Islami after a split. He was the second acting President of ISA under the Islamabad Accords from March 1993 to June. In 1996 he left Kabul with Massoud as the Taliban approached, but remained President of Afghanistan until the US-supported Karzai regime was established.
Rafi, Abdullah	Representative of Taliban Foreign Office sent with author to survey Jegdalek's ruby and sapphire mines.
Rafiq, Abdul	American-educated Afghanistan Export Promotion Minister.

Rafiq, Faird M.   President, Export Promotion Department.

Rahim, Abdul   An emerald miner and friend of author's who divides his time between Peshawar, Pakistan and Panjsher Valley.

Rashuddien   A Panjsher Valley businessman and brother-in-law of Ahmed Shah Massoud.

Rokha   A village located at the southern end of Panjsher Valley.

Salom-o-alaikum   Welcome, peace be upon you. A Moslem greeting. Spelled in a variety of ways.

Samarkand   A large city in Uzbekistan where Timur was born and ruled.

Sar-e-Sang   The lapis mining area of Badakhshan in northern Afghanistan.

SAVAK   The Iranian Intelligence Service.

Sayyef, Mohammad   Horseman who traveled with the author from Eskazer to Shah Saleem during his 2001 expedition.

Shah, Haider Ali   Owner of the Mountain Inn located in Chitral, Pakistan near the Kalash Valley. A close friend of the author's since 1985.

Shah, King Zahir   King of Afghanistan until overthrown in a 1972 coup d'etat

Shalwar-kamese (shalwar-kameez)

        Long knee-length shirts, worn tails out over baggy trousers (pantaloons) with a drawstring to keep them up on the hips.

Sharia (Shariat)   Islamic law.

Shia (Shi'a) parties (Shiite)

        The party of Ali. The political groups of the pro Iran Hesb-i-Wahdat and Harkat-i-Islami. Their views conflict with the Sunni principle that Muhammad's successor, khalifa (caliph), should be elected. Shias divide into three major sects according to which of their imams is believed to be the Expected One who will return on judgment day: the fifth, seventh, or twelfth.

Shighnan (Shignon)   A district in northern Badakhshan, Afghanistan that was an independent Tajik khanate until 1859. The Shighnanis speak a language of their own and are generally Isma'ili Shi'as.

Shigley, James. Dr.   Director of research for the Gemological Institute of

	America and a long-time friend of the author's. Dr. Shigley co-authored three articles with the author and has conducted research on gem materials from Afghanistan.
Shura	A Persian term meaning a consultative body of elders or leaders whose goal is to reach a consensus on communal matters. Islamic modernists base their demands for a representative government on this principle.
Snee, Dr. Lawrence	A Director at the U.S. Geological Survey (USGS) in Denver, Colorado. He has assisted the author with articles on Afghanistan and arranged for testing of materials in the USGS laboratory. He has lectured at four of the author's Symposiums and assisted with mapping.
Sorobi (Sorubi)	An Afghan village located between Kabul and Jalalabad. South of Sorobi is the village of Jegdalek with its ruby mines.
Spinzar hotels	A chain of Afghan hotels.
Stark, Hanoh	An Israeli gem merchant, cutter and emerald dealer.
Stingers	US-made, shoulder-fired anti-aircraft missiles. Deadly accurate.
Sufism	Islamic mysticism, emerged in eighth century A.D. and rapidly spread over most of the Islamic world. It was long in conflict with Islamic orthodoxy because it sought the personal experience of union with God, rather than rational knowledge, the scholasticism of Sunni Islam.
Sunnites	A version of Islam subdivided into four mazkhabs, named after their founders: Hanifite, Shafiite, Hanbalite and Malikite schools. The overwhelming majority of Afghans are Hanifites who, as distinct from the followers of the other Islamic doctrines, are more tolerant of other religions.
Tajik (Tadjik, Tadzhik)	
	People of Persian descent living in Afghanistan and Tajikistan. They are the second largest tribal group in Afghanistan. They are descended from the ancient population of Khorasan and Sistan who were sedentary and made a living as traders. They are largely Sunni Moslems, except for the mountain Tajiks who are Ismailis.

Tajikistan A previous Soviet Union-bloc country which borders Afghanistan, Uzbekistan, Kyrgistan and China.

Tajuddin Ahmed Shah Massoud's father-in-law and one of top officers.

Takhar A province in northeastern Afghanistan in which Taloqan is the capital. It is known for its salt, silver and gold mining.

Taliban "Seekers of Knowledge." Afghan refugee students educated in Pakistan Moslem schools who emerged in 1994 with the goal to conquer Afghanistan.

Taloqan (Taluqan, Taliqan)
 The capital of Takhar Province.

Taraki, Nur Muhammad
 Born 1917, a self-educated writer from Ghazni who became the founder and general secretary of PDPA as leader of the Khalq. He was President of the Revolutionary Council and Prime Minister of DRA in April 1978. On September 17, 1979 he was smothered to death in a coup d'etat.

Tashakur Thank you in Dari language.

Tavernier, Jean Baptiste
 French gem merchant who completed seven voyages to India, Ceylon and Southeast Asia from 1641-1667.

Timargarha A Pakistani village between Peshawar and Dir, containing Aryan graves made of stone slabs, a hill with a corundum deposit (ruby/sapphire) and a large bazaar with a bus transfer station.

Timur, Tugha (Tamerlane or Timur-I-Lenk)
 (AD 1369-1405) Founded the Timurid dynasty. Conquored India, Persia and Afghanistan and ruled Central Asia with an iron hand. Known for killing masses of people. He was a Turco-Mongol who by some accounts descended from a brother of Gengis Khan. Other accounts state that Timur traced his lineage to Abu-al-Atrak, Father of the Turks, the son of Japhet.

Tirich Mir A Hindu Kush multi-peaked mountain north of Chitral with an elevation of 25,229 ft (7,690-7750 m). It is the highest mountain in the Hindu Kush. Local inhabitants believe it is the home of the fairies who are guarded by large frogs known as bugzai.

Torkham   A Pakistani village at the Khyber Pass.

Turban   A typical male headdress in Afghanistan usually made
                   out of long pieces of cotton or silk. Different areas of
                   the country have different styles of wrapping their tur-
                   bans. For example, in the southern regions, men leave
                   a tail and an extension up on top, while in the northern
                   or central regions, this is not seen. At one time, an ex-
                   tension on top of the turban signified a man's wealth.
                   The higher the extension, the wealthier he was.

Turkic   People descended from Central Asian Turks who fre-
                   quently invaded Afghanistan from the north. The most
                   populous group is the Uzbeks who are kinsmen of
                   Uzbekistan. Less numerous are the Turkmen who live
                   along the Amu Darya and speak an archaic form of
                   Turkish and Persian.

ul-Mulk, Khush Ahmad, Major
                   A retired Pakistani Air Force pilot whose father was
                   the late Shuja ul-Mulk, Ruler of Chitral. Lives in Drosh,
                   just south of Chitral.

ul-Mulk, Shazada Kushwaqt, Col.
                   A former military officer and friend of the author, who
                   lives in the palace-fort in Mastuj, NWFP, Pakistan once
                   occupied by the British. His father was the former Ruler
                   of Chitral.

Ulema   General term for a body of scholars, particularly schol-
                   ars of Islamic theology. Alim is used to denote a single
                   scholar.

ur-Rehman, Shuja   Son of His Highness Saif Ur Rehman, the late ruler of
                   Chitral. Spends his time among Peshawar, Chitral and
                   Garam Chasma.

Uzbek (Uzbak)   The largest Turkic-language group in Afghanistan but
                   an ethnic minority.

Uzbekistan   A country bordering Afghanistan, Tajikistan,
                   Turkmenistan and Kazakhstan. It was formerly a mem-
                   ber of the Soviet Union.

Wahkhan   The extreme northeastern district of Badakhshan prov-
                   ince, extending from Ishkashim in the west to the bor-
                   ders of China. The inhabitants are Uzbeks, Wakhis and
                   Kirghiz.

Waikiki   A well-known beach area located in Honolulu, Hawaii

Wali Kom Salom (Wallaikhum salaam) Many variant spellings.

                                Unto you also peace! Said in reply to Salaam Aliakom.

Weerth, Andreas   A German mineral dealer and friend of author's. He was an instructor at the Chitral Symposium.

Woods, Captain John 1800's British soldier and explorer.

Yahya   One of Ahmed Shah Massoud's younger brothers.

Yeltsin, Boris   President of the Soviet Federation from 1990-2000.

Yousaf, Brigadier (retd.) Mohammad

                                In charge of the Afghan Bureau ISI under General Akhtar.

Zahir Shah, Muhammad

                                Son of Muhammad Nadir Shah and King of Afghanistan (1933-1973). He was educated in France and now lives in Rome.

Zia ul-Haq, General Pakistan General and Chief of Army Staff appointed by Zulfikar Ali Bhutto in 1974. He staged a coup d'etat in July 1977 and became the chief martial law administrator. He executed Bhutto in April 1979, ended martial law and proclaimed himself president. He died on August 17, 1988 when his military aircraft exploded.

Zia-Zadah, Dr. Ahmed Qu

                                President of the Mineral Exploitation Department, Kabul during 1979.

References

Abdullah, S., & Chmyiov V. M., Stazhilo-Alekseev, K.F., Dronov, V.I., Gannon P. J., Lubemov B.K., Kafarskiy A. Kh. & Malyarov E.P. (1977). *Mineral Resources of Afghanistan* (2nd ed). Afghanistan Geology Survey. United Nations Development Program, Program Support Project AFG/74/012, Kabul.

Adamec, L. W. (1991). *Historical Dictionary of Afghanistan.* London: The Scarecrow Press, Inc.

Ball, V. (1889). *Travels in India by Jean Baptiste Tavernier* v. 1. New York: Macmillian and Company.

Ball, V. (1894). A description of two large spinel rubies, with Persian characters engraved upon them. *Proceedings of the Royal Irish Academy 3rd series, 2 (3),* 380-400.

Bowersox, G. W. (1985). A Status Report on Gemstones from Afghanistan. *Gems & Gemology, 21*(4), pp. 191-204.

Bowersox, G. W. & Anwar, J. (1989). The Gujar Killi Emerald Deposit, Northwest Frontier Province, Pakistan. *Gems & Gemology, 25*(1). pp. 16-24.

Bowersox, G. W.; Snee, L.; Foord, E.; & Seal, R. (1991). Emeralds of Panjsher Valley, Afghanistan. *Gems & Gemology, 27* (1). pp. 26-39.

Bowersox, G. W. & Chamberlin, B.E. (1995). *Gemstones of Afghanistan.* Tucson: Geoscience Press.

Bowersox, G. W.; Foord, E.; Laurs, B.& Shigley, J. (2000). Rubies and Sapphires of Jegdalek Afghanistan. *Gems &Gemology.*

Bretschneider, E. (1887). *Medieval Resources from Eastern Asiatic Sources. vol. I.* London: Kegan Paul, Trench, Trubner and Company.

Cho K. (1887). *Hui-Hui shi t' on Precious Stones of the Mohammedans. vol. 1.* Fourteenth Century. London: Mediaeval Researches for Eastern Asiatic Sources, Kegan Paul, Trench, Trubner and Co., Ltd.

Darby, P., M.D. (1986). *Tears of the Oppressed: An American Doctor In Afghanistan.* Texas: Self- published.

Davis, Anthony (1990, October). The Mujahedin's Secret Weapon, Asian Times.

Dupree, L. (1980). *Afghanistan.* Princeton, NJ: Princeton University Press.

Dupree, N. (1970). *An Historical Guide to Afghanistan.* Tokyo: Jagra, Ltd.

Dunn, R. (1986). *The Adventures of Ibn Battuta 1325-1354.* Los Angeles: University of California Press.

Elliot, J. (1999). *An Unexpected Light.* London: Picador.

Elphinstone, M. (1972). *An Account of the Kingdom of Caubul and its Dependencies in Persia, Tartary, and India.* Karachi: Oxford University Press.

Emadi, H. (1997). *State, Revolution, and Superpowers in Afghanistan.* Karachi: Royal Book Company.

Gankovsky, Y., Arunova, M.R., Korgun, V.G., Masson, V.M., Muradov, G.A., Polyakov, G.A., & Romodin, V.A. (1982). *A History of Afghanistan.* Union of Soviet Socialist Republics: Progress Publishers.

Hedin, Sven. (1910). *Overland To India. vol. I, II.* London: MacMillan and Company, Limited.

Herrman, G. (1966). *Lapis lazuli: The early phases of its trade.* Oxford University Dissertation.

Herrman, G. (1968). Lapis lazuli: The early phases of its trade. *IRAQ Journal, 30*, part 1, 21-57.

Holden, E. (1895). *The Mongul Emperors of Hindustan.* New York: Charles Scribner's Sons.

Kabul Mines. (1979). USSR Offer for 50 Tons of Lapis. Personal correspondence with G. W. Bowersox, November, 25.

Marsden, P. (1999). *The Taliban.* Karachi: Oxford University Press.

Meyer, K. & Brysac, S. (1999). *Tournament of Shadows: The Great Game and the Race for Central Asia.* Washington, DC: Counterpoint.

Naseri, A.(1963). The History of Lapis Lazuli in Afghanistan (part III). *Afghanistan Revue Trimestester Soc. Etudes d'Afghan, 18*, 23-28.

O' Donnel, P. (1990, October). Afghan rebels dig up financial help. *Los Angeles Times.*

Olufsen, O. (1904). *Through the Unknown Pamirs. The Second Danish Pamir Expedition.* London: William Heinemann.

Prawdin, M. (1963). *The Builders of the Mongul Empire.* London: George Allen and Unwin Ltd.

Prokofiev, V. (1979). Letter Referencing $864,000 Purchasing of Lapis by USSR c/o Almazjuvelir Export and Inspection of Additional 50 tons of Lapis. Personal correspondence between G.W. Bowersox and V. Prokofiev, ITC Project Manager, Kabul, December 8.

Rashid, A. (2000). *Taliban, Militant Islam, Oil,and Fundamentalism in Central Asia.* New Haven: Yale University Press.

Rossovsky, L. N., & Zilberfarb, L. S. (1963). *Spinel-forsteritovye obazovanniya mestorozhdeniya Kukhi-lal (Spinel-forsterite formation of the Kukhi-lal deposit). Materialy po geologii Pamira (Data of the geology of the Pamirs), part 1.* Dushanbe.

Rossovsky, L.N. (1980). Mestorozhdeniya dragotsennykh kamney Afghanistana *(Gemstone deposits of Afghanistan). Geologiya Rudnykh Mestorozhdenii (Geology of Ore Deposits), 22,* 74-88, Translated by E. Foord.

Rossovsky, L. N. (1981). Rare metal pegmatite's with precious stones and conditions of their formation (Hindu Kush). *International Geology Review, 23,* (11), 1312-1320.

Rubin, Barnett. (1995). *The Search for Peace In Afghanistan.* New Haven and London: Yale University Press.

Seragli. (1670). The Six Voyages of John Baptiste Tavernier, A Noble Man of France Now Living Through Turkey into Persia and the East Indies. London.

Stanford, E. (1879). *India North.* London: Stanford's Geological Establishment, map.

Stanford, E. (1879). *The Hindu Kush and Passes between Kabul and Oxus.* Published for the Proceedings of the Royal Geographic Society, London, map.

Stewart, G. (1880). *Ruby mines of Afghanistan.* Preceedings Asiatic Society of Bengal.

Ward, Fred (1990). Emeralds. *National Geographic, 178,* (1), pp. 38-69.

Wood, John (1841). *A Personal Narrative of a Journey to the Source of the River Oxus.* London: I. Murray.

Wood, John. (1872). *A Journey to the Source of the River Oxus. London:* John Murray.

Yousef, M. (1991). *Silent Soldier.* Lahore: Jang.

Yule, Col. Sir Henry, (Ed.). (1903). *The Book of Sir Marco Polo The Venetian Concerning the Kingdoms and Marvels of the East.* London: John Murray.

National Leaders

Recent Afghanistan Leaders

	Dates
Amir Abdur Rahman Khan	1880–1901
Amir Habibullah	1901–1919
King Amanullah	1919–1929
Bacha–I–Saqao (Habibullah II Ghazi)	1929–1929
King Nadir Shah	1929–1933
King Mohammed Zahir Shah (July)	1933–1973
Mohammad Daoud Khan, President & Prime Minister	1973–1978
Nur Mohammed Taraki, President (September)	1978–1979
Hafizullah Amin, Chairman Revolutionary Council, Prime Minister and Secretary General of the Peoples Party (December)	1979–1979
Babrak Karmal, President	1979–1986
Dr. Najibullah, President	1986–1992
Sibghatullah Mujaddedi, Chairman Leadership Council	1992–1992
Professor Burhanuddin Rabani, President	1992–2001

Recent Pakistan Leaders

	Dates
General Mohammad Zia ul–Haq, Military Leader	1976–1977
General Mohammad Zia ul–Haq, President	1977–1988
Mohammad Khan Junejo, Prime Minister	1986–1988
Ghulam Ishaq Khan, President	1988–1993
Benzir Bhutto, Prime Minister	1988–1990
Nawaz Sharif, Prime Minister	1990–1993
Farooq Ahmed Khan Laghari, President	1993–1996
Benazir Bhutto, Prime Minister	1993–1996
Mohammad Rafiq Tarar, President	1996–1999
Nawaz Sharif, Prime Minister	1997–1999
General Pervez Musharraf	1999–

Recent Soviet Leaders | **Dates**

Recent Soviet Leaders	Dates
Lennid Illyich Brezhnev, President	1977-1982
Yuri Vladimirovich Andropov, President	1982-1983
Konstantin U. Chernenko	1983-1985
Mikhail Gorbachev, First Secretary Soviet Union	1985-1991
Mikhail Gorbachev, President Soviet Union	1986-1991
Boris N. Yeltsin, President Soviet Federation	1991-2000
Vladimir Putin, President	2000-to date

Recent Presidents of the United States of America	Dates
Jimmy Carter, President	1977-1981
Ronald Reagan, President	1981-1989
George Bush, President	1989-1993
William Clinton, President	1993-2001
George W. Bush, President	2001-to date

Chronology of Events

Dates	Events

Dates   **Events**

4000 BC   Ancestors of today's Afghans lived in one-room branched huts or mud-brick houses with a single opening. Tribesmen raised wheat and domesticated dogs, goats and sheep. They buried their dead in shallow graves often with crude beads of lapis.

3500-2500 BC First cities existed in an area now known as Afghanistan. Carvans delivered lapis lazuli to merchants in the Indus Valley who shipped it to Egypt. Lapis was carved into seals and beads.

2700 BC   Cities built along River Indus.

2600 BC   Date of lapis carvings found in Ur.

2000 BC   First wave of Aryan migration; horses used for riding.

521-485 BC   Conquest and reign of Darius I divides current Afghanistan into Gandhara and Bactria.

328 BC   Alexander the Great invades Afghanistan.

330-327 BC   Alexander the Great rules. Bactria (Balkh) becomes province of empire.

45 AD   Kadphises founds Kushan dynasty.

50-250 AD   Afghanistan area is part of Kushanid empire.

78 AD   Khushan under Kanisha invade northern India.

225-600 AD   Sassanids establish control.

241 AD   Invasion of Shadpur.

460 AD   Invasion of white Huns (Ephthalities).

571 AD   Birth of Muhammad in Mecca (died 632 AD).

642 AD   Arabs invade Afghanistan and introduce Islam.

997-1150   Ghaznavid rule.

1018   Mahmud of Ghazni destroys Hindu city of Kanauj.

1175   Mohmmed of Ghazni establishes Moslem rule in India.

1220   Gengis Khan (name at birth-Temujin 1167 -1227) invades Afghanistan. Gengis Khan devastates Balk, Bamian, and Sarakhs.

1270's   Marco Polo obtains information on ruby, lapis and silver mines in Afghanistan.

1332   Moslem adventurer Ibn Battuta visits Afghanistan.

1370	Tugha Timur (Timerlane) (1338-1351) becomes king at Balkh, Afghanistan.
1405-1506	Timurid rule in Herat and Balk.
1505(1504)	Babur Zehir (Uddin Mahammad Babar 1482-1530) captures Kabul.
1526	Babur victorious at Battle of Panipat; conquers Delhi and founds Mughal (Moslem) dynasty.
1550	Aryans invade Indus Valley and northern India.
1600's	British start trading in Indian region.
1631-1667	Jean Baptiste Tavernier trades gems with Mongols.
1747	Ahmed Shah Durani (a Pashtun) became king and founded what is known today as Afghanistan by assassinating Persian (Iranian) ruler Nadir Shah.
1748	The Afghan empire extends to Punjab, Baluchistan, Sind, and hence to the Arabian Sea.
1773	Timur Shah begins 20-year rule. Moves capital from Kandahar to Kabul.
1793	Afghans lose areas in the Indus river basin.
1803	British defeat Mahrattas and occupy Delhi, establishing a protectorate over the Moghul Emperor.
1819-1826	Afghanistan divided into fiefdoms among competing Durrani families in Kabul, Kandahar, and Peshawar.
1823	Baluchistan and large parts of later Northwest Frontier Province lost to Afghan rulers.
1829	Dost Mohammad Khan establishes Muhammadzai dynasty in Kabul and begins to unite the country.
1830's	Collision between British and Soviet Empires – the Great Game begins.
1834	Sikhs annex Peshawar.
1839	British begin annexing Sikh territory conquered from Afghanistan.
1839-42	Afghans destroy British forces in the First Anglo-Afghan war. However, Dost Muhammad flees to Balk and later surrenders to British. British puppet Shah Shuja is placed on throne.
1849	Afghans regain control of north Afghanistan.
1855	Anglo-Afghan agreement to prevent Persian and Soviet territorial incursions leads to Treaty of Peshawar.
1859	British annex Baluchistan.

1872	Anglo-Soviet agreement on Afghan independence.
1878-80	Second Anglo-Afghan War (Amir Shir Ali refused British in Kabul). British invade Afghanistan fearing Soviet dominance in Kabul.
1879	Treaty of Gandomak gives British control of Khyber Pass.
1880-1901	Amir Abdur Rahman supported by Britain comes to power and Britain and Russia agree on the boundaries of Afghanistan.
1885	Russia invades Panjdeh, defeats Afghan army, and annexes it to Soviet Central Asia.
1892	Uprising of Hazaras suppressed.
1893	Durand line fixed under British pressure as Afghan-British Indian boundary, although it divides ethnic Pushtuns in two.
1895	Amir Abdur Rahman subdued Kaffiristan *Land of Infidels* and changed the name to Nuristan *Land of Light*.
1895	The Wahkan annexed by Afghanistan at British insistence to separate British and Soviet empires.
1895	Abdur Rahman abolishes slavery in Afghanistan.
1896	Kafiristan brought under Afghan control.
1914	World War I breaks out. Afghanistan remains neutral.
1919	Amir Habibullah, Abdur Rahman's son and successor is assassinated by members of anti- British group. Modernist Amanullah, Habibullah's third son, seizes throne.
1919-1929	King Amanullah, Abdur Rahman's grandson attacks British India.
1921	Soviet military and civilian advisors enter Afghanistan. British recognize Afghanistan and send an ambassador to Kabul the next year.
1923	First Afghanistan constitution, based on Belgian, Turkish, and Iranian constitutions, is ratified.
1929	Habibullah II Ghazi also known as Bacha-i-Saqao, a Tajik, captures Kabul and declares himself as Amir.
1929	Nadir Khan captures Kabul and executes Habibullah Kalakani. (Bacha-i-Saqao). The purge of Habibullah's followers further deteriorates the strained relations between non-Pashtuns and Pashtuns.
1930	The concept of a separate Moslem state put forth by Alama Iqbal, the great Moslem poet. Three years later named Pakistan by Chowdry Ramat Ali.

1933-1973	Mohammad Zahir Shah, Nadir Khan's son becomes king after father's assassination.
1934	Diplomatic relations begin with the U.S.A. Zahir Shah orders general election for National Assembly.
1941	Russia joins hands with Britain against Germany, and Afghanistan declares neutrality in World War II.
1942	America legation opens in Kabul; it is raised to Embassy status in 1948.
1945	American company Morrison-Knudsen begins US aid project in Helmand valley.
1946	Amu Darya midchannel fixed as boundary of Afghanistan with Russia.
1947	India split into two countries forming Moslem Pakistan, *Land of the Pure*. Afghanistan becomes a founding member of the United Nations.
1949	Pakistan one of the first countries to recognize China at its emergence.
1950	Russia accuses America of aggression in Afghanistan.
1953–1963	Sadar Mohammed Daoud Khan, King Zahir's cousin is Prime Minister.
1955	Pakistan and Afghanistan riots over Pushtunistan. Pakistan closes border. Nikita Khrushchev visits Afghanistan. Russia supplies US$100 million in development loans and secret military aid.
1957	Jamiat-i-Islami (Islamic Society) organized at Kabul University by Professor Ghulam Muhammad Niazi.
1958	Soviet Union agrees to survey oil deposits in Afghanistan.
1959	Women of the royal family and high officials appear unveiled at Afghan national celebrations, thus ending the practice of police-enforced veiling.
1961	Pakistan breaks relations with Afghanistan over Pushtun regions. On July 23rd, the Afghanistan ambassador, Muhammad Hashem Maiwandwal, meets President Kennedy and expresses his government's grave concern over Pakistan's use of American arms against Pashtun tribes.
1963	Daoud supported creation of Pashtun State, tensions with Pakistan caused his dismissal as Prime Minister by Zahir Shah. Dr. Mohammad Yusuf, a Tajik, is appointed.

1964	A liberal Constitution was promulgated and signed by Afghanistan's King Zahir Shah. Leonid Brezhnev visits Kabul to establish new Soviet supported polytec institute and assistance to open Salang Tunnel for linking north and south with an all-weather road.
1965	India attacks Pakistan. The People's Democratic Party of Afghanistan (PDPA) is established by Nur Mohammad Taraki and Babrak Karmal as the Khalq party. The United States and Russia fund infrastructure projects for US$7.7 million and US$11.1 million, respectively. PDPA members led student demonstrations forcing resignation of Dr. Yusuf's government.
1967	Natural gas export to the Soviet Union begins via a 97-kilometer pipeline. The Democratic Party (PDPA) with close ties to the Soviet Union split two rival Parties: (1) the Khalq (Masses) supported by the military and headed by Nur Muhammad Taraki and (2) the Parcham (Banner) faction led by Babrak Karmal.
1969	Author and future *Gem Hunter* resigns as Major US Army
1969	Author Purchases Jewelry Store in Hawaii.
1970	The USSR sign a protocol for the export of 2.5 billion cubic meters of Afghan natural gas in 1970. Sibghatullah Mujaddidi leads religious opposition, which condemns communist influence in government.
1971	Engineer Muhammad Yaqub Lali appointed Minister of Mines and Industries.
1972	Author's adventure begins in Afghanistan. The United States sends a special envoy to inform Kabul of termination of U.S. aid.
1973 (July)	Daoud seizes power, abolishes the monarchy, abrogates the constitution, and declares Afghanistan a republic with himself as President and Prime Minister. The pro-Soviet Parcham faction of the PDPA supports this move. King Zahir Shah abdicates from Italian exile and receives pensions from Daoud. Pakistan is blamed for attempted coup against Daoud.
1974	Soviets pledge US$600 million to Afghanistan. Daoud moves against Islamists at Kabul University, forcing many into Pakistan exile.
1975	Fall of Saigon, Vietnam in April. A group of young men,

including Massoud and Hekmatyar, form a loosely knit Islamic movement in response to the increasing Communist influence.

1976   Author receives status as U.S.A. Exclusive Lapis Importer. Daoud runs afoul of Brezhnev and begins to turn toward Iran and the Arab world for development funding and support.

1977   Military coup in Pakistan led by Zia ul-Haq. Daoud convenes the Loyal Jirgah or Grand Assembly to approve the draft of a new constitution. A new constitution is approved. Daoud becomes president. Martial Law imposed in Pakistan.

1978   Daoud visits Pakistan to improve relations.

Pakistan provides Hekmatyar, Massoud and others support against Afghan the government which sponsors a revolt in Nuristan.

Daoud clashes with Brezhnev over NATO members in Afghanistan and walks out of meeting.

Members of the PDPA gain power in a coup led by insurgents in the armed forces.

The military revolutionary council form a new government. Defense Minister Ghulam Haidar Rasuli, Interior Minister Abdul Qadir Nuristani, and Vice Presdient Sayyid Abdullah are killed along with President Daoud, his brother, and most of his family. This is referred to as the April 27th Sour Revolution or Marxist coup.

Babrak Karmal becomes Deputy Premier and Hafizullah Amin becomes Deputy Premier and Foreign Minister.

Pakistan's Prime Minister Bhutto is arrested, tried and hanged in a military coup that brings General Zia ul-Haq to the presidency.

More than fifty people are arrested and accused of a plot to overthrow the government.

Afghanistan adopts a red flag as its new national emblem.

Pakistan initiates nuclear program.

The USA expands its military presence in the Middle East.

In December, Russia signs a new bilateral treaty with Afghanistan and increases military assistance.

1979   Guerrillas fighting government troops in the eastern provinces.

(February) Overthrow of the Shah of Iran, the principle pillar of Western security by the Islamic Revolution led by Ayatollah Sayyid Ruhollah Musavi Khomeini.

(February) US Ambassador Adolph Dubs murdered in Kabul

U.S. President Jimmy Carter orders withdrawal of most diplomatic workers from U.S.A. Embassies in Asia.

First non-congress government in India headed by Mr. Morarji Desai.

Zulfikai Ali Butto, ex-Prime Minister of Pakistan is hanged.

Rebellion in Herat (Afghanistan's third largest city) led by Captain Ismail Khan.

Soviet military intelligence forms and trains elite battalion of Turkman, Tajik, and Uzbek soldiers for Afghanistan.

Amin becomes President of Afghanistan and publishes list of 12,000 people killed by Taraki regime.

Author and Joao Monteiro visit Kabul.

Fighting breaks out in Kabul and at Rishkur barracks.

The government crushes an army mutiny.

Soviet arms being moved into Kabul.

On December 24th, the Soviet Union invades Afghanistan with 80,000 – 120,000 troops.

On December 27th a large airborne force occupies Kabul and kills Amin while Karmal's Parcham takes the reins of the government.

The American CIA starts covert action.

Armed counter-revolutionary detachments operated in 18 of 26 provinces of Afghanistan.

1980-1986   Iraq-Iran War.

U.S. President Jimmy Carter signs presidential finding authorizing supply of weapons to the Afghan resistance through Pakistan.

President Carter in State of Union address (Carter Doctrine) calls any attempt by an outside force to gain control of Persian Gulf region subject to U.S. intervention, including military force.

U.S. CIA begins supplying Soviet Arms to the Afghan Mujahideen.

Demonstrations and rioting against government and Soviet

Union take place in Kabul followed by mass arrest.

(March) First Symposium on Gems and Minerals of Afghanistan.

Massoud takes Khenj emerald mines.

1981   Prominent Shia leader and scholar Allama Arif ul Hussaini is assassinated in Peshawar.

The Reagan administration undertakes a five-year program of US$3.2 billion in assistance to Pakistan's military thus overlooking Pakistan's nuclear weapons program.

1982   CIA commits hundreds of millions of dollars to Pakistan for Afghanistan operations.

Soviets mine Pakistan border areas to stem flow of arms and supplies.

Soviets divide Afghanistan into seven military districts, each headed by a Soviet General.

In November Brezhnev dies and is succeeded by Yuri Andropov who desires a political settlement.

1983   Commander Ahmed Shah Massoud accepts Soviet offer of one-year truce in Panjsher Valley but refuses to negotiate with Karmal regime.

With consent of Jamiat-i-Islami leader Burhanuuddin Rabani, Commander Massoud invites Jamiat commanders from six provinces (Kapisa, Parwan, Takhar, Baglan, Kunduz, and Badakhshan) to join in the North to coordinate military and administrative work. The Council tries to extend influence to all commanders north of the Hindu Kush, regardless of party.

1984   Andropov dies and is replaced by Konstantin Chernenko.

Saturation bombing of Panjsher Valley begins.

President Reagan declares his support for the Afghan counter-revolutionaries to defeat communism with a billion-dollar budget (National Security Decision Directive 166).

At the suggestion of CIA chief William Casey, with support of Pakistan intelligence, Afghan Mujahideen begin sending Islamic propaganda missions into Soviet Central Asia. Afghan planes cross Pakistan border bombing and shelling.

1985   *Gems & Gemology* publishes author's first article on Gemstones of Afghanistan

Author has inventory stolen in Hawaii and in Tel Aviv.

Chernenko dies.

Mikhail Gorbachev succeeds to Kremlin leadership as president and general secretary.

Peshawar resistance groups form a seven-party union called Islamic Unity of Afghan Mujahideen, with rotating presidency.

United States begins to supply Pakistan with Sidewinder air-to-air missiles and Stinger ground-to-air missiles.

1986   (April 17th) American military bomb Libya; angry demonstrations and marches are held in Pakistan.

Mohammad Najibullah, former chief of KHAD, replaces Karmal as party secretary. He purges PDPA of Karmal men.

Karmal removed from ceremonial presidency position and replaced by non-PDPA member Haji Mohammad Samkanai.

Gorbachev announces unilateral withdrawal of six regiments by end of year.

U.S. Government sends Milton Beardon, CIA, with 100 Stinger missiles to Afghanistan. This ends *Plausibility Deniability* and starts open war between the U.S.A. and the Soviet Union. Aid from all sources to the Mujahideen was rumored to be over one billion dollars in 1986 and for the subsequent three years.

Afghan government planes cross into Pakistan and drop bombs.

The U.S. Stinger missiles result in destruction of three Soviet MI-24 helicopter gunships at the Jalalabad airport.

U.S. 7th Fleet arrive at Karachi, Pakistan port.

1987   Author has inventory stolen in Hawaii.

In Afghanistan Stinger missiles destroy fifty-three Soviet-Kabul aircraft in May and sixty in June.

Geneva VII convened at Kabul's government's initiative. Kabul government agrees to reduce Soviet troop withdrawal time to sixteen months.

1988   On April 10th the ISI arms depot at Ojri camp (Rawalpindi) explodes, destroying 10,000 tons of arms and ammunition for Afghan resistance, killing 100 and injuring 1,000.

The Afghan Interim Government (AIG) is formed in Peshawar.

	(August) Pakistan President Zia ul-Haq killed with General Aktar,

(August) Pakistan President Zia ul-Haq killed with General Aktar,

U.S.A. Ambassador Raphel, American General Wasson and eight Pakistani generals when their plan exploded.

Five Afghan planes bomb two Peshawar villages

Soviets deliver SCUD missiles into Afghanistan and increase fighting.

Geneva Accords signed by Afghanistan, Pakistan, Russia and USA (Mujahideen not a party to this agreement) Soviets agree to move out of Afghanistan in phases.

Benazir Bhutto becomes Prime Minister of Pakistan.

1989   The Afghanistan Interim Government (AIG) is formed in Pakistan with Sibghtullah Mojaddedi as President.

Gem Hunter, Gary Bowersox, meet's Ahmed Shah Massoud in Afghanistan

Hesb-i-Islami (Hekmatyar) commanders ambush and kill 17 Jamiat Commanders after meeting in Takhar, Afghanistan.

Hesb-i-Islami (Hekmatyar) and Jamiat-i-Islami (Massoud) troops clash in Northern Afghanistan killing more than 17 Jamiat commanders.

Author Sponsors Gem and Mineral Symposium at Chitral.

Article on the Gujar Killi Emerald Deposit co-authored by Gary

Bowersox and Jawaid Anwar is published in *Gems & Gemology.*

The last Soviet Troops leave Afghanistan.

1990   A Scud Missile from Afghanistan lands near Islamabad, the Capital of Pakistan.

The Gem Hunter explores Badakshan, Panjsher Valley and Nuristan.

The Gem Hunter sponsors a symposium at Chitral on the Gem and Minerals of Hindu Kush.

Soviet Union Communist Party is declared defunct after an abortive coup.

1991   A second symposium titled "The Gems and Minerals of Central Asia" is sponsored by the Gem Hunter in Chitral Pakistan.

Mujahideen conquers Wahkan corridor.

Mujahideen (Jamiat) conclude local truce with Soviet border guards in Tajikistan to keep bridge at Ishkashim open for local use.

"Emeralds of Panjsher Valley" is published in *Gems & Gemology.*

Formal end of Soviet Union (December 8th).

1992 General Abdul Rashid Dostam and Uzbek militia defect to Mujahideen.

Professor B. Rabani leads delegation of Mujahideen to Moscow to discuss end of war. At Afghan suggestion, representatives of Ukraine, Uzbekistan, Tajikistan, and Kazakistan participate. They agree that all powers should be transferred to Islamic interim government and elections under international supervision be held within two years.

Abdul Rasul, Sayyaf, Khalis, and Hekmatyar denounce Rabani as engaging in anti-Mujahideen activities.

A third symposium on the Gems and Minerals of the Hindu Kush and Central Asia is held in Tucson, Arizona. Professor Sibghatullah Mojaddedi is sworn in as caretaker Interim President of the Islamic State of Afghanistan (April).

Massoud's forces capture Charikar and Bagram military air base south of Hindu Kush from Najibullah's forces.

Najibullah announces his resignation on Kabul TV and takes refuge in the UN compound after being stopped at the airport.

(June) President Rabani elected President and heavy fighting breaks out in Kabul with rival factions, particularly with Hekmatyar's Hesb-i-Islami.

Khalis withdraws from leadership council in protest of Rabani's decision to admit Wahdat (Shi'a) representatives to council.

Trouble in Namak Mandi between the Shiite and Sunni Moslems.

The Gem Hunter visits ruby mines at Jegdalek.

Dostam's militia leaves Kabul for Marar-i-Sharif.

1993 Hekmatyar calls Rabani's election as president of Islamic Republic Afghanistan (IRA) a fraud.

Fractional fighting disrupts Kabul.

Dostam and Massoud forces join to squeeze out Hekmatyar.

1994 General Dostam switches sides joining Hekmatyar and

attacks Massoud's forces.

Dostam forces join Hekmatyar to seize presidential palace and other key Kabul installations.

Dostam's airplanes bomb Kabul.

Gem Hunter visits Kabul and the Sar-e-sang lapis mines.

Taliban becomes active and capture parts of Kandahar.

Rabani extends his term in office for a third time, claiming as justification the lack of legal authority acceptable to all.

Massoud vs. Taliban 1994 – 2001.

1995   Wahdat leader Ali Mazari threatens to launch SCUD missiles against Massoud's forces. Massoud attacks the Wahdat forces. Wahdat forces turn over some weapons to the Taliban.

Taliban launch attack on Herat (April).

The United Nations representative warns that if Rabani does not step down, the UN members will not recognize him.

The Gem Hunter makes an historic trip to the Kuh-i-Lal mines located on the Afghanistan border with Tajikistan.

The book *Gemstones of Afghanistan* is published by Geoscience Press.

The Taliban capture Herat.

Afghanistan accuses envoy Mestiri at UN of supporting the Taliban.

1996   Hekmatyar defeated by the Taliban.

Taliban take over Jalalabad and Kabul as Massoud moves out without a fight.

1997   A consortium of U.S. and Saudi companies agree to fund a multi-billion dollar pipeline crossing Afghanistan.

A revolt by General Malik, Dostam second in command, forces Dostam to flee the country.

Commander of Dostam's airforce and two fellow pilots defect to the Taliban.

1998   An important symposium on gems and minerals of Central Asia held in Tucson, Arizona, USA.

The Gem Hunter meets with Taliban Commanders and Minister of Mines and Industry.

Mapping surveys begin in the Jegdalek ruby mines and the Panjsher Valley emerald mines.

U.S.A. military fire missiles into Afghanistan.

1999	GPS/satellite mapping of Panjsher emerald mines.
	Expedition team lead by the Gem Hunter escapes from Panjsher Valley as Taliban army breaks Massoud's lines of defense.
	Massoud recaptures lost territory.
2000	The Gem Hunter visit Panjsher Valley to continue work but is forced to leave.
	Massoud loses Taloqan.
	The author's article "The Rubies and Sapphires of Jegdalek, Afghanistan" is published by *Gems & Gemology*.
2001	The Gem Hunter films the mining operations at Sar-e-Sang.
	Commander Ahmed Shah Massoud assassinated.
	USA attacked.
	USA and British Soldiers attack Afghanistan.
2002	Northern Alliance moves in to Kabul
	Interim Afghanistan Government is established.

Afghanistan Provinces

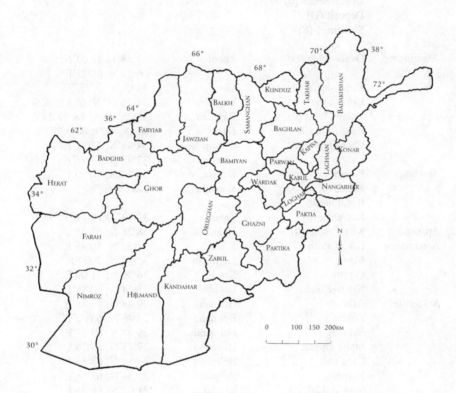

Coordinates Where to Locate Afghanistan
Gems and Minerals

Mineral	Field (F) Occurrences (O) Deposit (D) Showings (S)	Province	Coordinates
Aluminum	Ovatu-shela (D)	Zabul	31°58' to 32°03'N; 66°12' to 66°22'E
	Kohe-safed (0)	Ghor	34°05'N; 63°20'E
	Estoma (0)	Baghlan	34°26'08"N; 68°l 1'16"E
	Nalag (Tala) (0)	Baghlan	35°25'16"N; 68°09'20"E
	Esnpushta (0)	Baghlan	35°18'44"N; 68°06'22"E
	Char-Qala (0)	Ghazni	34°46'N; 68°12'E
	Tanghi (0)	Ghazni	32°45'N; 67°25'E
Amethyst	Parian	Kapisa	35°50'N; 70°10'E
	Kandahar	Kandahar	unknown
	Badakhshan		
	Korothka (0)	Zabul	32°33'18"N; 66°39'56"E
Apatite	Khanneshin (0)	Helmand	38°28'N; 63°35'E
Aquamarine	Dhray-Pech	Konar	34°50'N; 70°45'E
	Mawi	Laghman	35°10'N; 70°12'E
	Papruk	Konar	36°30'N; 71°09'E
	Nilaw-Kolum	Laghman	35°14'N; 70°18'E
Aragonite	Arbu	Helmand	29°49'N; 68°58'E
	Zoldag	Helmand	29°46'N; 63°52'E
	Sukalog	Helmand	29°43'N; 63°27'E
	Malik Dukan	Helmand	29°43'N; 63°36'E
	I'anawuk	Helmand	29°34'N; 63°54'E
	Muzdan	Helmand	29°34'N; 63°58'E
	Spin-Boldak	Kandahar	31°02'N; 66°23'E
Asbestos	Loe-Dakka	Nangarhar	34°l 1'N; 70°56'E
	Loghar (D)	Loghar	34°06'30"N; 69°01'30"E
	Shodal (D)	Paktia	33°14'N; 69°35'E
	Farenjal (0)	Parwan	34°59'N; 68°41'E
	Spinkala (0)	Loghar	34°11'50"N; 68°55'15"E
	Baghram (0)	Parwan	34°50'30"N; 69°28'30"H
	Gerdab (0)	Nangarhar	34°23'N; 70°43'E
	Kohe Moghu Aba (O)	Loghar	34°l4'30"N; 69°02'45"E
	Abparan (0)	Loghar	34°ll'55"N; 69°15'15"E
	Waghjan (0)	Loghar	34°07'50"N; 39°03'35°E
	Shakhsi (0)	Loghar	34°07'05"N; 69°04'15"E
	Sperkaw (0)	Paktia	33°15'N; 69°36'E.
	Kopra (0)	Paktia	33°13'll"N; 69°34'00"E
	Roghay (0)	Paktia	33°12'55"N; 69°32'45"E

	Rosana (0)	Paktia	33°12'25"N; 69°36'35°E
	Afdzalkhel (0)	Paktia	33°11'05"N; 69°32'22"E
	Samandkay (0)	Paktia	33°10'05"N; 69°40'46"E
	Kandinkhel (0)	Paktia	33°09'45"N; 69°38'30"E
	Sperkhay (0)	Paktia	33°08'40"N; 69°38'35°E
	Frontierside (0)	Paktia	32°35'N; 69°22'E
	- (S)	Badakhshan	38°13'31"N; 70°41'33"E
	- (S)	Badakhshan	36°57'10"N; 70°44'20"E
	Saidy-kayon - (S)	Baghlan	35°37'39"N; 68°21'20"E
	- (S)	Loghar	34°13'40"N; 68°59'30"E
	- (S)	Loghar	34°12'25"N; 68°57'55"E
	- (S)	Loghar	34°11'45"N; 68°59'40"E
	- (S)	Loghar	34°08'50"N; 68°58'05"E
Barite	I'eranjal	Parwan	35°10'N; 68°50'E
	Sangilyan (D)	Herat	34°45'55"N; 62°01'40"E
	Farenjal (D)	Parwan	34°59'N; 68°41'E
	Gardin-burida (0)	Herat	35°20'25"N; 61°25'00"E
	Gulron (0)	Herat	34°51'30"N; 61°44'00"E
	Zandadshon (0)	Herat	34°17'30"N; 61°53'40"E
	Kushkak (0)	Ghor	34°34'N; 64°31'E
	Durbas (0)	Farah	32°50'N; 63°13'E
	North Farenjal (0)	Parwan	45°00'30"N; 68°41'00"E
	Tanghi-loli (0)	Parwan	34°59'N; 68°34'E
	Zerak (0)	Parwan	34°46'07"N; 68°16'10"E
	Rokul (0)	Bamiyan	34°42'10"N; 68°08'05"E
	Chapqul (0)	Bamiyan	34°41'45"N; 68°08'00"E
	Hajigat (0)	Bamiyan	34°40'20"N; 68°03'45"E
	- (S)	Parwan	35°02'N; 68°38'E
	- (S)	Parwan	35°01'00; 68°37'30"E
	- (S)	Parwan	34°59'00"N; 68°37'30"E
Beryl	Deh Rarar	Badakhshan	35°57"N; 70°28 E
	Chawki- Sarhani	Konar	34°48'N; 70°11'8
	Darra-i-Pec	Konar	35°00"N; 70°37'E
	Pechaghan	Kapisa	35°02'N'; 69°43'E
	Sundurar	Laghman	34°52'N; 70°16'E
	Nilaw-Kolum	Laghman	35°10'N; 70°21'E
Beryllium	Talbuzanak Field (F)	Badakhshan	37°12'06"N; 70°33'36"E
	Mundel Field (F)	Laghman	35°17'28"N; 70°09'57"E
	Nilaw-Kolum Field (F)	Laghman	35°10'00" to 35°15'36"N; 70°14'56" to 70°21'14"E
	Pachaghan Field (P)	Parwan	35°02'03"N; 69°43'10"E
	Darra-i-Pech Field (F)	Nangarhar	34°52'30" to 34°59'00"N; 70°42'10" to 70 6 45'40"E
	Chawki Field (F)	Nangarhar	34°40'20" to 34°49'10"N; 70°46'56" to 70°52'50"E
	Darrahe-Nur Field (F)	Laghman	34°37'00" to 34°39'14"N; 70°16'17" to 70°45'00"E
	Shahidan Field (F)	Laghman	34°29'00" to 34°34'00"N;

			69°49'00" to 69°59'30"E
	Nilaw (D)	Laghman	35°ll'18" to 35°15'36"N; 70°15'18" to 70°18'10"E
	Kolum (D)	Laghman	35°12'07"N; 70°20'04"E
	Darrahe-Pech (D)	Nangarhar	34°55'02" to 34°55'53"N; 70°44'12" to 70°44'53"E
	Darrahe-nur (D)	Nangarhar	34°39'40"N; 70°32'30"E
	Talbuzanak (0)	Badakhshan	37°13'35"N; 70°33'21"E
	Darava- Su (0)	Badakhshan	36°09'N; 70°48'E
	Alama (0)	Nangarhar	35°30'08"N; 71°10'52"E
	Pachaghan (0)	Parwan	35°02'03"N; 64°43'10"E
	Ghursalak (0)	Nangarhar	34°57'15" to 34°57'45"N; 70°43'55" to 70°44'55"E
	Awraghal (0)	Nangarhar	34°56'10" to 34°57'00"N; 70°42'30" to 70°44'10"E
	Kashmund (0)	Nangarhar	34°37'30"N; 70°28'00"E
	Shabidan (0)	Laghman	34°29'54"N; 63°56'04"E
	Jalalabad (0)	Nangarhar	34°28'00"N; 69°27'30"E
	Maydan-Ahu (0)	Zabul	32°46'24"N; 66°54'38"E
	Band (0)	Zabul	32°45'32"N; 66°53'01"E
	- S	Maydan	34°23'N; 68°52'E
	- S	Laghman	34°38'N; 69°50'E
	- S	Oruzghan	33°37'02"N; 66°15'l0"E
	- S	Oruzghan	33°35'23"N; 66°16'06"E
Bismuth	Qara-Jelga (0)	Badakhshan	37°14'35"N; 74°25'14"E
	Podar (0)	Herat	33°59'; 62°33'E
	Shand (0)	Farah	33°00'30"N; 60°51'00"E
	Gharghey (0)	Kandahar	32°13'N; 65°42'E
	Kochak (0)	Oruzghan	32°58'N; 63°43'E
	Koh-i-Sohi (0)	Oruzghan	32°56'N; 66°48'E
	Oruzghan (0)	Oruzghan	32°55'20"N; 66°39'20"E
	Qarya-i-Baki (0)	Ghazni	32°55'30"N; 66°52'30"E
	outcrop #914 (0)	Oruzghan	34°41'N; 66°28'30"E
	- S	Oruzghan	
Borosilicate	Neylak (0)	Ghazni	33°18'30"N; 67°24'40"E
	- (S)	Ghazni	33°09'25"N; 67°44'15"E
Cadmium	Kalai-Asad (D)	Kandahar	32°05' to 32°07'N; 65°31' to 65°33'E
Calcite	Robaty-Payin (0)	Badakhshan	37°55'25"N; 71°34'45"E
	Gulron (0)	Herat	34°51'30"N; 61°44'00"E
	Gizaw (0)	Oruzghan	33°23'20"N; 66°17'09"E
	Manjlek (0)	Paktia	33°31'50"N; 69°57'50"E
	Kasha (0)	Paktia	33°16'00"N; 69°35'40"E
Celestite	(unknown)	Takhar	36°17'N; 69°28'E
	Kartaw (D)	Kunduz	36°42'N; 38°35'E
	Tangi-murch (D)	Baghlan	36°16'13"N; 69°12'24"E
Cesium/Rubidium			
	Parun Field (P)	Nangarhar	34°54'34"N; 70°52'15"E

	Nilaw/Kolum Field (1)	Laghman	35°10'00" to 35°15'36"N; 70°14'56" to 70°21'14"E
	Korghal Field (1)	Laghman	35°04'06"N; 70°18'29"E
	Alinghar (P)	Laghman	34°52'41"N; 70°16'48"E
	Surkh-rod Field (F)	Nangarhar	34°26'05"N; 70°15'23"E
	Tatang (D)	Nangarhar	34°26'05"N; 70°15'23"E
	Paskhi (D)	Nangarhar	35°17'30"N; 70°57'30"E
	Kolum (D)	Laghman	35°12'07"N; 70°20'04"E
	Wozghul (0)	Nangarhar	35°29'l0"N; 70°59'l0"E
	Korghal (0)	Laghman	35°04'06"N; 70°18'29"E
	Kalatan (0)	Laghman	35°00'26"N; 70°26'40"E
Chromite	Hezarak	Nangarhar	34°04'N; 69°58'E
	Mohammad Agha (Deposit #2)	Kabul	34°13'N; 69°08'E
	Kulangar (Deposit #10)	Kabul	34°06'N; 69°08'E
Clays, Refractory			
	Rafak	Samanghan	35°31'49"N; 67°51'09"E
	Nalak	Baghlan	35°25'27"N; 68°09'26"8
	Talin	Baghlan	35°21'00"N; 68°07'30"E
Clays, Brick	Karukh	Herat	34°30'00"N; 62°34'30"E
	Malumat	Herat	34°29'N; 62°44"E
	Surkhab	Baghlan	35°58'25"N; 68°40'32"E
	Kaukpar	Baghlan	35°56'55"N; 68°52'36"E
	Dahane-Tor	Samanghan	35°43'13"N; 67°15'41"E
	Shabashak	Samanghan	34°41'36"N; 67°27'00"E
	Deh-Kepal	Kabul	34°37'00"N; 66°04'30"E
Clays, Porcelain/Pottery			
	Topcha-Khana	Takhar	36°35'N; 69°37'E
	Tala-Barfak	Baghlan	35°21'49"N; 68°10'40"E
Coal	Kinjan	Kunduz	35°39'N; 68°5'8'E
	Sar-i-Asia (D)	Samanghan	36°19'37"N; 68°05'29"E
	Darra Suf	Balkh	35°42'N; 67°28'E
	Sabzak	Herat	35°33'42"N; 67°33'28"E
	(unknown)	Ghor	36°01'57"N; 68°46'36" E
	(unknown)	Bamiyan	34°30'N; 62°40'E
	(unknown)	Paktia	34°42'N; 66°l6'E
	Dudkash (D)	Baghlan	35°26'N; 57°50'E
	Majid-i-Chubi (D)	Herat	36°01'00"N; 68°46'35°E
	Dahane-Tor (D)	Samanghan	34°36'00"N; 63°09'30"E
	Karkar (D)	Baghlan	36°01'57"N; 68°46'36" E
	Ishpushta (D)	Baghlan	36°19'37"N; 68°05'29"E
	Sar-i-Asia (D)	Samanghan	35°33'42"N; 67°33'28"E
	Dudkash (D)	Baghlan	36°01'00"N; 68°46'35°E
	Majid-i-Chubi (D)	Herat	34°36'00"N; 63°09'30"E
	Dahane-Tor (D)	Samanghan	35°42'20"N; 67°17'34"E
	Sabashak (D)	Samanghan	34°41'36"N; 67°27'00"E
	Darwaza (D)	Samanghan	35°40'00"N; 67°23'00"E

	Lela (D)	Samanghan	35°38'30"N; 67°10'35"6
	Mirza-Wolang (0)	Jowzjan	36°01'N; 65°45'E
	Western Dudkash (0)	Baghlan	36°00'30"N; 68°45'00"E
	Bangi	Takhar	36°22"N; 69°32"E
	(Unknown)	Takhar	36°12"N; 38°22"E
	Farkhar (0)	Takhar	36°47'51"N; 69°43'16"E
	Kishakton (0)	Takhar	36°36'36"N; 69°41'56"E
	Roshgh (0)	Takhar	36°35'25"N; 69°40'52"E
	Zamburak (0)	Takhar	36°31'25"N; 69°34'42"E
	Namakab (0)	Takhar	36°31'04"N; 69°41'16"E
	Sangylyashm (0)	Takhar	36°30'49"N; 69°36'13"E
	Sayed-i (0)	Takhar	36°30'32"N; 69°33'32"E
	Kalta-taw (0)	Takhar	36°30'22"N; 69°30'41"E
	Chal (0)	Takhar	36°30'll"N; 69°29'20"E
	Zumrab (0)	Takhar	36°30'13"N; 69°42'12"E
	Darra-i-Kolon (0)	Takhar	36°30'00"N; 69°31'10"E
	Syakh-Darra (0)	Takhar	36°30'03"N; 69°29'52"E
	Sayed II (0)	Takhar	36°30'00"N; 69°40'12"E
	Chalay-Khurd (0)	Takhar	36°29'10"N; 69°37'41"E
	Bazarak (0)	Takhar	36°38'36"N; 69°35'45"E
	Narin (0)	Baghlan	36°02'23"N; 69°09'48"E
	Palowana (0)	Herat	34°23'50"N; 62°46'45"E
	Shere-Arman (0)	Badghis	34°37'N; 63°52'E
	Western Sangach (0)	Baghlan	34°59'13"N; 68°46'30"E
	Western Garmak (0)	Samanghan	35°44'00"N; 67°18'28"E
	Eastern Garmak (0)	Samanghan	35°43'40"N; 67°21'05"E
	Balkhab (0)	Balkh	35°43'N; 66°59'E
	Karamkol (0)	Samanghan	35°41'23"N; 67°23'06"E
	Oilokhak (0)	Balkh	35°41N; 67°05'E
	Sary-Tor (0)	Samanghan	35°38'23"N; 67°21'20"E
	Sabzak-Kotal (0)	Samanghan	35°30'54"N; 67°35'12"E
	Awkhorak (0)	Samanghan	35°29'53"N; 67°41'04"E
	Estoma (0)	Baghlan	35°25'24"N; 68°09'42"E
	Amir-Amand (0)	Baghlan	35°25'23"N; 68°09'28"E
	Nalak (0)	Baghlan	35° 24'02"N; 68°10'40"E
	Barfak (0)	Baghlan	35°19'55"N; 68°07'12"E
	Kamard (0)	Bamiyan	35°15'25"N; 67°57'40"E
	Mazar-Kol (0)	Bamiyan	35°14'40"N; 67°53'32"E
	Faraghard (0)	Parwan	34°58'30"N; 68°52'30"E
Chromium	Loghar (D)	Loghar	34°05'N; 68°56'E
	Jurgati (0)	Parwan	34°51'30"N; 69°26'10"E
	Werek (0)	Loghar	34°18'55"N; 69°04'05"E
	Makhmudgazi III (0)	Loghar	34°08'20"N; 69°01'00"E
	Makhmudgazi 1 (0)	Loghar	34°07'40"N; 69°02'10"E
	Mokhmudgazi II (0)	Loghar	34°07'10"N; 69°02'10"E
	Koh-i-Kalawur (0)	Loghar	34°05'45"N; 69°07'45"8
	Sperkaw (0)	Paktia	34°15'N; 69°36'E
	Shodal (0)	Paktia	34°14'N; 69°36'E

	- (S)	Loghar	34°16'20"N; 68°53'10"E
	- (S)	Loghar	34°14'l0"N; 68°52'20"E
	- (S)	Loghar	34°08'50"N; 68°58'05"E
	- (S)	Kandahar	31°53'14"N; 65°59'29"E
	- (S)	Kandahar	31°41'30"N; 65°14'40"E
Combustible Shales			
	Taj-Kala (0)	Faryiab	35°54'N; 65°31'E
Copper	Doab	Bamiyan	35°22'N; 68°06'E
	(unknown)	Wardak	34°33'N; 68°27'E
	(unknown)	Oruzghan	33°46'N; 67°08'E
	(unknown)	Ghazni	33°21'N; 67°15'E
	Kundalen	Zabul	32°20'N; 66°30'E
	(unknown)	Parah	32°l6'N; 62°21'E
	(unknown)	Kandahar	32°18'N; 65°54'E
	Kako Kili	Kandahar	30°57'N; 66°07'E
	(unknown)	Kabul	34°28'N; 69°05'E
	(unknown)	Loghar	33°57'N; 69°18'E
	Hesa-i-Awal	Parwan	35°21'N; 69°46'E
	(unknown)	Parwan	35°15'N; 69°35'E
	Shaida (D)	Herat	33°51'N; 61°51'E
	Jawkhar (D)	Kabul	34°18'57"N; 69°18'10"E
	Aynak (D)	Loghar	34°l5'58"N; 69°18'02"E
	Darband (D)	Kabul	34°16'N; 69°24'E
	Kundalyan (D)	Zabul	32°18'46"N; 66°31'58"E
	Chosnudi-Bolo (0)	Badakhshan	37°48'10"N; 71°34'39"E
	Glick (0)	Badakhshan	37°21'25"N; 71°00'35°E
	Furmorah I (0)	Badakhshan	37°05'10"N; 70°50'20"E
	Boi-Qara (0)	Badakhshan	36°59'30"N; 73°53'52"E
	Sim-Koh (0)	Herat	35°20'25"N; 61°20'00"E
	Nayak (0)	Herat	34°26'N; 62°27'E
	Du-Berodar (0)	Herat	34°08'N; 61°05'E
	Rabot-i-Sapcha (0)	Herat	34°06'30"N; 62°l9'00"E
	Seh-Koh (0)	Faryiab	35°l7'N; 65°22'E
	Ahankashan (0)	Badghis	34°39'N; 64°23'E
	Kushkak (0)	Ghor	34°30'N; 64°31'E
	Taghab- Soni (0)	Herat	34°26'30"N; 63°42'30"E
	Taghab I (0)	Herat	34°26'N; 63°48'E
	Bedan (0)	Ghor	34°25'N; 64°31'E
	Khasan-Sansalaghei (0)	Ghor	34°41'08"N; 64°35'00"E
	Zawar (0)	Ghor	34°10'N; 63°55'E
	Minora (0)	Ghor	34°10'N; 63°58'E
	Minora II (0)	Ghor	34°09'N; 63°59'E
	Mir-Ali (0)	Herat	33°54'N; 62°l2'E
	Shaida I (0)	Herat	33°52'N; 61°50'E
	Shaida Ill (0)	Herat	33°51'10"N; 61°49'00"E
	Shaida II (0)	Herat	33°50'50"N; 61°49'00"E
	Pudar (0)	Herat	33°50'N; 62°33'E
	Dahana (0)	Herat	33°46'N; 62°01'E

Tonura (0)	Farah	35°45'N; 61°41'E
Kalmurgh (0)	Herat	33°45'N; 61°55'E
Northern Occurrence (0)	Herat	33°43'N; 61°12'E
Dusar (0)	Herat	33°43'N; 61°17'E
Sar Dakhana (0)	Farah	33°25'N; 61°48'E
Gologha I (0)	Farah	33°21'N; 61°21'E
Border- Side (0)	Farah	33°15'N; 60°40'E
Korezak (0)	Farah	33°06'N; 60°44'E
- (0)	Farah	33°02'55"N; 61°41'40"E
Ghuri-Safed (0)	Farah	32°56'N; 61°06'E
Chohe-Hrusi (0)	Farah	32°51'45"N; 61°13'00"E
Markoh (0)	Farah	32°46'N; 60°58'E
Siab (0)	Farah	32°39'N; 62°53'E
Farah II (0)	Farah	33°18'N; 64°13'E
Durbas 11 (0)	Farah	32°51'N; 63°12'E
Rode-Duzd (0)	Farah	32°44'N; 63°03'E
Ghurma (0)	Farah	33°42'N; 63°18'E
- (0)	Kandahar	32°15'17"N; 65°59'02"E
Shin-char (0)	Kandahar	32°14'09"N; 65°43'03"E
Gharghey (0)	Kandahar	32°13'N; 65°42'E
Chinar (0)	Kandahar	32°11'15"N; 65°35'10"8
Chawni (0)	Kandahar	32°10'N; 65°25'E
- (0)	Kandahar	32°05'N; 68°55'E
Andarab (0)	Baghlan	35°38'00"N; 68°56'30"E
Balkhab (0)	Jawzjan	35°35'N; 66°46'E
Gazoghel (0)	Baghlan	35°34'00"N; 68°50'40"E
Gazoghel I (0)	Baghlan	35°32'N; 68°50'E
Andarab1 (0)	Baghlan	35°31'N; 68°46'E
Tanghy-Eshpusshta (0)	Bamiyan	35°21'50"N; 68°05'46"E
Darra-Alasang (0)	Baghlan	35°18'59"N; 68°07'16"E
Eshpushta (0)	Baghlan	35°18'32"N; 68°04'50"E
Surkh-i-Parso (0)	Parwan	34°51'N; 68°39'E
Kushk (0)	Ghor	34°30'N; 66,00'E
Maydan (0)	Maydan	34°28'24"N; 68°46'12"E
Waraz (0)	Bamiyan	34°13'N; 66°53'E
Ghulbina (0)	Bamiyan	34°03'N; 67°36'E
Shoshon (0)	Baghlan	35°51'N; 69°23'E
Ghuly-Sang (0)	Baghlan	35°46'N; 69°24'E
Tele-Doab (0)	Baghlan	35°38'N; 69°41'E
Bazarak (0)	Kapisa	35°21'N; 69°31'E
Godo-China (0)	Kabul	34°40N; 69°40'E
Khaidarabad (0)	Kabul	34°30'42"N; 69°01'00"E
Sultan Padshah (0)	Kabul	34°25'25"N; 69°08'10"E
Taghar (0)	Kabul	34°25'53"N; 69°22'43"E
Yakhdarra (0)	Kabul	34°25'25"N; 69°15'00"E
Ghuldarra II (0)	Kabul	34°24'25"N; 69°15'35°E
Mirzakhan (0)	Kabul	34°24'05"N; 69°21'35°E
Dawrankhel (0)	Kabul	34°24'00"N; 69°24'00"E

Ghuldarra 1 (0)	Kabul	34°23'53"N; 69°18'20"E
Kharuti I (0)	Kabul	34°23'12"N; 69°20'50"E
Gharwazi I (0)	Kabul	34°22'10"N; 69°19'30"E
Khurdkabul (0)	Kabul	34°22'20"N; 69°22'40"E
Kharuti II (0)	Kabul	34°22'05"N; 69°21'00"E
Gharari (0)	Kabul	34°22'00"N; 69°23'20"E
Charwazi II (0)	Kabul	34°21'55"N; 69°18'45"E
Zakhel II (0)	Kabul	34°21'20"N; 69°17'20"E
Barkhei (0)	Kabul	34°21'15"N; 69°18'30"E
Charwazi Ill (0)	Kabul	34°20'50"N; 69°18'00"E
Charazi IV (0)	Kabul	34°20'20"N; 69°19'05"E
Zakhel I (0)	Kabul	34°20'05"N; 69°16'00"E
Palanghar (0)	Kabul	34°20'00"N; 69°17'55"E
Shinwar (0)	Kabul	34°19'N; 69°37"E
Kelaghey (0)	Loghar	34°18'40"N; 69°ll'20"E
Lalmi-Tanghi (0)	Kabul	34°18'33"N; 69°20'35"E
Gezghaz (0)	Kabul	34°18'N; 69°22'E
Umar (0)	Kabul	34°17'55"N; 69°26'10"E
Akarkhel (0)	Kabul	34°17'30"N; 69°17'00"E
Janguzay IV (0)	Kabul	34°16'40"N; 69°24'00"E
Rjan (0)	Kabul	34°16'36"N; 69°27'36"E
Batkhel II (0)	Kabul	34°16'20"N; 69°22'10"E
Batkhel III (0)	Kabul	34°16'10"N; 69°22'45"E
Janguzay Ill (0)	Kabul	34°15'40"N; 69°23'20"E
Janguzay II (0)	Kabul	34°15'40"N; 69°24'00"E
Batkhel1 (0)	Kabul	34°15'35°N; 69°22'30"E
Janguzay 1 (0)	Kabul	34°15'l0"N; 69°23'10"E
Batkhel IV (0)	Loghar	34°14'50"N; 69°21'50"E
Pachi (0)	Loghar	34°14'05"N; 69°16'50"E
Kundara (0)	Loghar	34°13'55"N; 69°l5'40"E
Gurghi Mayden (0)	Loghar	34°13'40"N; 69°22'00"E
Manay (0)	Loghar	34°04'55"N; 69°19'20"E
Darh (0)	Loghar	34°02'35°N; 69°22'40"E
Kunduli (0)	Ghazni	33°25'55"N; 67°30'40"E
Saydo (0)	Ghazni	33°14'00"N; 67°l5'40"E
Khanabad (0)	Ghazni	33°10'20"N; 67°15'30"E
Luman (0)	Ghazni	33°06'20"N; 67°40'10"E
Kareztu (0)	Ghazni	32°58'02"N; 67°41'52"E
Kochak (0)	Oruzghan	32°58'N; 66°43'E
Alaghzar (0)	Ghazni	32°57'10"N; 67°32'55"E
Koh-i- Sokhi (0)	Oruzghan	32°56'N; 66°40'E
Qarya-i-Baki (0)	Ghazni	32°55'30"N; 66°52'30"E
Khinjaktu (0)	Ghazni	32°54'N; 67°44'E
Lashkar-Qala (0)	Ghazni	32°53'40"N; 67°31'05"E
Tangha (0)	Ghazni	32°47'30"N; 67°25'30"E
Saydan (0)	Zabul	32°42'06"N; 66°52'18"E
Outcrop #914 (0)	Oruzghan	32°41'00"N; 66°28'30"E
Outcrop #1305 (0)	Zabul	32°36'32"N; 66°37'16"E

Hazarbuz (0)	Zabul	32°33'00"N; 66°31'40"E
Ekrak (0)	Zabul	32°30'57"N; 66°44'10"E
Kunag (0)	Zabul	32°29'34"N 66°35'55"E
Daryabghar (0)	Zabul	32°27'22"N; 66°35'00"E
Sare-Surkh (0)	Zabul	32°26'18"N; 66°36'28"E
Buzghala II (0)	Zabul	32°25'13"N; 66°35'46"E
Tughra (0)	Zabul	32°21'26"N; 66°34'03"E
Garangh (0)	Zabul	32°21'N; 66°35'E
Outcrop #543 (0)	Zabul	32°20'23"N; 66°35'16"E
Arghatu (0)	Zabul	32°18'00"N; 66°30'20"E
Chokrak (0)	Zabul	32°16'40"N; 66°28'38"E
Anaghay (0)	Zabul	32°16'31"N; 66°33'51"E
Jurwa (0)	Zabul	33°15'59"N; 66°29'30"E
Bolo (0)	Zabul	32°14'04"N; 66°03'34"E
Baghawan (0)	Zabul	32°12'56"N; 66°30'04"E
Dorushka (0)	Zabul	32°10'40"N; 66°21'49"E
Arghasu (1, II, Ill) (0)	Zabul	32°06'02"N; 66°20'07"E
Azanzay (0)	Kandahar	32°03'25"N; 66°12'16"E
Charsu (0)	Zabul	32°02'54"N; 66°18'10"E
Outcrop #7273 (0)	Zabul	32°02'34"N; 66°18'16"E
Zanda Gharay (0)	Paktia	33°12'30"N; 69°32'00"E
Zanda 1 (0)	Kandahar	31°57'01"N; 65°55'00"E
- (S)	Badakhshan	38°15'N; 70°44'E
- (S)	Badakhshan	38°11'00"N; 70°31'30"E
- (S)	Badakhshan	38°10'N; 70°37'E
- (S)	Badakhshan	38°09'10"N; 71°10'08"E
- (S)	Badakhshan	38°07'30"N; 70°32'00"E
- (S)	Badakhshan	37°50'30"N; 71°11'30"E
- (S)	Badakhshan	37°21'05"N; 71°09'42"E
- (S)	Badakhshan	37°19'20"N; 71°01'40"E
- (S)	Badakhshan	36°52'N; 70°41'E
- (S)	Baghlan	36°02'22"N; 69°11'14"E
- (S)	Baghlan	36°00'00"N; 69°11'16"E
- (S)	Ghor	34°31'N; 65°25'E
- (S)	Ghor	34°09'N; 64°17'E
- (S)	Herat	33°47'N; 61°17'E
- (S)	Herat	33°44'N; 61°17'E
- (S)	Herat	33°41'N; 71°14'E
- (S)	Farah	32°43'N; 62°56'E
- (S)	Farah	32°35'N; 61°30'E
- (S)	Farah	32°20'N; 62°19'E
- (S)	Kandahar	32°18'17"N; 65°57'20"E
- (S)	Samanghan	35°28'40"N; 67°48'57"E
- (S)	Baghlan	35°24'14"N; 68°11'25"E
- (S)	Baghlan	35°19'N; 68°10'E
- (S)	Baghlan	35°18'24"N; 68°05'32"E
- (S)	Bamiyan	35°10'02"N; 67°31'41"E
- (S)	Kabul	34°28'00"N; 68°57'15"E

- (S)	Kabul	34°27'N; 68°55'H
- (S)	Kabul	34°26'10"N; 68°59'20"E
- (S)	Baghlan	35°36'N; 69°09'E
- (S)	Kabul	34°25'10"N; 69°01'53"E
- (S)	Kabul	34°24'30"N; 69°06'00"E
- (S)	Kabul	34°21'40"N; 69°39'15"E
- (S)	Loghar	34°02'N; 69°22'E
- (S)	Oruzghan	33°57'41"N; 66°35'00"E
- (S)	Oruzghan	33°57'12"N; 66°45'08"E
- (S)	Oruzghan	33°53'40"N; 66°41'00"E
- (S)	Oruzghan	33°53'03"N; 66°37'28"H
- (S)	Oruzghan	33°51'40"N; 66°34'53"E
- (5)	Oruzghan	33°48'30"N; 66°34'00"E
- (S)	Oruzghan	33°48'20"N; 66°44'22"E
- (S)	Oruzghan	33°47'16"N; 66°36'18"E
- (S)	Oruzghan	33°47'21"N; 66°45'09"E
- (S)	Oruzghan	33°43'17"N; 66°20'46"E
- (S)	Oruzghan	33°38'55"N; 66°04'33"E
- (S)	Oruzghan	33°35'09"N; 66°30'02"E
- (S)	Ghazni	33°18'10"N; 67°30'20"E
- (S)	Ghazni	33°11'50"N; 67°48'40"E
- (S)	Ghazni	33°10'35°N; 67°47'05"E
- (S)	Ghazni	33°10'35°N; 67°38'45"E
- (S)	Ghazni	33°09'25"N; 67°44'15"E
- (S)	Ghazni	33°07'40"N; 67°23'10"E
- (S)	Oruzghan	33°06'N; 67°26'E
- (S)	Ghazni	33°04'25"N; 67°40'05"E
- (S)	Ghazni	33°01'50'N; 67°15'40"E
- (S)	Oruzghan	33°01'30"N; 66°52'00"E
- (S)	Oruzghan	33°01'N; 66°50'E
- (S)	Oruzghan	33°0'40"N; 66°51'20"E
- (S)	Oruzghan	32°58'N; 66°45'E
- (S)	Oruzghan	32°58'30"N; 66°49'00"E
- (S)	Ghazni	32°57'50"N; 67°10'15"E
- (S)	Ghazni	32°57'05"N; 67°12'50"E
- (S)	Ghazni	32°55'05"N; 67°19'10"E
- (S)	Ghazni	32°49'56"N; 67°13'59"E
- (S)	Zabul	32°46'30"N; 66°45'30"E
- (S)	Zabul	32°45'59"N; 67°03'13"E
- (5)	Zabul	32°44'26"N; 67°04'33"H
- (S)	Ghazni	32°44'25"N; 67°16'45"E
- (S)	Zabul	32°44'27"N; 67°04'51"E
- (S)	Zabul	32°43'22"N; 67°01'22"E
- (S)	Zabul	32°43'44"N; 67°02'30"E
- (S)	Zabul	32°42'10"N; 67°13'45"E
- (S)	Zabul	32°38'18"N; 66°33'08"E
- (S)	Zabul	32°38'18"N; 66°55'27"E
- (S)	Zabul	32°36'07"N; 67,05'35"E

- (S)	Zabul	32°34'1 l"N; 66°33'01"E
- (S)	Zabul	32°30'34"N; 66°40'56"E
- (S)	Zabul	32°29'17"N; 67°01'30"E
- (S)	Zabul	32°28'07"N; 66°37'13"E
- (S)	Zabul	32°14'll"N; 66°25'45"E
- (S)	Zabul	32°13'27'N; 66°37'10"E
- (S)	Paktia	33°16'06"N; 69°36'35"E
- (S)	Paktia	33°15'10"N; 69°37'32'E
- (S)	Kandahar	31°57'08"N; 65°51'32"E
- (S)	Kandahar	31°54'49"N; 65°59'32"E
- (S)	Kandahar	31°54'11"N; 65°53'22"E
- (S)	Kandahar	31°46'48"N; 65°53'00"E
- (S)	Kandahar	31°51'17"N; 66°04'l6"E
- (S)	Kandahar	32°23'N; 66°23'E
- (S)	Kandahar	31°08'N; 66°13'E
- (S)	Kandahar	31°07'N; 66°10'E
- (S)	Kandahar	30°17'N; 66°10'E
- (S)	Kandahar	30°03'N; 66°08'E
Dolomite	Hajigak	Bamiyan	34°36'N; 68°08'E
Emerald	Khenj	Parwan	35°24'50"N; 69°45'30"E
	Mikeni	Parwan	35°25'20"N; 69°46'45"E
	Butak	Parwan	35°27'00"N; 69°50'00"E
	Buzmul	Parwan	35°28'35°N; 69°50'00"E
	Bakhi	Parwan	35°29'00"N; 69°50'00"E
	Darun	Parwan	35°29'15"N; 69°54'15"E
	Badel	Parwan	34°50'20"N; 70°56'30"E
	Rewat	Parwan	35°28'00"E; 69°52'30"N
Epidote	Baghawak	Konar	35°N; 71°15'E
Fluorite	Bakhud (D)	Oruzghan	32°27'17"N; 65°53'58"E
	Chura (0)	Oruzghan	32°43'N; 65°49'E
	Anaghey (0)	Oruzghan	32°39'N; 65°46'E
	Saraw (0)	Oruzghan	32°28'N; 35°49'E
	Ganighay (0)	Oruzghan	32°23'N; 65°53'E
	- (S)	Badakhshan	37°30'33"N; 70°32'42"E
	- (S)	Baghlan	35°44'20"N; 69°20'00"E
Fuller's Earth	Loghar Valley	Loghar	34°10'N; 69°10'E
Garnet (Almandine)			
	Pachighram	Nangarhar	35°45'00"N; 71°11'40"E
Garnet (Spessartite)			
	Mawi	Laghman	

garnets are found throughout the northeastern part of Afghanistan, but few
are of gem quality

Gold	Zahghar	Badakhshan	38°23'N; 70°55'E
	Ab-i-Panja	Badakhshan	37°58'N; 70°24'E
	Vicador	Badakhshan	37°17'N; 70°23'E
	near Rustak	Takhar	37°07'N; 59°44'E
	Mugur	Ghazni	32°56'N; 67°44'E
	Baghtu	Kandahar	32°03'N; 66°03'E

Gold, Lode	Vekadur (D)	Badakhshan	37°30'50"N; 70°35'37"E
	Zarkashan	Ghazni	32°53' to 32°55'N; 67°40' to 67°42'E
	Kundalyan (D)	Zabul	32°18'46"N; 66°31'58"E
	Kalar (0)	Badakhshan	37°36'33"N; 70°35'50"E
	Neshebdur (0)	Badakhshan	37°35'53"N; 70°36'31"E
	Shenghan (0)	Badakhshan	37°30'20" to 37°38'00"N; 70°16'00" to 70°21'15"E
	Rishaw (0)	Badakhshan	37°30'10"N; 70°38'05"E
	Chilkonshar (0)	Badakhshan	37°26' to 37°30'N; 70°15' to 70°17'E
	NakhchirPar (0)	Badakhshan	37°21'00"N; 71°05' 50"'E
	Dog-Glat (0)	Badakhshan	37°07'35"N; 70°21'00"E
	Furmorah I (0)	Badakhshan	37°05'10"N; 70°50'20"E
	Pusida (0)	Takhar	36°05' to 36° 10'N, 70° 08' to 70°11'E
	Ahankashan (0)	Ghor	34°39'N; 64°23'E
	Kushkak (0)	Ghor	34°04'N; 64°31'E
	Taghab- Soni (0)	Herat	34°26'00"N; 63°42'30"E
	Chinar (0)	Kandahar	32°11'15"N; 65°39'10"E
	Khanabad (0)	Ghazni	33°10'20"N; 67°15'30"E
	Tamaki (0)	Ghazni	33°10'50"N; 67°46'30"E
	Luman (0)	Ghazni	33°06'20"N; 67°40'10"E
	Kareztu (0)	Ghazni	32°57"45"N' 67°42'15"E
	Belaw (0)	Ghazni	32°57'50"N; 67°33'20"E
	Alaghzar (0)	Ghazni	32°57'10"N; 67°32'55"E
	Mirzaka (0)	Ghazni	32°56'37"N; 67°41'46"E
	Basharghar (0)	Ghazni	32°56'46"N; 67°40'43"E
	Ukul (0)	Ghazni	32°55'50"N; 67°33'40"E
	Anghuri (0)	Ghazni	32°55'00"N; 67°32'10"E
	Bolo (0)	Ghazni	32°54'30"N; 67°32'40"E
	Dynamitic (0)	Ghazni	32°54'38"N; 67°41'01"E
	Sufi-Kamedi (0)	Ghazni	32°54'21"N; 67°41'38"E
	Choh-i-Surkh (0)	Ghazni	32°54'22"N; 67°40'24"E
	Khinjaktu (0)	Ghazni	32°54'N; 67°44'E
	Lashkar-Qala (0)	Ghazni	32°53'40"N; 67°31'05"E
	Zardak (0)	Ghazni	32°53'40"N; 67°44'05"E
	Gulyakhel (0)	Ghazni	32°53'15"N; 67°41'20"E
	Tangha (0)	Ghazni	32°47'30"N; 67°25'30"E
	Ludin (0)	Zabul	32°35'08"N; 66°31'47"E
	Ekrak (0)	Zabul	32°30'57"N; 66°40'10"E
	Kunag (0)	Zabul	32°29'34"N; 66°35'55"E
	Daryabghar (0)	Zabul	32°27'22"N; 66°35'00"E
	Sara-surkh (0)	Zabul	32°26'18"N; 66°36'18"E
	Buzghala II (0)	Zabul	33°25'13"N; 66°35'46"E
	Assanak (0)	Zabul	32°22'04"N; 66°34 25"E
	Tughra (0)	Zabul	32°21'26"N; 66°34'03"E
	Gharang (0)	Zabul	32°21'N; 66°35'E

outcrop #543 (0)	Zabul	32°20'23"N; 66°35'16"E
Baghawan (0)	Zabul	32°12'56"N; 66°30'04"E
Kadilak (0)	Zabul	32°07'20"N; 66°20'09"E
Arghasu (0)	Zabul	32°06'02"N; 66°20'07"E
Asanzay (0)	Kandahar	32°03'25"N; 66°12'16"E
Charsu (0)	Zabul	32°02'54"N; 66°18'10"E
outcrop #7273 (0)	Zabul	32°02'34"N; 66°18'16"E
Zanda I (0)	Kandahar	31°57'01"N; 65°55'00"E
Jaffur-Kalay (0)	Kandahar	31°55'15"N; 65°38'17"E
Kandahar (0)	Kandahar	31°40'N; 65°45'E
- S	Badakhshan	38°13'12"N; 70°42'24"E
- S	Badakhshan	38°07'40"N; 71°18'00"E
- S	Badakhshan	37°42'40"N; 70°56'40"E
- S	Badakhshan	37°37'07"N; 70°29'10"E
- S	Badakhshan	37°35'35°N; 70°26'30"E
- S	Badakhshan	37°34'30"N; 70°27'30"E
- S	Badakhshan	37°21'05"N; 71°09'42"E
- S	Badakhshan	37°19'20"N; 71°01'40"E
- S	Badakhshan	37°16'10"N; 70°42'09"E
- S	Badakhshan	37°15'30"N; 70°38'10"E
- S	Badakhshan	37°15'30"N; 70°42'20"E
- S	Badakhshan	37°11'45"N; 70°40'30"E
- S	Badakhshan	37°11'22"N; 70°42'41"E
- S	Badakhshan	37°08'08"N; 70°40'45"E
- S	Badakhshan	37°06'55"N; 70°43'40"E
- S	Takhar	36°19'06"N; 70°16'10"E
- S	Ghazni	33°21'15"N; 67°19'30"E
- S	Ghazni	33°15'25"N; 67°24'20"E
- S	Ghazni	33°02'40"N; 67°17'25"E
- S	Ghazni	33°02'40"N; 67°38'30"E
- S	Ghazni	33°00'05"N; 67°36'20"E
- S	Ghazni	32°51'15"N; 67°23'15"E
- S	Zabul	32°44'26"N; 67°04'33"E
- S	Zabul	32°44'32"N; 67°03'09"H
- S	Zabul	32°44'27"N; 67°04'51"E
- S	Ghazni	32°42'40"N; 67°21'30"E
- S	Zabul	32°38'27"N; 66°39'30"E
- S	Zabul	32°35'52"N; 66°40'09"E
- S	Zabul	32°35'28"N; 66°46'09"E
- S	Zabul	32°34'11"N; 66°45'35°E
- S	Zabul	32°33'31"N; 66°33'29"E
- S	Zabul	32°31'48"N; 66°47'28"E
- S	Zabul	32°30'07"N; 66°43'55"E
- S	Zabul	32°30'34"N; 66°40'56"E
- S	Zabul	32°29'13"N; 66°41'03"E
- S	Zabul	32°17'00"N; 66°34'37"E
- S	Zabul	32°14'll"N; 66°25'45"E
- S	Zabul	32°13'27"N; 66°37'10"E

	- S	Zabul	32°13'17"N; 66°26'20"E
	- S	Zabul	32°02'10"N; 66°21'34"E
	- S	Kandahar	31°53'38"N; 66°01'17"E
Gold, Placer			
(commercial)	Samty	Takhar	37°34' to 37°36'N; 69°49' to 69°54'E
	Nooraba, Khasar, Anjir	Takhar	37°29' to 37°36'N; 69°49' to 69°54'E
(marginal)	Chah-i-ab	Takhar	37°25'N; 69°49'E
	Jar-Bashi	Takhar	37°33'N; 69°42'E
	Zarkashan	Ghazni	32°54'30"N; 67°44'00"E
Graphite	Yagh-darra (0)	Badakhshan	36°59'15"N; 71°22'00"E
	Sanglich (0)	Badakhshan	36°40'N; 71°21'E
	Istrombi (0)	Badakhshan	36°12'00"N; 70°46'30"E
	Shahkabul (0)	Maydan	34°19'10"N; 69°49'15"E
	Khawai (0)	Kabul	34°13'N; 69°45'E
	Charkh (0)	Loghar	33°45'N; 68°53'E
Gypsum	Dudkash (0)	Baghlan	36°00'55"N; 68°47'30"E
	Sary-kan (0)	Takhar	36°34'47"N; 69°39'14"E
	Chal (0)	Takhar	36°33'03"N; 69°32'14"E
	Shuraw (0)	Baghlan	36°03'45"N; 69°08'56"E
	Cherulang (0)	Herat	34°44'00"N; 62°02'30"E
	Pusht-koh (0)	Herat	34°09'N; 62°10'E
	Rabot-i-sapcha (0)	Herat	34°05'N; 62°19'E
	Pir-i-surkh (0)	Herat	34°03'N; 62°27'E
	Laman (0)	Badghis	34°45' to 34°47'N; 63°07' to 63°10'E
	Pushma-i-Bidak (0)	Ghor	34°08'N; 64°45'E'
	Sary-assya I (0)	Samanghan	35°31'32"N; 67°30'02"E
	Sary-assya (0)	Samanghan	35°30'32"N; 67°36'08"E
	Nadr (0)	Bamiyan	35°26'25"N; 67°48'03"H
	Nalak (0)	Baghlan	32°24'06"N; 68°12'30"E
	Kamard (0)	Bamiyan	35°18'32"N; 67°54'00"E
	Dasht-i- Safed (0)	Bamiyan	35°17'09"N; 67°53'08"E
	Surkh-Rod (0)	Nangarhar	34°2 1'N; 70°05'E
Halite	Andkhoi (D)	Faryiab	36°45'N; 65°21'E
	Dawlatabad (D)	Faryiab	36°36'15"N; 64°56'00"E
	Maymana (D)	Faryiab	36°06'00"N; 64°42'30"E
	Tashkurghan (D)	Samanghan	36°50'00"N; 67°42'30"E
	Taqcha Khana (D)	Takhar	36°35'00"N; 69°37'30"E
	Chal 1 (D)	Takhar	36°33'N; 69°32'E
	Chal II (D)	Takhar	36°32'N; 69°31'E
	Namaksar (D)	Herat	34°05'N; 60°45'E
	Rugh (D)	Ghor	34°16'N; 64°24'E
	Kavir-i-Naizar (D)	Herat	33°40'N; 60°52'E
	Kushk-i-nakhub (D)	Kandahar	31°36'30"N; 65°04'00"E
	Rukhabad (D)	Kandahar	31°24'40"N; 65°42'00"E
	Spin-Boldak (D)	Kandahar	31°19'N; 65°56'£

	Usdursihar (0)	Parwan	35°03'N; 68°55'E
Hematite	Nukrakhana	Parwan	35°08'N; 69°12'E
Iron Ore	Manwa	Herat	34°12'N; 62°53'E
	Hajigak	Bamiyan	34°40'N; 68°04'E
	(unknown)	Ghazni	33°30'N; 67°0'E
	(unknown)	Farah	33°25'N; 63°15'E
	Tirin Rurl	Kandahar	32°35'N; 65°38'E
	Shakar-Dara	Parwan	34°43'N; 68°46'E
	Bagram	Parwan	34°57'N; 69°14'E
	Hesa-i-Bowum	Parwan	35°29'N; 69°54'E
Iron	Syakh Jar (D)	Badakhshan	37°07'12"N; 70°52'35°E
	Furmarak (D)	Badakhshan	37°05'30"N; 70°49'55"E
	Zerak (D)	Baghlan	34°46'36"N; 68°15'12"E
	Khaish (D)	Bamiyan	34°43'55"N; 68°12'30"E
	Hajigak (D)	Bamiyan	34°40'N; 68°04'E
	Zanif (0)	Badakhshan	38°18'00"N; 71°15'31"E
	Dozah-dara (0)	Badakhshan	37°24'30"N; 70°54'00"E
	Kalawoch (0)	Badakhshan	37°17'N; 70°53'E
	Furamorah-i (0)	Badakhshan	37°05'10"N; 70°50'20"E
	Skazar (0)	Badakhshan	36°00'30"N; 70°40'30"E
	Eshon (0)	Badakhshan	36°58'54"N; 72°38'53"E
	Taghab (0)	Herat	34°36'11"N; 62°57'12"E
	Kushast (0)	Herat	34°38'05"N; 62°59'26"E
	Chashma-i-Reg (0)	Herat	34°09'N; 62°26'E
	Band-i-sarah (0)	Herat	34°04'N; 64°47'E
	Palang- Sor (0)	Herat	34°00'N; 63°00'E
	Kohi (0)	Fariab	35°22N; 65°15'E
	Sekoh (0)	Fariab	35°17'N; 65°22'E
	Espesang (0)	Ghor	34°43'N; 64°36°'E
	Rod-i-Karuh (0)	Herat	34°34'50"N; 63°08'20"E
	Kajnaw (0)	Ghor	34°18'N; 64°36°'E
	Kohe Pod (0)	Herat	34°19'N; 63°24'E
	Karezak (0)	Fariab	33°06'N; 60°44'E
	Aumiyt (0)	Kandahar	32°22'N; 65°38'E
	Haji-Alam (0)	Kandahar	32°18'N; 65°33'E
	Chinar (0)	Kandahar	32°14'N; 65°32'E
	Tambil (0)	Kandahar	32°10'17"N; 65°35'32"E
	Ghala-i-Assad (0)	Kandahar	32°05'N; 65°28'E
	Dara-i-Neel (0)	Parwan	34°54'N; 64°34'E
	Chuy (0)	Bamiyan	34°45'37"N; 68°13'00"E
	Sausang (0)	Bamiyan	34°45'08"N; 68°15'45"E
	Harzar (0)	Bamiyan	34°41'46"N; 68°09'12"E
	Paghman (0)	Kabul	34°40'N; 69°00'E
	Mangasak (0)	Maydan	34°21'N; 67°44'E
	Razer (0)	Badakhshan	35°59'N; 70°44'E
	Pinawi (0)	Badakhshan	35°59'N; 70°38'E
	Chukri-Naw (0)	Kapisa	35°36'24"N; 69°53'40"E
	Nukra-Khana (0)	Kapisa	35°35'N; 69°54'E

	Panjshir (0)	Kapisa	35°32'30"N; 69°52'30"E
	Durnama (0)	Kapisa	35°30'N; 69°51'E
	Dehe-Kolon (0)	Parwan	35°13'N; 69°18'E
	Hazar (0)	Parwan	35°12'N; 69°19'E
	Saraj (0)	Parwan	35°09'42"N; 69°15'00"E
	Doz Dara (0)	Kapisa	35°08'N; 69°24'E
	Dangam (0)	Konar	35°01'N; 71°28'E
	Shaykhu (0)	Kabul	34°46'N; 69°13'E
	Deh-i-Sabz (0)	Kabul	34°37'N; 69°25'E
	Khaidarabad (0)	Kabul	34°30'35ᵒN; 69°00'45"E
	Sheenky (0)	Kabul	34°19'50"N; 69°15'00"E
	Gezghay (0)	Kabul	34°17"10"N; 69°21'50"E
	Kwali-kushi (0)	Ghazni	33°18'55"N; 67°23'10"E
	Naylak (0)	Ghazni	33°18'30"N; 67°24'40"E
	Lar (0)	Ghazni	33°09'00"N; 67°48'15"E
	Dodi (0)	Ghazni	33°08'30"N; 67°07'10"E
	Pir Khana (0)	Ghazni	34°49'40"N; 67°25'50"E
	Lom (0)	Kandahar	31°40'N; 65°26'E
	Myen Boldak (0)	Kandahar	30°56'N; 66°18'E
	- (S)	Badakhshan	37°33'30"N; 71°06'00"E
	- (S)	Badakhshan	37°31'15"N; 71°02'00"E
	- (S)	Badakhshan	37°09'15"N; 70°48'30"E
	- (S)	Badakhshan	37°08'51"N; 70°48'05"E
	- (S)	Badakhshan	37°03'00"N; 70°50'38"E
	- (S)	Badakhshan	36°40'25"N; 70°50'00"E
	- (S)	Badakhshan	36°13'00"N; 71°08'40"E
	- (S)	Ghor	34°34'N; 64°55'E
	- (S)	Ghor	34°22'N; 64°33'E
	- (S)	Ghor	34°19'N; 64°04'E
	- (S)	Bamiyan	34°47'30"N; 68°14'00"E
	- (S)	Zabul	32°43'1 1"N; 66°46'08"E
Kunzite	Kolum (D)	Konar	35°12'07"N; 70°20'04"E
	Kantiwa (0)	Nangarhar	35°17'00"N; 70°44"30"E
		Konar	35°35'N; 71°05'E
		Konar	35°50'N; 71°15'E
		Konar	35°42'N; 71°07'E
		Konar	35°22'N; 70°68'E
		Konar	35°28'N; 71°09'E
		Konar	34°52'N; 70°43'E
	12 other known deposits in the Kamdesh area through Rossovsky		
Lapis Lazuli	Sar-e-Sang	Badakhshan	36°10' to 36°12'N; 70°47' to 70°49'E
	Chilak	Badakhshan	36°22'N; 71°13'E
	Shoka	Badakhshan	36°22'N; 71°13'E
	Lagharaan	Badakhshan	36°22'N; 71°13'E
	Strambi Valley	Badakhshan	36°22'N; 71°13'E
	Kohe Madan	Badakhshan	(unknown)
	Robate Bola	Badakhshan	(unknown)

	Jurm	Badakhshan	36°50'N; 70°50'E
Lead and Zinc	Saheb Khan	Badghis	35°08'N; 62°46'E
	Nalbandan- Sarghol	Ghor	34°15'N; 63°46'E
	(unknown)	Ghor	34°30'N; 66°00'E
	(unknown)	Ghor	34°32'N; 66°11'E
	Jalraiz	Wardak	34°24'N; 68°29'E
	area of Khakriz-Dahla	Kandahar	32°17'N; 66°47'E
	Feranjal	Parwan	35°10'N; 68°50'E
	Nalbandon (D)	Ghor	34°07'N; 63°55'E
	Darra-i-Nur (D)	Kandahar	32°12'N; 65°41'E
	Kalai-Assad (D)	Kandahar	32°05'N; 65°31'E
	Farenjal (D)	Parwan	34°59'N; 68°41'E
	Spira (D)	Paktia	33°08'N; 69°33'E
	Boi-Qara (0)	Badakhshan	36°59'30"N; 73°53'52"E
	Rabat-i- Sapcha (0)	Herat	34°06'30"N; 62°19'00"E
	Jari-Chokoor (0)	Ghor	34°43'00"N; 65°05'00"E
	Kushkak (0)	Ghor	34°34'N; 64°31'E
	Tagabi-Soni (0)	Herat	34°26'00"N; 63°42'30"E
	Tagabi-Soni I (0)	Herat	34°26'N; 63°48'E
	Bedan (0)	Ghor	34°25'N; 64°31'E
	Ustoowa (0)	Ghor	34°21'N; 64°34'E
	Kajnaw (0)	Ghor	34°18'N; 64°36'E
	Gawmazarl V (0)	Ghor	34°16'36"N; 64°38'00"E
	Gawmazar I and 11 (0)	Ghor	34°15'45"N; 64°37'06"E
	Gawmazar ill (0)	Ghor	34°16'N; 64°38'E
	Shekhlawast (0)	Ghor	34°15'32"N; 64°37'00"E
	Talah (0)	Oruzghan	34°14'18"N; 65°55'50"E
	Hasan Sansalaghay (0)	Ghor	34°14'08"N; 64°35'00"E
	Gharghanaw II and III (0)	Ghor	34°13'N; 64°33'E
	Karimdad (0)	Oruzghan	34°10'28"N; 65°59'14"E
	Minora (0)	Ghor	34°10'N; 63°58'E
	Minora 11 (0)	Ghor	34°09'N; 63°59'E
	Rangin (0)	Oruzghan	34°08'52"N; 65°55'20"E
	Palang-Khana (0)	Ghor	34°09'N; 64°01'E
	Sarghul (0)	Ghor	34°05'N; 64°46'E
	Mir Ali (0)	Herat	34°54'N; 62°12'E
	Shayda1 (0)	Herat	33°52'N; 61°50'E
	Shayda III (0)	Herat	33°51'10"N; 61°49'00"E
	Shayda II (0)	Herat	33°50'50N; 61°49'00"E
	Dakana (0)	Herat	33°46'N; 62°01'E
	Tanora (0)	Farah	35°45'N; 61°41'E
	Gologa I (0)	Farah	33°21'N; 61°21'E
	Bulghaja (0)	Farah	33°09'N; 61°49'E
	Korezak (0)	Farah	33°06'N; 60°44'E
	Seh Kuta (0)	Farah	33°05'N; 61°42'E
	Sy-Ab (0)	Farah	32°39'N; 62°53'E
	Doshk (0)	Ghor	33°55'N; 63°49'E
	Gariba (0)	Farah	33°18'N; 64°1 3'E

Saraw 1,11,111 (0)	Oruzghan	32°28'N; 65°49'E
Bakhud (0)	Oruzghan	32°27'17"N; 65°53'58"E
#7757 (0)	Kandahar	32°15'17"N; 65°59'02"E
#9390 (0)	Kandahar	32°05'N; 65°55'E
Darrah-Alasang (0)	Baghlan	35°18'59"N; 68°07'16"E
Kushk (0)	Ghor	34°30'N; 66°00'E
Shashan (0)	Baghlan	35°51'N; 69°23'E
Godo-China (0)	Kabul	34°40'N; 69°40'E
Manay (0)	Loghar	34°04'55"N; 69°19'20"E
Zardghelak (0)	Bamiyan	33°57'N; 67°24'E
Gudry-Mazar (0)	Bamiyan	33°55'N; 67°27'E
Eskan (0)	Oruzghan	33°45'N; 66°47'E
Kwali-Kushi (0)	Ghazni	33°18'55"N; 67°23'10"E
Tamaki (0)	Ghazni	33°10'50"N; 67°46'30"E
Sare luman (0)	Ghazni	33°08'40"N; 67°41'00"E
#551 (0)	Ghazni	33°01'30"N; 67°03'00"E
Larga (0)	Ghazni	33°01'00"N; 67°42'50"E
Kareztu (0)	Ghazni	32°58'02"N; 67°41'52"E
Tangi (0)	Ghazni	32°57'08"N; 67°40'08"E
Anguri (0)	Ghazni	32°55'00"N; 67°32'10"E
Pir Khana (0)	Ghazni	34°49'40"N; 67°25'50"E
Ludin (0)	Zabul	32°35'08"N; 66°31'47"E
Assanaka (0)	Zabul	32°22'04"N; 66°34'25"E
Tugra (0)	Zabul	32°21'26"N; 66°34'03'E
Surkhbed (0)	Kandahar	32°20'36"N; 66,01'08"
Kadilak (0)	Zabul	32°07'20"N; 66°20'09"E
- S	Takhar	36°27'53"N; 69°30'31"E
- S	Badakhshan	36°12'30"N; 70°46'30"E
- S	Baghlan	36°04'14"N; 69°18'40"E
- S	Ghor	35°46'N; 65°53'E
- S	Ghor	34°31'N; 65°25'E
- S	Ghor	34°17'N; 64°34'E
- S	Ghor	34°16'00"N; 64°35'30"E
- S	Ghor	34°15'30"N; 64°34'00"E
- S	Ghor	34°14'N; 64°54'E
- S	Farah	33°10'45"N; 61°55'04"E
- S	Farah	32°43'N; 62°56'E
- S	Farah	32°23'N; 61°19'E
- S	Helmand	33°04'N; 65°00'E
- S	Baghlan	35°58'16"N; 69°06'32"E
- S	Baghlan	35°39'42"N; 69°16'36"E
- S	Kapisa	35°29'12"N; 69°48'00"E
- S	Oruzghan	33°46'N; 66°06'E
- S	Ghazni	33°18'10N; 67°40'20"E
- S	Ghazni	34°14'N; 67°48'E
- S	Ghazni	33°12'55"N; 67°28'00"E
- S	Ghazni	33°10'35°N; 67°47'05"E
- S	Ghazni	32°09'25"N; 67°44'15"E

	- S	Ghazni	33°06'50"N; 67°23'40"E
	- S	Ghazni	33°06'20"N; 67°16'10"E
	- S	Oruzghan	33°00'30"N; 66°51'20"E
	- S	Paktia	33°10'48"N; 69°37'23"E
Lignite	Tozaghol (0)	Parwan	35°01'N; 68°36'E
	Samykhel (0)	Parwan	34°58'N; 68°50E
	Safed-Kob (Shinwar) (0)	Nangarhar	34°12'N; 70°47'E
Limestone/Dolomite			
	Hajigak	Bamiyan	34°36'N; 68°08'E
Lithium	Talbuzanak Field (F)	Badakhshan	37°12'06"N; 70°33'36"E
	Kokcha Field (F)	Badakhshan	36°36'35°N; 70°53'15"E
	Eshkashim Field (F)	Badakhshan	36°27'19"N; 71°36'23"E
	Pachighram Field (F)	Nangarhar	35°31'40" to 35°52'00"N 71°00'00" to 71°18'00"E
	Parun Field (P)	Nangarhar	34°54'34" to 35°40'18"N 70°52'15" to 71°14'40"E
	Kantiwa Field (F)	Nangarhar	35°26'10"N; 70°46'20"E
	Marid Field (F)	Nangarhar	35°06'40" to 35°21'40"N 71°13'50" to 71°26'40"E
	Alinghar Field (F)	Laghman	34°52'41" to 35°01'05"N 70°16'48" to 70°27'51"E
	Darra-i-Pech Field (F)	Nangarhar	34°52'30" to 34°59'00"N 70°42'10' to 75°45'40"E
	Shamakat Field (F)	Laghman	34°40'10" to 34°44'00"N 70°00'20" to 70°02'15"E
	Shahidan Field (F)	Laghman	34°29'00" to 34°34'00"N 69°49'00" to 69°59'30"E
	Taghawlor Field (F)	Oruzghan	33°42'30" to 33°47'00"N 66°19'30" to 66°29'00"E
	Pasghushta (D)	Nangarhar	35°23'34"N; 71°00'56"E
	Jamanak (D)	Nangarhar	35°23'12"N; 70°59'06"E
	Yryhgul (D)	Nangarhar	35°22'40"N; 70°50'51"E
	Lower Pasghushta (D)	Nangarhar	35°22'53"N; 71°03'06"E
	Drumgal (D)	Nangarhar	35°19'08"N; 71°01'21"E
	Paskhi (D)	Nangarhar	35°17'30"N; 70°57'30"E
	Tsamgal (D)	Nangarhar	35°17'45"N; 71°02'31"E
	Dara-i-Pech (D)	Nangarhar	34°55'02" to 34°55'53"N; 70°44'12" to 70°44'53"E
	Shamakat (D)	Laghman	34°40'10" to 34°44'00"N; 70°00'20" to 70"02'15"E
	Taghaqlor (D)	Oruzghan	33°45'00"N; 66°25'30"E
	Talbuzanak (0)	Badakhshan	37°13'35°N; 70°33'21"E
	- (0)	Badakhshan	36°40'N; 71°40'E
	Futur (0)	Badakhshan	36°38'N; 71°39'E
	Nawshah (0)	Badakhshan	36°38'N; 71°45'E
	Dehghal (0)	Badakhshan	36°22'N; 71°27'E
	Pachighram (0)	Nangarhar	35°45'54"N; 71°11'07"E
	Tsanigal (0)	Nangarhar	35°43'02"N; 71°07'00"E

	Degha (0)	Nangarhar	35°38'33"N; 71°03'30"E
	Pakawalpet (0)	Nangarhar	35°33'44"N; 71°07'24"E
	Alma (0)	Nangarhar	35°30'08"N; 71°10'52"E
	Wozgal (0)	Nangarhar	35°29'10"N; 70°59'10"E
	Prangal (0)	Nangarhar	35°23'34"N; 71°04'50"E
	Inshakhar (0)	Nangarhar	35°13'56"N; 70°59'18"E
	Boni (0)	Nangarhar	35°10'54"N; 70°49'39"E
	Marid (0)	Nangarhar	35°08'00"N; 71°17'58"E
	Aranch (0)	Nangarhar	35°09'36"N; 70°58'31"E
	Kalatan (0)	Laghman	35°00'26"N; 70°26'40"E
	Nanghalam (0)	Nangarhar	34°59'27"N; 70°53'22"E
	Kalagush (0)	Laghman	35°58'08"N; 70°23'17"E
	Awragal (0)	Nangarhar	34°56'10" to 34°57'00"N; 70°42'30" to 70°44'10"E
	Shahidan (0)	Laghman	34°29'54"N; 69°56'04"E
	- S	Oruzghan	33°43'29"N; 66°29'45"E
Magnesite	(unknown)	Ghazni	33°38'N; 67°06'E
	Achin (D)	Nangarhar	34°03'N; 70°43'E
	Mamadugha (0)	Loghar	34°19'30"N; 69°07'30"E
Malachite	Baghawak	Oruzghan	
	Farenjal		
	Oghankashan		
	Bakhud		
Manganese	(unknown)	Parwan	35°10'N; 58°50'E
	Farenjal (0)	Parwan	34°59'N; 68°41'E
	- (S)	Oruzghan	33°53'30"N; 66°51'48"E
Marble	Kandahar area	Kandahar	31°43'N; 65°27'E
	Kabul area	Kabul	34°15'N; 69°08'E
	Jalalabad area	Nangarhar	34°35'N; 70°25'E
	Bini-Kama	Badakhshan	38°18'30"N; 71°17'00"E
	Mayden	Maydan	34°26'N; 68°47'E
	Kariz-Amir	Kabul	34°39'00"N; 69°05'30"E
	Alghoi	Kabul	34°38'N; 69°09'E
	Dex Kenak	Kabul	34°35'00"N; 69°03'00"E
	Gezak	Kabul	34°33'30"N; 69°27'00"E
	Khojarawas	Kabul	34°33'00"N; 69°07'30"E
	Sharar	Kabul	34°30'N; 69°10'E
	Shanai-Baranty	Kabul	34°25'30"N; 69°14'00"E
	Sultan Padshah	Kabul	34°25'30"N; 69°08'30"E
	Wardak	Maydan	33°47'N; 68°31'E
	Anghuri	Ghazni	33°19'15"N; 67°41'05"E
	Alaghzar	Ghazni	32°59'25"N; 67°45'25"E
Marl (quarries)	Jamarchi-Bolo	Badakhshan	38°15'15"N; 71°21'10"E
	Ghumay	Badakhshan	38°08'30"N; 71°15'30"E
	Sabz	Badakhshan	38°08'10"N; 70°33'00"E
	Bakunvij	Badakhshan	38°04'50"N; 71°12'00"E
	Shenivaghur	Baghlan	35°43'47"N; 68°33'00"E
	Dudkash	Baghlan	36°00'40"N; 69°46'00"E

	Benosh Darrah	Herat	34°34'30"N; 62°46'20"E
	Darra-i-chartagh	Herat	34°26'20"N; 62°46'00"E
	Rod-i-sangur	Herat	34°26'N; 62°44'E
	Laman	Badghis	34°45'50"N; 63°06'30"E
	Pur-i-Khumry	Baghlan	35°58'24"N; 68°40'56"E
	Sawak	Bamiyan	35°19'00"N; 67°53'42"E
	Jabal-ur-Saraj	Parwan	35°09'20"N; 69°16'30"E
(fluxes)	Dudkash	Baghlan	36°00'47"N; 68°47'20"E
	Bamiyan	Bamiyan	34°52'N; 67°44'E
	Bamiyan	Bamiyan	34°51'N; 67°44'E
	Hajigak	Bamiyan	34°40'20"N; 68°04'00"E
Mercury	Nayak (0)	Herat	34°26"N; 62°27'E
	Tilak (0)	Ghor	34°14'24"N; 64°06'30"E
	Zarmardan (0)	Farah	32°57'N; 62°44'E
	Khanjar (0)	Oruzghan	33°57'12"N; 65°23'50"E
	Darwvaza (0)	Oruzghan	33°54'34"N; 65°58'48"E
	Alibali (0)	Oruzghan	33°51'50"N; 65°13'20"E
	Gulgadam (0)	Oruzghan	33°51'26"N; 65°11'50"E
	Alibali I (0)	Oruzghan	33°51'26"N; 65°13'52"E
	Sahebad (0)	Oruzghan	33°47'57"N; 65°05'30"E
	Qalat (0)	Oruzghan	33°47'21"N; 65°05'27"E
	Pasaband (0)	Oruzghan	33°40'40"N; 64°51'00"E
	Sebak (0)	Ghor	33°30'03N; 64°40'30"E
	Surkhnow (0)	Ghor	33°28'26"N; 64°41'15"E
	Kharnak (0)	Ghor	33°27'30"N; 64°31'42"E
	Katif (0)	Ghor	33°27'25"N; 64°38'04"E
	Duwalak (0)	Ghor	33°27'22"N; 64°38'45"E
	Panjshah (0)	Ghor	33°27'N; 64°19'E
	Koh-i-katif (0)	Ghor	33°26'32"N; 64°38'10"E
	Mullayan (0)	Ghor	33°26'N; 64°22'E
	Qasem (0)	Ghor	33°25'05"N; 64°37'14"E
	Pushwara (0)	Ghor	33°20'N; 64°33'E
	Mushkan (0)	Farah	32°57'N; 63°53'E
	Sewak (0)	Bamiyan	34°14'15"N; 66°52'33"E
	(0)	Oruzghan	33°59'N; 66°36'E
Mica	Aera	Loghar	34°03'N; 69°38'E
	(unknown)	Loghar	33°50'N; 69°42'E
Molybdenum	Kundalyan (D)	Zabul	32°18'46"N; 66°31'58"E
	Tundara (0)	Baghlan	35°41'25"N; 68°22'20"E
	Andar (0)	Loghar	34°16'36"N; 68°46'48 "E
	- S	Badakhshan	36°10'30"N; 70°49'00"E
Morganite	found with Kunzite	Laghman	
Muscovite	Pachaghan Field	Parwan	35°02'03"N; 69°43'10"E
	Pachaghan (D)	Parwan	35°02'03"N; 69°43'10"E
	Sorobi (D)	Laghman	34°29' to 34°30'N; 69°55' to 69°58'E
	Bashlang (0)	Helmand	32°56'N; 64°56'E
	Tokana (0)	Maydan	34°26'N; 68°35'E

	Andar (0)	Maydan	34°16'N; 68°47'E
	Andarab (0)	Baghlan	35°33'N; 69°38'E
	Manjyadar (0)	Parwan	35°28'N; 69°40'E
	Kamdesh (0)	Nangarhar	35°25'N; 71°22'E
	Awshoba (0)	Parwan	35°25'N; 69°30'E
	Parandeh (0)	Parwan	35°22'N; 69°28'E
	Tambona (0)	Parwan	35°18'N; 69°27'E
	Gulin (0)	Parwan	35°06'30"N; 69°40'00"E
	Zuri (0)	Parwan	35°06'N; 69°38'E
	Esshni (0)	Parwan	35°04'N; 69°36'E
	Dewoz (0)	Nangarhar	35°01'N; 71°05'E
	Kuzuk (0)	Laghman	34°55'N; 70°06'E
	Kohe-babo-sanghun (0)	Parwan	34°52'N; 69°38'E
	Jalalabad (0)	Nangarhar	34°28'00"N; 69°27'30"E
	Jegdalek (0)	Kabul	34°26'N; 69°50'E
	Kunak (0)	Oruzghan	34°00'00"N; 66°41'30"E
	Band-i-sultan (0)	Ghazni	33°43'N; 68°23'E
Natural Gas	Shebanghan	Jawzjan	36°41'N; 66°09'E
Olivine	Shodal	Loghar	
Opal	Alburs	Badakhshan	36°20'N; 71°15'E
	Sanglich		
	Gugirt		
Peat	Nawdeho (D)	Ghazni	33°45'N; 67°46'E
	Andemin (0)	Badakhshan	37°20'23"N; 74°19'05"E
	Bedsh-Kunak (0)	Badakhshan	37°20'55"N; 73°22'38"E
	Tegher-Maneu (0)	Badakhshan	37°21'28"N; 74°44'19"E
	Ahazde-Kol (0)	Badakhshan	37°23'24"N; 73°30'00"E
	Yal-Kumak (0)	Badakhshan	37°23'40"N; 73°17'05"E
	Boi-Tibat (0)	Badakhshan	37°20'22"N; 73°11'13"E
	Kara-Jelga (0)	Badakhshan	37°17'20"N; 74°15'41"E
	Wahkhan	Badakhshan	37°03'30"N; 73°54'03"E
Phosphorite	Kotal-i-Sebzak (0)	Herat	34°39'30"N; 63°09'00"E
Quartz	Kantiwa Field (F)	Nangarhar	35°26'10"N; 70°46'20"E
	Kolum (D)	Laghman	35°12'07"N; 70°20'04"E
	Mandoghol (0)	Badakhshan	36°23'N; 71°29'E
	Darawa-su (0)	Badakhshan	36°09'N; 70°48'E
	Petaw (0)	Kandahar	32°09'31"N; 65°41'39"E
	Kantiwa (0)	Nangarhar	35°17'00"N; 74°44'30"E
	Khawre-Khawre (0)	Kabul	34°44'N; 69°30'E
	Korthka (0)	Zabul	32°33'18"N; 66°39'56"E
	Alamkan (0)	Paktia	33°19'05"N; 69°40'24"E
	Shamal (0)	Paktia	33°18'55"N; 69°37'00"E
	Zanda-Gheray (0)	Paktia	33°12'10"N; 69°31'00"E
	- (S)	Badakhshan	37°55'00"N; 71°13'15"E
	- (S)	Badakhshan	37°52'15"N; 71°13'50"E
	- (S)	Badakhshan	37°51'30"N; 70°15'40"E
	- (S)	Badakhshan	37°41'15"N; 71°14'15"E
	- (S)	Ghor	33°48'N; 64°16'E

	- (S)	Ghor	33°47'N; 64°20'E
	- (S)	Nangarhar	34°15'N; 69°50'E
Rhodochrosite	Maghn		
	Syaghar		
Ruby/Sapphire	near Ab-i-Panja	Badakhshan	37°15'N; 71°27'E
	Sorobi		(unknown)
	Bhkshar		(unknown)
	Jegdalek (D)	Kabul	34°26'N; 69°49'E
Salt (Rock)	Nemakab	Takhar	36°43'N; 69°37'E
	(unknown)	Balkh	36°33'N; 66°48'E
	Heri Rud	Ghor	34°21'N; 64°14'E
Salt (Brines)	NamaksarTashkanhan	Samanghan	36°57'N; 67°27'E
	Namaksar Andkhui	Pariah	36°37'N; 65°04'E
	Namaksar Herat	Herat	34°05'N; 60°46'E
	Spia Baldak	Kandahar	31°01'N; 66°24'E
	Takhta Pul	Kandahar	31°19'N; 65°57'E
	Ruhabad Oirishek,	Kandahar-	
		Helmand	31°27'N; 65041'E
	Qala Bist Saline Belt,		31°25'N; 64°23'E
	(on north bank Dori-Agahandab Rivers, between listed coordinates)		
	Daqq-i-Tundi	Pariah	32°26'N; 61°05'E
	Chakhansar		31°ll'N; 61°58'E
Sand/Gravel	Nusay	Badakhshan	38°26'40"N; 70°50'00"E
(quarries)	Maymay	Badakhshan	38°25'00"N; 71°02'00"E
	Ghuch	Badakhshan	38°25'N; 71°06"E
	Waris	Badakhshan	38°23'30"N; 71°07'30"E
	Zangerya	Badakhshan	38°20'00"N; 70°37'30"E
	Zanif	Badakhshan	38°18'N; 71°15'E
	Murghan Darra	Badakhshan	38°17'30"N; 71°l8'30"E
	Rawanak	Badakhshan	38°11'30"N; 70°32'40"E
	Amury	Badakhshan	38°10'50"N; 71°21'20"E
	Warv	Badakhshan	38°01'l0"N; 71°17'00"E
	Shewa	Badakhshan	38°00'N; 71°16'E
	Krunch	Badakhshan	37°27'00"N; 71°30'30"E
	Shabnam	Ghazni	32°56'45"N; 67°49'15"E
	Abdul-Qala	Ghazni	32°51'40"N; 37°49'20"E
	Aghonan	Ghazni	32°44'15"N; 67°37'40"E
Sandstone	(unknown)	Balkh	36°34'N; 67°09'E
	Hajigak	Bamiyan	34°38' to 34°40'N;
			68°04' to 68°08'E
	Koh-i-alburz	Balkh	36°35'N; 66°51'E
	Farkhar	Takhar	36°32'00" to 36°36'30"N;
			69°49'30" to 69°51'00"E
Serpentine	Zamburak	Kandahar	32°10'N; 65°30'E
	Syry-Dach	Kandahar	32°08'28"N; 65°23'50"E
	Lajar	Zabul	32°l3'55"N; 66°28'51"E
	Sharhmaxud	Kandahar	31°40'00"N; 65°25'00"E
Silica	Sand/ Sheghnan	Badakhshan	37°21'N; 71°29'E

Silver	#7757(O)	Kandahar	32°15'17"N; 65°59'02"E
	Chukri-naw (0)	Kapisa	35°36'24"N; 69°53'40"E
	Mirzaka (0)	Ghazni	32°56'37"N; 67°41'46"E
	Surkhbed (0)	Kandahar	32°20'36"N; 66°01'08"E
	- (S)	Baghlan	35°44'20"N; 69°20'00"E
Smoky Quartz	Papruk	Konar	35°36'N; 71°10'E
	Petaw (0)	Kandahar	32°09'31"N; 65°41'39"E
Spinel	Zarkashan		
	Jegdalek	Kabul	34°26'N; 64°14'E
Sulfur	near Rabatak	Kunduz	36°08'N; 68°33'E
	(unknown)	Balkh	36°24'N; 67°12'E
	Elbura		36°37'N; 66°43'E
	(unknown)		36°05'N; 64°41'E
	Murghab	Badghis	35°07'N; 68°12'E
	Alburz (D)	Balkh	36°35'N; 66°35'E
	Astana (0)	Samanghan	36°27'00"N; 67°42'90"E
	Shadian (0)	Samanghan	36°20'N; 67°55'E
	Sanglich (0)	Badakhshan	36°20'N; 71°15'E
	Gugirt (0)	Bamiyan	34°10'N; 67°01'E
	- S	Badakhshan	36°14'N; 71°09"E
	Doshk (S)	Ghor	33°54'N; 63°48'E
	Dasht-i- Safed (S)	Bamiyan	35°18'32"N; 67°57'24"E
Talc	Los-Dakka	Nangarhar	34°11'N; 74°56'E
	Narzi	Konar	35°12'N; 71°32'E
	Ghunday (D)	Nangarhar	34°11'N; 70°01'E
	Achin (D)	Nangarhar	34°03'N; 70°43'E
	Danay Ghury (0)	Baghlan	35°43'55"N; 68°17'56"E
	Farenjal (0)	Parwan	34°59'N; 68°51'E
	Landar (0)	Kabul	34°23'48"N; 69°01'48"E
	- (S)	Maydan	33°54'N; 68°44'E
	- (S)	Ghazni	33°35'N; 68°38'E
Tantalum/Niobium			
	Shewa Field (F)	Badakhshan	37°22'07"N; 70°24'43"E
	Talbuzanak Field (F)	Badakhshan	37°12'06"N; 70°33'36"E
	Kokcha Field (F)	Badakhshan	36°36'35°N; 70°53'15"E
	Eshkashim Field (F)	Badakhshan	36°27'19"N; 71°36'23"E
	Parun Field (F)	Nangarhar	34°54'34"N; 70°52'15"E
	Panjshir Field (F)	Parwan	35°15' to 35°20'N; 69°12' to 69°20'E
	Nilaw/Kolum Field (F)	Laghman	35°10'00" to 35°15'36"N; 70°14'56" to 70°21'14"E
	Korghal Field (F)	Laghman	35°04'06"N; 70°18'20"E
	Dara-i-Pech Field (F)	Nangarhar	34°52'30" to 34°59'00"N; 70°42'10" to 70°45'40"E
	Daram Daram Field (P)	Parwan	34°48' to 34°53'N; 69°45' to 69°47'E
	Chawki Field (F)	Nangarhar	34°40'20"N; 70°46'56"E
	Shamakat Field (F)	Laghman	34°40'10" to 34°44'00"N;

		70°00'20" to 70°02'15"E
Dara-i-Nur Field (F)	Laghman	34°37'N; 70°45'E
Taghawlor Field (P)	Oruzghan	33°42'30" to 33°47'00"N;
		66°19'30" to 66°29'00"E
Drumghal (D)	Nangarhar	35°19'08"N; 71°01'21"E
Nilaw (D)	Laghman	35°11'18" to 35°15'36"N;
		70°15'18" to 70°18'10"E
Dara-i-Pech (D)	Nangarhar	34°55'02" to 34°55'53"N;
		70°44'12" to 70°44'53"E
Shamakat (D)	Laghman	34°40'10" to 34°44'00"N;
		70°00'20" to 70°O2'15"E
Taghawlor (D)	Oruzghan	33°45'05"N; 66°25'30"E
Talbuzanak (0)	Badakhshan	37°13'35"N; 70°33'21"E
Tundara (0)		
Futur (0)	Badakhshan	36°38'N; 71°45"E
Baghlan		35°41'25"N; 68°22'20"E
Besud Field (0)	Maydan	34°23'N; 67°50'E
Dardang (0)	Maydan	34°22'40" to 34°24'30"N;
		67°48'30" to 67°49'40"E
Pachighram (0)	Nangarhar	35°45'54"N; 71°11'07"E
Wozgul (0)	Nangarhar	35°29'10"N; 70°59'10"E
Salang (0)	Parwan	35°18'00"N; 69°16'30"E
Taghma (0)	Parwan	35°11'15"N; 69°12'30"E
Sumte- Shamir (0)	Parwan	35°09'30"N; 69°13'30"E
Gursalak (0)	Nangarhar	34°57'15" to 34°57'45"N;
		70°43'55" to 70°44'55"E
Daram Daram (0)	Parwan	34°50'16"N; 69°46'18"E
Karbah (0)	Laghman	34°34'14"N; 70°18'17"E
Tin	Shewa Field	Badakhshan	37°22'07"N; 70°24'43"E
Kokcha Field	Badakhshan	36°36'35"N; 70°53'15"E
Eshkashim Field	Badakhshan	36°27'19"N; 71°36'23"E
Besud Field	Maydan	34°23'N; 67°50'E
Panjshir Field	Parwan	35°20'N; 69°20'E
Dara-i-daram Field	Kapisa	34°53'N; 69°45'E
Taghawlor Field	Oruzghan	33°42'30"N to 33°47'00"N
		66°19'30"E to 66°29'00"E
Misgaran (D)	Herat	33°49'30"N; 62°06'00"E
- (D)	Farah	33°05'45"N; 61°40'00"E
Taghawlor (D)	Oruzghan	33°45'00"N; 66°25'30"E
Chosnudi-Bolo (0)	Badakhshan	37°48'10"N; 71°34'39"E
- (0)	Badakhshan	37°40'N; 71°40'E
Futor (0)	Badakhshan	36°38'N; 71°39'E
Dehgal (0)	Badakhshan	36°22'N; 71°27'E
Qara Jelga (0)	Badakhshan	37°14'35°N; 74°25'14"E
Tagab- Sony-1 (0)	Herat	34°26'N; 63°48'E
Bandi-Medira (0)	Herat	33°47'10"N; 62°01'20"E
Dacite (0)	Herat	33°47'N; 62°02'E
Sardakna (0)	Farah	33°25'N; 61°48'E

Sarkoro (0)	Farah	33°09'30"N; 61°45'00"E
Bulgaja (0)	Farah	39°09'N; 61°49'E
Kuchi (0)	Farah	33°05'20"N; 61°45'27"E
Seb-Kuta (0)	Farah	33°05'N; 61°42'E
Kelkak (0)	Farah	33°02'55"N; 61°41'40"E
Shand (0)	Farah	33°00'30"N; 69°51'00"E
Bisar (0)	Farah	32°58'56"N; 61°40'57"E
Shin-gar (0)	Kandahar	32°14'09"N; 65°43'03"E
Ziadan (0)	Kandahar	32°14'05"N; 65°44'32"E
Ziadan1 (0)	Kandahar	32°13'23"N; 65°43'28"E
Ghbargei (0)	Kandahar	32°13'N; 65°42'E
Chinar (0)	Kandahar	32°11'15"N; 65°39'10"E
Dara-alasang (0)	Baghlan	35°18'59"N; 68°07'16"E
Dardang (0)	Maydan	34°22'40" to 34°24'30"N 67°48'30" to 67°49'40"E
Gulbina (0)	Bamiyan	34°03'N; 67°36'E
Salang (0)	Parwan	35°18'00"N; 69°16'30"E
Tagma (0)	Parwan	35°11'15"N; 69°12'30"E
Sumte-shamir (0)	Parwan	35°09'30"N; 69°13'30"E
Awraghal (0)	Konar	34°56'10" to 34°57'00"N 70°42'30" to 70°44'10"E
Daram-Daram (0)	Kapisa	34°50'16"N; 69°46'18"E
Dariw-Sheng	Oruzghan	33°43'00" to 33°48'30"N 66°41'00" to 66°50'00"E
Sheng (0)	Oruzghan	33°45'N; 66°40'E
Eskan (0)	Oruzghan	33°45'N; 66°47'E
Largha (0)	Ghazni	33°01'00" to 33°01'30"N 67°42'50" to 67°44'20"E
Kareztu (0)	Ghazni	32°58'02"N; 67°41'53"E
Mirzaka (0)	Ghazni	32°56'37"N; 67°41'46"E
Syaghar (0)	Ghazni	32°56'20"N; 67°40'20"E
Maghn (0)	Ghazni	32°55'20"N; 67°38'00"E
Khinjak (0)	Ghazni	32°51'45"N; 67°37'05"E
Maydan - Ahu (0)	Zabul	32°46'24"N; 66°54'38"E
Baytamur (0)	Zabul	32°46'06"N; 66°48'06"E
Adamkhel (0)	Zabul	32°46'05"N; 66°57'54"E
Boraghana I (0)	Kandahar	32°08'25"N; 66°03'36"E
Boraghana (0)	Kandahar	32°08'N; 66°05'E
Bakhtu (0)	Kandahar	32°07'N; 66°02'E
- S	Farah	33°10'45"N; 61°55'04"E
- S	Farah	32°59'30"N; 62°45'26"E
- S	Oruzghan	34°03'N; 66°40'E
- S	Baghlan	35°47'N; 69°17'12"E
- S	Oruzghan	34°00'N; 66°40'E
- S	Oruzghan	33°52'48"N; 66°35'35°E
- S	Oruzghan	33°49'05"N; 66°44'10"E
- S	Oruzghan	33°48'36"N; 66°43'11 "E
- S	Oruzghan	33°48'20"N; 66°44'22"E

	- S	Oruzghan	33°47'15"N; 66°45'27"E
	- S	Oruzghan	33°46'05"N; 66°41'33"E
	- S	Oruzghan	33°44'24"N; 66°32'12"E
	- S	Oruzghan	33°40'55"N; 66°13'50"E
	- S	Oruzghan	33°37'02"N; 66°15'10"E
	- S	Oruzghan	33°35'23"N; 66°16'06"E
	- S	Oruzghan	33°28'49"N; 66°21'01"E
	- S	Ghazni	33°18'10"N; 67°40'20"E
	- S	Ghazni	33°14'50"N; 67°16'20"E
Topaz	Sheng		
	Baroghana		
Tourmaline	Kantiwa Field	Nangarhar	35°26'10"N; 70°46'20"E
	KorghalField	Laghman	35°04'06"N; 70°18'20"E
	Nilaw and Kolum	Laghman	35°12'N; 70°20'E
	Papruk (0)	Konar	35°36'30"N; 71°10'00"E
	Kantiwa (0)	Nangarhar	35°17'00"N; 70°44'30"E
	Korghal (0)	Laghman	35°04'06"N; 70°18'29"E
	Mualevi	Konar	35°46'N; 71°05'E
	Tsotsum	Konar	35°35'N; 71°0'E
	Mandanesha	Badakhshan	35°40'N; 70°42'E
	Vora Desh	Laghman	34°55'N; 70°45'E
	Dhray-Pech	Nangarhar	34°50'N; 70°45'E
Tungsten	Kelkak (0)	Farah	33°02'55"N; 61°41'40"E
	Farah 11(0)	Farah	32°14'30"N; 62°18'00"E
	Farahl (0)	Farah	32°11'50"N; 62°16'30"E
	Gulbina (0)	Bamiyan	34°03'N; 67°36'E
	Charh II (0)	Oruzghan	33°54'00"N; 66°38'15"E
	Salej (0)	Oruzghan	33°51'30"N; 66°20'30"E
	Dariw-Sheng (0)	Oruzghan	33°43'00"N to 33°48'30"N 66°41'00"E to 66°50"00"E
	Nili (0)	Oruzghan	33°43"20"N; 66°12'30"E
	Chak (0)	Oruzghan	33°41'40"N; 66°10'40"E
	Shakhzadah I (0)	Ghazni	33°27'48"N; 68°10'40"E
	Maraghol (0)	Ghazni	33°07'05"N; 67°24'40"E
	Kakrak (0)	Ghazni	33°06'40"N; 67°27'50"E
	Kochak (0)	Oruzghan	32°58'N; 66°43'E
	Oruzghan (0)	Oruzghan	32°55'20"N; 66°39'20"E
	Qarya-i-baki (0)	Ghazni	32°55'30"N; 66°52'30"E
	Qarya-i-Saraw (0)	Ghazni	32°55'N; 66°57'E
	Kharnay (0)	Ghazni	32°47'55"N; 67°20'00"E
	Maydane Ahu (0)	Zabul	32°46'24"N; 66°54'38"E
	Baytamur (0)	Zabul	32°46'06"N; 66°48'06"E
	Adamkhel (0)	Zabul	32°46'05"N; 66°57'04"E
	Band (0)	Zabul	32°45'32"N; 66°53'01"E
	Kashmirak II (0)	Zabul	32°43'48"N; 66°41'46"E
	Ghumbad (0)	Zabul	32°11'15"N; 66°23'22"E
	Baraghana I (0)	Kandahar	32°08'25"N; 66°03'36"E
	- S	Badakhshan	37°38'25"N; 70°54'50"E

	- S	Badakhshan	37°14'08"N; 71°01'25"E
	- S	Bamiyan	34°47'18"N; 68°00'25"E
	- S	Oruzghan	33°59'15"N; 66°48'46"E
	- S	Oruzghan	33°55'50"N; 66°09'53"E
	- S	Maydan	33°55"03"N; 68°37'10"E
	- S	Oruzghan	33°54'01"N; 66°58'38"E
	- S	Maydan	33°54'10"N; 68°37'00"E
	- S	Oruzghan	33°51'11"N; 66°39'29"E
	- S	Oruzghan	33°44'17"N; 66°44'02"E
	- S	Oruzghan	33°43'23"N; 66°46'33"E
	- S	Ghazni	33°27'48"N; 68°10'20"E
	- S	Ghazni	33°08'40"N; 67°27'30"E
	- S	Zabul	32°46'56"N; 67°03'03"E
	- S	Ghazni	32°46'12"N; 67°21'30"E
	- S	Zabul	32°45'56"N; 66°50'14"E
	- S	Zabul	32°44'04"N; 66°43'20"E
	- S	Zabul	32°44'07"N; 66°55'05"E
	- S	Zabul	32°36'51"N; 66°55'36"E
	- S	Zabul	32°32'32"N; 66°34'55"E
	- S	Zabul	32°30'40"N; 66°40'40"E
Uranium/Thorium			
	Surkh-i-Parso (0)	Parwan	34°51'N; 68°39'E
Rare Earths	No. Khanneshin (0)	Helmand	39°29'40"N; 63°35'00"E
	Khanneshin (0)	Helmand	38°28'N; 63°35'E
	So. Khanneshin (0)	Helmand	30°27'20"N; 63°34'30"E

Note: The mine locations, coordinates, and names of mines have been compiled from the authors' experiences, from research of literature, and notes from interviews. In that there are discrepancies, all sites need verification. In some cases old mine sites along veins have been closed, and new sites have been opened, resulting in a mix of old and new names, and much confusion.

Articles, Books, and Films
by Gary W. Bowersox

Articles:

A Status Report On Gemstones From Afghanistan
The Gujar Killi Emerald Deposit, Northwest Frontier Province,
  Pakistan
Emeralds of Panjsher Valley, Afghanistan
Ruby and Sapphire from Jegdalek, Afghanistan

Articles are free on-line at:
www.gems-afghan.com/articles.htm

Films:

The Gem Hunter In Afghanistan

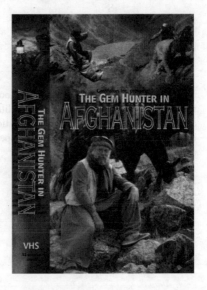

This video, a 50 minute TV documentary, was filmed in August 2001. It
follows The Gem Hunter, Gary Bowersox,
from the Peshawar gem market over the
high mountain passes of the Hindu Kush
to the lapis and the emerald mines of
Afghanistan.

Along the trail, The Gem Hunter
meets the ghost of Marco Polo and
Alexander the Great on the Silk Road.
The last scene of the film is The Gem
Hunter interviewing the legendary Commander Ahmed Shah Massoud, the Lion
of Panjsher, twenty-one days before his
assassination on September 9, 2001.

This video, available in both VHS and DVD formats, is an excellent
companion to *The Gem Hunter.*

Order your copy on-line at:
www.gems-afghan.com/bookstore.htm

Books:

Gemstones of Afghanistan

Take this opportunity to learn about this hidden source of gems: their history, lore, and properties. A Smithsonian quality collection of gems and one-of-a-kind custom-made pieces are shown in this book – many of which are available for sale.

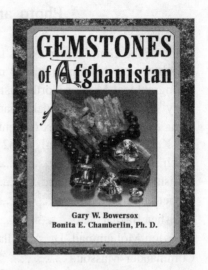

GEMSTONES of Afghanistan

Gary W. Bowersox
Bonita E. Chamberlin, Ph. D.

Gemstones of Afghanistan is the first comprehensive, fully-documented book on the geology, history, and lore of the gems and minerals of this war-ravaged crossroads between the Near East and the Far East.

This book features stunning color photographs, original maps, and geographic coordinates of significant mines. The authors have compiled a wide-ranging and thorough set of references that, like the book, will prove invaluable to jewelers, gem buyers, geologists, historians, and those who seek to make a careful assessment of the riches Afghanistan has to offer.

It is the first complete reference on gemstones of Afghanistan – the results of 23 years of researching over 6,500 years of history.

√ Hardcover, glossy 8 1/2" x 11", 244-page collection edition

√ 110 photographs, maps, and figures, including 52 in color

√ History of geology and gem mining in Afghanistan, describing mining methods and production

√ Detailed topographical and geological maps pinpoint gem and mineral deposits

√ Over 1,400 gem and mineral locations by coordinates

√ Based on 2,000 years of geological, geographical, and gemological exploration

√ Over 500 references and suggested readings

√ Color photographs of new cutting styles, carved gems, and new jewelry designs

Order your copy on-line at:
www.gems-afghan.com/bookstore.htm

Photo and Map Index

Index